LONDON STORIES
and Other Writings

There have been few writers more dedicated to their art than Henry James (1843–1916). Novels such as *The Portrait of a Lady, The Bostonians, The Wings of the Dove, The Ambassadors* and *The Golden Bowl* have passed into the canon of great English literature, as have stories like *The Aspern Papers* and *The Lesson of the Master*. An American who spent most of his life in Europe, he also wrote a great deal of non-fiction: essays, reviews, travel, biography and reminiscences were all part of his range, as well as a wonderful gift for letter-writing. By the time of his death he was almost universally acknowledged as 'the Master'.

David Kynaston was born at Aldershot in 1951 and educated at Wellington College, before reading modern history at New College, Oxford. He has written six books, all on historical subjects: one on the Victorian working class; two on offices of state; two on cricket; and the centenary history of the *Financial Times*. In 1983 he completed a doctoral thesis at the University of London on the London Stock Exchange, 1870–1914. He is currently writing the history of the stockbrokers Cazenove & Co and hopes one day to complete a major work on late-Victorian London.

Other books by the Editor

King Labour: The British Working Class, 1850–1914
The Secretary of State
The Chancellor of the Exchequer
Bobby Abel, Professional Batsman
Archie's Last Stand: MCC in New Zealand, 1922–23
The Financial Times: A Centenary History

LONDON STORIES
and Other Writings

Edited and with an Introduction
by
David Kynaston

TABB HOUSE

Published by Tabb House 1989
7 Church Street, Padstow, Cornwall, PL28 8BG

Introduction and other editorial matter © David Kynaston, 1989

Paperback edition ISBN 0 907018 67 X
Hardback edition ISBN 0 907018 75 0

Cover illustration: Photo Bulloz, Paris

Phototypeset by Exe Valley Dataset Ltd, Exeter
Printed by Bookcraft (Bath) Ltd, Midsomer Norton, Bath

I WOULD LIKE to thank my wife Lucy for all her help, both in conceiving this collection and helping to decide which stories to include.

I also wish to acknowledge permission to use the painting of the National Gallery and St Martin-in-the-Fields by Joseph de Nittis, part of which is reproduced on the cover by courtesy of the Ville de Paris, Musée du Petit Palais, Paris.

David Kynaston

CONTENTS

INTRODUCTION

HENRY JAMES, briefly in London as an infant, returned there with his family at the age of twelve. He was to recall (in the third person) how a New York childhood spent poring over the pages of *Punch* had helped to prepare him for the city he now saw, a city with which he would develop such intimate relations:

He remembers today [1883] vividly his impression of the London streets in the summer of 1855; they had an extraordinary look of familiarity, and every figure, every object he encountered, appeared to have been drawn by Leech. He has learned to know these things better since then; but his childish impression is subject to extraordinary revivals. The expansive back of an old lady getting into an omnibus, the attitude of a little girl bending from her pony in the park, the demureness of a maid-servant opening a street-door in Brompton, the top-heavy attitude of the small 'Ameliar-Ann', as she stands planted with the baby in her arms on the corner of a Westminster slum, the coal-heavers, the cabmen, the publicans, the butcher-boys, the flunkeys, the guardsmen, the policemen (in spite of their change of uniform), are liable at this hour, in certain moments, to look more like sketchy tail-pieces than natural things.

And he added of Leech's drawings of London streets, with their 'damp blackness', that 'long before I had it I was acquainted, through his sketches, with the aspect of Baker Street in December'.[1]

But if London seemed familiar and reassuring to the boy, that was not at all how it felt to the young man. After a long absence, James paid his first adult visit to the city in 1869 and after ten days was writing to his sister as one almost overwhelmed:

I may say that up to this time I have been crushed under a sense of the mere magnitude of London – its inconceivable immensity – in such a way as to paralyse my mind for any appreciation of details. This is gradually subsiding; but what does it leave behind it? An extraordinary intellectual depression, as I may say, and an indefinable flatness of mind. The place sits on you, broods on you, stamps on you with the feet of its myriad bipeds and quadrupeds. In fine, it is anything but a cheerful or a charming city.[2]

A broadly hostile tone persisted during periodic visits over the next three years. 'This *beastly* London', he declared to his mother in 1870, referring in sweeping terms to 'its darkness and grim and grime and filth and misery'. By contrast Paris, which he had just left, seemed 'the perfect model of a mighty capital'.[3] And in 1872, again just arrived at the Charing Cross Hotel after a stay in 'blood-drenched' but 'graceful' Paris, he informed his parents that 'London is the same terrible great murky Babylon as ever' and described how 'the autumn fogs magnify all the swarming street vistas and give them a kind of monstrous immensity'. In short: 'Oh, the grimness of London! And oh! the cookery of London!'[4]

It was not surprising therefore that when in 1875 James came to Europe to assume permanent residence ('I take possession of the old world – I inhale it – I appropriate it!'[5]) his first choice of domicile should be Paris, with its thriving literary culture in addition to its other charms. Within a year, however, he had come to feel that he would always be treated there as an outsider; and in the closing weeks of 1876, prompted by his brother William, he moved to London and settled in rooms at 3 Bolton Street, Piccadilly. For such a dedicated writer it proved an inspired decision, not so much on account of the wide circle of acquaintances which he quickly developed, but rather because, as he told his friend Grace Norton in August 1877, 'my interest in London is chiefly that of an observer in a place where there is most in the world to observe'.[6] Disenchantment with London society and 'the Season' soon set in, but not with London itself, and by 1879 there was a definitive tone in an affirmation to his fellow American writer, William Dean Howells: 'London continues to possess and please me; I have passed a bargain with it forever. The die is cast and the deed is done. The harm, I mean, is done. You can live elsewhere *before* you have lived here – but not after. Not that it is any great "harm" to live in this multitudinous world-centre'.[7]

Why exactly London and at what cost? While on a visit to America in 1881, his first time there for six years, James sought to set down his innermost thoughts:

It is difficult to speak adequately or justly of London. It is not a pleasant place; it is not agreeable, or cheerful, or easy, or exempt from reproach. It is only magnificent. You can draw up a tremendous list of reasons why it should be insupportable. The fogs, the smoke, the dirt, the darkness, the wet, the distances, the ugliness, the brutal size of the place, the horrible numerosity of society, the manner in which this senseless bigness is fatal to amenity, to convenience, to conversation, to good manners – all this and much more you may expatiate upon. You may call it dreary, heavy, stupid, dull, inhuman, vulgar at heart and tiresome in form. I have felt these things at times so strongly that I have said – 'Ah London, you too then are impossible?' But these are occasional moods; and for one who takes it as I take it, London is on the whole the most possible form of life. I take it as an artist and as a bachelor; as one who has the passion of observation and whose business is the study of human life. It is the biggest aggregation of human life – the most complete compendium of the world. The human race is better represented there than anywhere else, and if you learn to know your London you learn a great many things.[8]

In January 1882 his mother died, prolonging his stay in America, and from Boston the following month he wrote in heartfelt fashion to his friend Lord Rosebery that he was 'desperately homesick for London'.[9]

It was during the mid-1880s that James wrote his great London novel, *The Princess Casamassima*, a novel remarkable for its vivid, sympathetic depiction of the drab underside of London life. It marked a clear stage in James's metropolitan journey, and in the course of writing it he moved, early in 1886, to an apartment in De Vere Gardens, Kensington. Bemoaning in a letter to William soon after his move 'the constant old story of London interruptions and distractions', he went on: 'Thank God I am out of them far more now than I have ever been before – in my chaste and secluded Kensington *quatrième*'.[10] Soon afterwards he wrote his full-scale essay on London included in this volume, a companion piece to earlier essays on Rome, Florence and Venice. To quote his incomparable biographer, Leon Edel: 'It is perhaps the best of the series, certainly the most saturated with the "sense of place" . . . It was his way of saying that he had at last taken root in the particular spot which communicated "the greatest sense of life"'.[11] London remained for James the indispensable place, even though he no longer wished to be in the very centre of things.

So, despite occasional appearance to the contrary, it would be for the rest of his life. The 1890s was a bruising decade for James, with the humiliating failure of his great theatrical venture, and during it his ostensible attitude towards London, as reflected in his correspondence, became increasingly detached. 'I am vaguely looking for a humble permanent cot beside the sea (preferably)', he told Grace Norton in 1893[12]; and five years later he indeed moved to Rye in Sussex, which he described to her as 'a little old brown and red and green and black hill-city' where he could find 'peace ineffable compared with London'.[13] A letter of November 1899 offered a retrospective rationale:

I am still, thank heaven, out of town – which is more and more my predominant and natural state. I am only reacting, I suppose, against many, many long years of London, which had ended by giving me a deep sense of the quantity of 'cry' in all that life compared to the almost total absence of 'wool'. By which I mean, simply, that acquaintances and relations there have a way of seeming at last to end in smoke – while having consumed a great deal of fuel and taken a great deal of time.[14]

The observer, it seemed, was not prepared to continue paying the human price of the observatory, perhaps because he no longer needed it for his art.

Yet within weeks he was writing, still from Rye, to old London friends in a quite different strain. 'I'm so homesick for the blessed Kensington fields that I gloat over the prospect of treading them, finally, afresh. Meanwhile I've felt remote and unfriended . . .'.[15] And: 'This second winter here has made me really homesick for town. Next year I shall, D.V., drink deep again'.[16] So it proved through the 1900s, as James gradually, by means of a permanent room at the Reform Club, developed a compromise through which he spent summers at Rye and, on the whole, wintered in London. His underlying attachment to his old stamping ground continued strong, perhaps especially when he was elsewhere. On one occasion the young Desmond MacCarthy asked him if he thought London 'beautiful'. James pondered. 'Hardly beautiful', he replied, but during his ensuing disquisition he dropped a wholly Jamesian remark about 'craving for a whiff of London's carboniferous damp'.[17]

For a time it even seemed that he would write a book-length study on the subject, signing an agreement to that effect with Macmillan and Co in 1903. The proposed book, to be called *London Town*, was envisaged by James as 'a romantic-psychological, pictorial-social volume'.[18] Other projects unfortunately intervened, but James during 1907 and 1909 did take some preparatory notes that survive.[19] Some observations one summer's afternoon catch something of the tone. After citing 'the deplorable Boer monument in the little garden under the new Admiralty' and 'the at present so *bête* and common curve of the – bulge of the – face of the Grand Hotel (round into Whitehall)', he continues:

> *Passages* in London, however, make vistas, and just at this hour I catch a little specimen of it and of the way that they make a little charm and a little picture. There is an opening at the end of the terrace through into Trafalgar Square at the end of (the shortness of) which just a bit of the Nat Gall, the ugly cupola itself, sits up and *speaks* to one. Speaks to one, that is, if one have the old London sense, the feeling and the fondness. How *all* one's appreciations here need that: nothing so fine, beautiful or artistic, as to work for much without it.

'The old London sense': while not wholly averse to the modern – 'the terrible Tower Bridge' is 'yet right and *fine* symbol of our time' – the notes are suffused with nostalgia for an earlier London. Thus on the south side of St Clement Danes, James refers regretfully to 'the note of the New London in the circular, the shallow-curved street where the big statued insurance building (or whatever) is replacing the little old sordidries that were yet the old world where that pleasant bookshop (Buxton Forman's), publisher, some time vanished, used to be'.

Or at St Giles in the City: 'No city churchyard has held its own better, more amply: with hideous workhouses and offices pressing hard, it seems still to bid them stand off – keep their distance civilly, and respect a little the precious history of things'. Perhaps most eloquently of all in these notes, there is his description of how 'the grey stone of the Law-Courts is in a good stage of that dusky-silvering which is the best that London buildings can look for in the so operative, so tormenting (no, find the right kindly, affectionate word) air'. The parenthesis is almost that of a lover.

Odd remarks have come down from the last years. While in Manhattan in 1910, he apparently found that 'the rhythm and beat and margin' of that archetypically twentieth-century city were all 'scant and inadequate' in comparison with his adopted metropolis.[20] The following autumn saw him in Rye and missing London badly: 'Dear old London and its ways and works, its walks and conversations, define themselves as a Prodigious Cure'.[21] There was to be one final London home. In 1913 he left the Reform Club and moved into an apartment in Carlyle Mansions, Cheyne Walk, overlooking the Thames. He could, in Edel's felicitous phrase, 'feel himself once more in harmony with the rumbling city'.[22] It was there that Henry James died in February 1916. The funeral was held at Chelsea Old Church and his body cremated at Golders Green. Sixty years later a memorial stone to him was unveiled in the Poet's Corner of Westminster Abbey.

REFERENCES

1. *Partial Portraits* (1888), pp 329–30, 339
2. *Letters, Volume I* (1974), p 90.
3. Ibid, p 194.
4. Ibid, pp 305–6.
5. Ibid, p 484.
6. *Letters, Volume II* (1978), p 135.
7. Ibid, p 227.
8. *The Complete Notebooks* (1987), pp 217–8.
9. *Letters, Volume II* (1978), p 380.

10. *Letters, Volume III* (1980), p 114.

11. Leon Edel, *The Life of Henry James* (1977), volume I, pp 756–7.

12. *Letters, Volume III* (1980), pp 431–2.

13. *Letters, Volume IV* (1984), p 92.

14. Ibid, p 121.

15. Ibid, p 128.

16. Ibid, p 129.

17. Leon Edel, *op cit*, volume II, p 680.

18. *Letters, Volume IV* (1984), p 278.

19. *The Complete Notebooks* (1987), pp 273–80.

20. Edel, *op cit*, volume II, p 727.

21. Ibid, p 731.

22. Ibid, p 754.

A NOTE ON THE TEXT

As in almost any selection of James's tales, the editor has to choose between the original magazine texts, the versions published in book form shortly afterwards, and the final texts as rewritten for the New York Edition towards the end of his life. For each of the three stories included here, the original book version has been chosen, offering a freshness that (in this editor's opinion) the New York Edition sometimes lacks. Moreover, as Edel points out in his edition of the complete tales, in that form it not only 'had the benefit of revision from magazine to volume', but also 'it was best known to James's generation'. In the case of the essay on *London*, the text is taken from its book publication.

LADY BARBERINA

Lady Barberina, first published in *The Century Magazine* (May–July 1884) and in book form in *Tales of Three Cities* (1884), was almost the last of James's 'international' tales. It offers not only one of his fullest, most piquant explorations of the differing *mores* of London and Manhattan 'society', but also one of his choicest opening scenes. 'You will happily never have cause', Robert Louis Stevenson wrote to him shortly after publication, 'to understand the despair with which a writer like myself considers (say) the park scene in *Lady Barberina*. Every touch surprises me by its intangible precision; and the effect when done, as light as syllabub, as distinct as a picture, fills me with envy'.[1]

1. *The Letters of Robert Louis Stevenson, Volume II* (1921), p 217.

LADY BARBERINA

I

IT IS WELL known that there are few sights in the world more brilliant than the main avenues of Hyde Park of a fine afternoon in June. This was quite the opinion of two persons who, on a beautiful day at the beginning of that month, four years ago, had established themselves under the great trees in a couple of iron chairs (the big ones with arms, for which, if I mistake not, you pay twopence), and sat there with slow procession of the Drive behind them, while their faces were turned to the more vivid agitation of the Row. They were lost in the multitude of observers, and they belonged, superficially, at least, to that class of persons who, wherever they may be, rank rather with the spectators than with the spectacle. They were quiet, simple, elderly, of aspect somewhat neutral; you would have liked them extremely, but you would scarcely have noticed them. Nevertheless, in all that shining host, it is to them, obscure, that we must give our attention. The reader is begged to have confidence; he is not asked to make vain concessions. There was that in the faces of our friends which indicated that they were growing old together, and that they were fond enough of each other's company not to object (if it was a condition) even to that. The reader will have guessed that they were husband and wife; and perhaps while he is about it he will have guessed that they were of that nationality for which Hyde Park at the height of the season is most completely illustrative. They were familiar strangers, as it were; and people at once so initiated and so detached could only be Americans. This reflection, indeed, you would have made only after some delay; for it must be admitted that they carried few patriotic signs on the surface. They had the American turn of mind, but that was very subtle; and to your eye – if your eye had cared about it – they might have been English, or even of Continental, parentage. It was as if it suited them to be colourless; their colour was all in their talk. They were not in the least verdant; they were grey, rather, of monotonous hue. If they were interested in the riders, the horses the walkers, the great exhibition of English wealth and health, beauty, luxury and leisure, it was because all this referred itself to other impressions, because they had the key to almost everything that needed an answer – because, in a word, they were able to compare. They had not arrived, they had only returned; and recognition much more than surprise was expressed in their quiet gaze. It may as well be said outright that Dexter Freer and his wife belonged to that class of Americans who are constantly 'passing through' London. Possessors of a fortune of which, from any standpoint, the limits were plainly visible, they were unable to command that highest of luxuries – a habitation in their own country. They found it much more possible to economise at Dresden or Florence than at Buffalo or Minneapolis. The economy was as great, and the inspiration was greater. From Dresden, from Florence, moreover, they constantly made excursions which would not have been possible in those other cities; and it is even to be feared that they had some rather expensive methods of saving. They came to London to buy their portmanteaus, their tooth-brushes, their writing-paper; they occasionally even crossed the Atlantic to assure themselves that prices over there were still the same. They were eminently a social pair; their interests were mainly personal. Their point of view always was so distinctly human that they passed for being fond of gossip; and they certainly knew a good deal about the affairs of other people. They had friends in every country, in every town; and it was not their fault if people told them their secrets. Dexter Freer was a tall, lean man, with an interested eye, and a nose that rather aspired than drooped, yet was salient withal. He brushed his hair, which was streaked with white, forward over his ears in those locks which are represented in the portraits of clean-shaven gentlemen who flourished fifty years ago, and wore an old-fashioned neckcloth and gaiters. His wife, a small, plump person, of superficial freshness, with a white face, and hair that was still perfectly black, smiled perpetually, but had never laughed since the death of a son whom she had lost ten years after her marriage. Her husband, on the other hand, who was usually quite grave, indulged on great occasions in resounding mirth. People confided in her less than in him; but that mattered little, as he confided sufficiently in herself. Her dress, which was always black or dark grey, was so harmoniously simple that you could see she was fond of it; it was never smart by accident. She was full of intentions, of the most judicious sort; and though she was perpetually moving about the world she had the air of being perfectly stationary. She was celebrated for the promptitude with which she made her sitting-room at an inn, where she might be spending a night or two, look like an apartment long inhabited. With books, flowers, photographs, draperies, rapidly distributed – she had even a way, for the most part, of having a piano – the place seemed almost hereditary. The pair were just back from America, where they had spent three months, and now were able to face the world with something of the elation which people feel who have been justified in a prevision. They had found their native land quite ruinous.

'There he is again!' said Mr Freer, following with his eyes a young man who passed along the Row, riding slowly. 'That's a beautiful thoroughbred!'

Mrs Freer asked idle questions only when she wished for time to think. At present she had simply to look and see who it was her husband meant. 'The horse is too big,' she remarked, in a moment.

'You mean that the rider is too small,' her husband rejoined; 'he is mounted on his millions.'

'Is it really millions?'

'Seven or eight, they tell me.'

'How disgusting!' It was in this manner that Mrs Freer usually spoke of the large fortunes of the day. 'I wish he would see us,' she added.

'He does see us, but he doesn't like to look at us. He is too conscious; he isn't easy.'

'Too conscious of his big horse?'

'Yes, and of his big fortune; he is rather ashamed of it.'

'This is an odd place to come, then,' said Mrs Freer.

'I am not sure of that. He will find people here richer than himself, and other big horses in plenty, and that will cheer him up. Perhaps, too, he is looking for that girl.'

'The one we heard about? He can't be such a fool.'

'He isn't a fool,' said Dexter Freer. 'If he is thinking of her, he has some good reason.'

'I wonder what Mary Lemon would say.'

'She would say it was right, if he should do it. She thinks he can do no wrong. He is exceedingly fond of her.'

'I shan't be sure of that if he takes home a wife who will despise her.'

'Why should the girl despise her? She is a delightful woman.'

'The girl will never know it – and if she should, it would make no difference; she will despise everything.'

'I don't believe it, my dear; she will like some things very much. Every one will be very nice to her.'

'She will despise them all the more. But we are speaking as if it were all arranged; I don't believe in it at all,' said Mrs Freer.

'Well, something of the sort – in this case or in some other – is sure to happen sooner or later,' her husband replied, turning round a little toward the part of the delta which is formed, near the entrance to the Park, by the divergence of the two great vistas of the Drive and the Row.

Our friends had turned their backs, as I have said, to the solemn revolution of wheels and the densely-packed mass of spectators who had chosen that part of the show. These spectators were now agitated by a unanimous impulse: the pushing back of chairs, the shuffle of feet, the rustle of garments and the deepening murmur of voices sufficiently expressed it. Royalty was approaching – royalty had passed. Freer turned his head and his ear a little; but he failed to alter his position further, and his wife took no notice of the flurry. They had seen royalty pass, all over Europe, and they knew that it passed very quickly. Sometimes it came back; sometimes it didn't; for more than once they had seen it pass for the last time. They were veteran tourists, and they knew perfectly when to get up and when to remain seated. Mr Freer went on with his proposition: 'Some young fellow is certain to do it, and one of these girls is certain to take the risk. They must take risks, over here, more and more.'

'The girls, I have no doubt, will be glad enough; they have had very little chance as yet. But I don't want Jackson to begin.'

'Do you know I rather think I do?' said Dexter Freer; 'It will be very amusing.'

'For us, perhaps, but not for him; he will repent of it, and be wretched. He is too good for that.'

'Wretched, never! He has no capacity for wretchedness; and that's why he can afford to risk it.'

'He will have to make great concessions,' Mrs Freer remarked.

'He won't make one.'

'I should like to see.'

'You admit, then, that it will be amusing, which is all I contend for. But, as you say, we are talking as if it were settled, whereas there is probably nothing in it, after all. The best stories always turn out false. I shall be sorry in this case.'

They relapsed into silence, while people passed and re-passed them – continuous, successive, mechanical, with strange sequences of faces. They looked at the people, but no one looked at them, though every one was there so admittedly to see what was to be seen. It was all striking, all pictorial, and it made a great composition. The wide, long area of the Row, its red-brown surface dotted with bounding figures, stretched away into the distance and became suffused and misty in the bright, thick air. The deep, dark English verdure that bordered and overhung it, looked rich and old, revived and refreshed though it was by the breath of June. The mild blue of the sky was spotted with great silvery clouds, and the light drizzled down in heavenly shafts over the quieter spaces of the Park, as one saw them beyond the Row. All this, however, was only a back-ground, for the scene was before everything personal; superbly so, and full of the gloss and lustre, the contrasted tones, of a thousand polished surfaces. Certain things were salient, pervasive – the shining flanks of the perfect horses, the twinkle of bits and spurs, the smoothness of the fine cloth adjusted to shoulders and limbs, the sheen of hats and boots, the freshness of complexions, the expression of smiling, talking faces, the flash and flutter of rapid gallops. Faces were everywhere, and they were the great effect; above all, the fair faces of women on tall horses, flushed a little under their stiff black hats, with figures stiffened, in spite of much definition of curve, by their tight-fitting habits. Their hard little helmets; their neat, compact heads; their straight necks; their firm, tailor-made armour; their blooming, competent physique, made them look doubly like amazons about to ride a charge. The men, with their eyes before them, with hats of undulating brim, good profiles, high collars, white flowers on their chests, long legs and long feet, had an air more elaborately decorative, as they jolted beside the ladies, always out of step. These were youthful types; but it was not all youth, for many a saddle was surmounted by a richer rotundity; and ruddy faces, with short white whiskers or with matronly chins, looked down comfortably from an equilibrium which was moral and social as well as physical. The walkers differed from the riders only in being on foot, and in looking at the riders more than these looked at them; for they would have done as well in the saddle and ridden as the others rode. The women had tight little bonnets and still tighter little knots of hair; their round chins rested on a close swathing of lace, or, in some cases, of silver chains and circlets. They had flat backs and small waists; they walked slowly, with their elbows out, carrying vast parasols, and turning their heads very little to the right or the left. They were amazons unmounted, quite ready to spring into the saddle. There was a great deal of beauty and a general look of successful development, which came from clear, quiet eyes, and from well-cut lips, on which syllables were liquid and sentences brief. Some of the young men, as well as the women, had the happiest proportions and oval faces, in which line and colour were pure and fresh and the idea of the moment was not very intense.

'They are very good-looking,' said Mr Freer, at the end of ten minutes; 'they are the finest whites.'

'So long as they remain white they do very well; but when they venture upon colour!' his wife replied. She sat with her eyes on a level with the skirts of the ladies who passed her; and she had been following the progress of a green velvet robe, enriched with ornaments of steel and much gathered up in the hands of its wearer, who, herself apparently in her teens, was accompanied by a young lady draped in scanty pink muslin, embroidered, aesthetically, with flowers that simulated the iris.

'All the same, in a crowd, they are wonderfully well turned

out,' Dexter Freer went on; 'take the men, and women, and horses together. Look at that big fellow on the light chestnut: what could be more perfect? By the way, it's Lord Canterville,' he added in a moment, as if the fact were of some importance.

Mrs Freer recognised its importance to the degree of raising her glass to look at Lord Canterville. 'How do you know it's he?' she asked, with her glass still up.

'I heard him say something the night I went to the House of Lords. It was very few words, but I remember him. A man who was near me told me who he was.'

'He is not so handsome as you,' said Mrs Freer, dropping her glass.

'Ah, you're too difficult!' her husband murmured. 'What a pity the girl isn't with him,' he went on; 'we might see something.'

It appeared in a moment that the girl was with him. The nobleman designated had ridden slowly forward from the start, but just opposite our friends he pulled up to look behind him, as if he had been waiting for someone. At the same moment a gentleman in the Walk engaged his attention, so that he advanced to the barrier which protects the pedestrians, and halted there, bending a little from his saddle and talking with his friend, who leaned against the rail. Lord Canterville was indeed perfect, as his American admirer had said. Upwards of sixty, and of great stature and great presence, he was really a splendid apparition. In exquisite preservation, he had the freshness of middle life, and would have been young to the eye if the lapse of years were not needed to account for his considerable girth. He was clad from head to foot in garments of a radiant grey, and his fine florid countenance was surmounted with a white hat, of which the majestic curves were a triumph of good form. Over his mighty chest was spread a beard of the richest growth, and of a colour, in spite of a few streaks, vaguely grizzled, to which the coat of his admirable horse appeared to be a perfect match. It left no opportunity, in his uppermost button-hole, for the customary gardenia; but this was of comparatively little consequence, as the vegetation of the beard itself was tropical. Astride his great steed, with his big fist, gloved in pearl-grey, on his swelling thigh, his face lighted up with good-humoured indifference, and all his magnificent surface reflecting the mild sunshine, he was a very imposing man indeed, and visibly, incontestably, a personage. People almost lingered to look at him as they passed. His halt was brief, however, for he was almost immediately joined by two handsome girls, who were as well turned out, in Dexter Freer's phrase, as himself. They had been detained a moment at the entrance to the Row, and now advanced side by side, their groom close behind them. One was taller and older than the other, and it was apparent at a glance that they were sisters. Between them, with their charming shoulders, contracted waists, and skirts that hung without a wrinkle, like a plate of zinc, they represented in singularly complete form the pretty English girl in the position in which she is prettiest.

'Of course they are his daughters,' said Dexter Freer, as they rode away with Lord Canterville; 'and in that case one of them must be Jackson Lemon's sweetheart. Probably the bigger; they said it was the eldest. She is evidently a fine creature.'

'She would hate it over there,' Mrs Freer remarked, for all answer to this cluster of inductions.

'You know I don't admit that. But granting she should, it would do her good to have to accommodate herself.'

'She wouldn't accommodate herself.'

'She looks so confoundedly fortunate, perched up on that saddle,' Dexter Freer pursued, without heeding his wife's rejoinder.

'Aren't they supposed to be very poor?'

'Yes, they look it!' And his eyes followed the distinguished trio, as, with the groom, as distinguished in his way as any of them, they started on a canter.

The air was full of sound, but it was low and diffused; and when, near our friends, it became articulate, the words were simple and few.

'It's as good as the circus, isn't it, Mrs Freer?' These words correspond to that description, but they pierced the air more effectually than any our friends had lately heard. They were uttered by a young man who had stopped short in the path, absorbed by the sight of his compatriots. He was short and stout, he had a round, kind face, and short, stiff-looking hair, which was reproduced in a small bristling beard. He wore a double-breasted walking-coat, which was not, however, buttoned, and on the summit of his round head was perched a hat of exceeding smallness, and of the so-called 'pot' category. It evidently fitted him, but a hatter himself would not have known why. His hands were encased in new gloves, of a dark-brown colour, and they hung with an air of unaccustomed inaction at his sides. He sported neither umbrella nor stick. He extended one of his hands, almost with eagerness, to Mrs Freer, blushing a little as he became aware that he had been eager.

'Oh, Doctor Feeder!' she said, smiling at him. Then she repeated to her husband, 'Doctor Feeder, my dear!' and her husband said, 'Oh, Doctor, how d'ye do?' I have spoken of the composition of his appearance; but the items were not perceived by these two. They saw only one thing, his delightful face, which was both simple and clever- and unreservedly good. They had lately made the voyage from New York in his company, and it was plain that he would be very genial at sea. After he had stood in front of them a moment, a chair beside Mrs Freer became vacant, on which he took possession of it, and sat there telling her what he thought of the Park and how he liked London. As she knew every one she had known many of his people at home; and while she listened to him she remembered how large their contribution had been to the virtue and culture of Cincinnati. Mrs Freer's social horizon included even that city; she had been on terms almost familiar with several families from Ohio, and was acquainted with the position of the Feeders there. This family, very numerous, was interwoven into an enormous cousinship. She herself was quite out of such a system, but she could have told you whom Doctor Feeder's great-grandfather had married. Every one, indeed, had heard of the good deeds of the descendants of this worthy, who were generally physicians, excellent ones, and whose name expressed not inaptly their numerous acts of charity. Sidney Feeder, who had several cousins of this name established in the same line at Cincinnati, had transferred himself and his ambition to New York, where his practice, at the end of three years, had begun to grow. He had studied his profession at Vienna, and was impregnated with German science; indeed, if he had only worn spectacles, he might perfectly, as he sat there watching the riders in Rotten Row as if their proceedings were a successful demonstration, have passed for a young German of distinction. He had come over to London to attend a medical congress which met this year in the British capital; for his interest in the healing art was by no means limited to the cure of his patients; it embraced every form of experiment, and the expression of his honest eyes would almost have reconciled you to vivisection. It was the first time he had come to the Park; for social experiments he had little leisure. Being aware, however, that it was a very typical, and as it were symptomatic, sight, he had conscientiously reserved an after-noon, and had dressed himself carefully for the occasion. 'It's quite a brilliant show,' he said to Mrs Freer, 'it makes me wish I had a mount.' Little as he resembled Lord Canterville, he rode very well.

'Wait till Jackson Lemon passes again, and you can stop him and make him let you take a turn.' This was the jocular suggestion of Dexter Freer.

'Why, is he here? I have been looking out for him; I should like to see him.'

'Doesn't he go to your medical congress?' asked Mrs Freer.

'Well, yes, he attends; but he isn't very regular. I guess he goes out a good deal.'

'I guess he does,' said Mr Freer; 'and if he isn't very regular, I guess he has a good reason. A beautiful reason, a charming reason,' he went on, bending forward to look down toward the beginning of the Row. 'Dear me, what a lovely reason!'

Doctor Feeder followed the direction of his eyes, and after a moment understood his allusion. Little Jackson Lemon, on his big horse, passed along the avenue again, riding beside one of the young girls who had come that way shortly before in the company of Lord Canterville. His lordship followed, in con-versation with the other, his younger daughter. As they advanced, Jackson Lemon turned his eyes toward the multitude under the trees, and it so happened that they rested upon the Dexter Freers. He smiled, and raised his hat with all possible friendliness; and his three companions turned to see to whom he was bowing with so much cordiality. As he settled his hat on his head he espied the young man from Cincinnati, whom he had at

first overlooked; whereupon he smiled still more brightly and
waved Sidney Feeder an airy salutation with his hand, reining in
a little at the same time just for an instant, as if he half expected
the Doctor to come and speak to him. Seeing him with
strangers, however, Sidney Feeder hung back, staring a little as
he rode away.

It is open to us to know that at this moment the young lady
by whose side he was riding said to him, familiarly enough;
'Who are those people you bowed to?'

'Some old friends of mine – Americans,' Jackson Lemon
answered.

'Of course they are Americans; there is nothing but Americans
nowadays.'

'Oh yes, our turn's coming round!' laughed the young man.

'But that doesn't say who they are,' his companion continued.
'It's so difficult to say who Americans are,' she added, before he
had time to answer her.

'Dexter Freer and his wife – there is nothing difficult about
that: every one knows them.'

'I never heard of them,' said the English girl.

'Ah, that's your fault. I assure you everybody knows them.'

'And does everybody know the little man with the fat face
whom you kissed your hand to?'

'I didn't kiss my hand, but I would if I had thought of it. He
is a great chum of mine, – a fellow-student at Vienna.'

'And what's *his* name?'

'Doctor Feeder.'

Jackson Lemon's companion was silent a moment. 'Are *all*
your friends doctors?' she presently inquired.

'No; some of them are in other businesses.'

'Are they all in some business?'

'Most of them; save two or three, like Dexter Freer.'

'Dexter Freer? I thought you said Doctor Freer.'

The young man gave a laugh. 'You heard me wrong. You
have got doctors on the brain, Lady Barb.'

'I am rather glad,' said Lady Barb, giving the rein to her
horse, who bounded away.

'Well, yes, she's very handsome, the reason,' Doctor Feeder
remarked, as he sat under the trees.

'Is he going to marry her?' Mrs Freer inquired.

'Marry her? I hope not.'

'Why do you hope not?'

'Because I know nothing about her. I want to know something about the woman that man marries.'

'I suppose you would like him to marry in Cincinnati,' Mrs Freer rejoined lightly.

'Well, I am not particular where it is; but I want to know her first.' Doctor Feeder was very sturdy.

'We were in hopes you would know all about it,' said Mr Freer.

'No; I haven't kept up with him there.'

'We have heard from a dozen people that he has been always with her for the last month; and that kind of thing, in England, is supposed to mean something. Hasn't he spoken of her when you have seen him?'

'No, he has only talked about the new treatment of spinal meningitis. He is very much interested in spinal meningitis.'

'I wonder if he talks about it to Lady Barb,' said Mrs Freer.

'Who is she, any way?' the young man inquired.

'Lady Barberina Clement.'

'And who is Lady Barberina Clement?'

'The daughter of Lord Canterville.'

'And who is Lord Canterville?'

'Dexter must tell you that,' said Mrs Freer.

And Dexter accordingly told him that the Marquis of Canterville had been in his day a great sporting nobleman and an ornament to English society, and had held more than once a high post in her Majesty's household. Dexter Freer knew all these things – how his lordship had married a daughter of Lord Treherne, a very serious, intelligent and beautiful woman, who had redeemed him from the extravagance of his youth and presented him in rapid succession with a dozen little tenants for the nurseries at Pasterns – this being, as Mr Freer also knew, the name of the principal seat of the Cantervilles. The Marquis was a Tory, but very liberal for a Tory, and very popular in society at large; good-natured, good-looking, knowing how to be genial and yet remain a *grand seigneur*, clever enough to make an occasional speech, and much associated with the fine old English pursuits, as well as with many of the new improvements – the purification of the Turf, the opening of the museums on Sunday, the propagation of coffee-taverns, the latest ideas on sanitary reform. He disapproved of the extension of the suffrage, but he positively had drainage on the brain. It had been said of him at least once (and I think in print) that he was just the man to convey to the popular mind the impression that the British aristocracy is still a living force. He was not very rich, unfortunately (for a man who had to exemplify such truths), and of his twelve children no less than seven were daughters. Lady Barberina, Jackson Lemon's friend, was the second; the eldest had married Lord Beauchemin. Mr Freer had caught quite the right pronunciation of this name; he called it Bitumen. Lady Louisa had done very well, for her husband was rich, and she had brought him nothing to speak of; but it was hardly to be expected that the others would do so well. Happily the younger girls were still in the school-room; and before they had come up, Lady Canterville, who was a woman of resources, would have worked off the two that were out. It was Lady Agatha's first season; she was not so pretty as her sister, but she was thought to be cleverer. Half a dozen people had spoken to him of Jackson Lemon's being a great deal at the Cantervilles. He was supposed to be enormously rich.

'Well, so he is,' said Sidney Feeder, who had listened to Mr Freer's little recital with attention, with eagerness even, but with an air of imperfect apprehension.

'Yes, but not so rich as they probably think.'

'Do they want his money? Is that what they're after?'

'You go straight to the point,' Mrs Freer murmured.

'I haven't the least idea,' said her husband. 'He is a very nice fellow in himself.'

'Yes, but he's a doctor,' Mrs Freer remarked.

'What have they got against that?' asked Sidney Feeder.

'Why, over here, you know, they only call them in to prescribe,' said Dexter Freer; 'the profession isn't – a – what you'd call aristocratic.'

'Well, I don't know it, and I don't know that I want to know it. How do you mean, aristocratic? What profession is? It would be rather a curious one. Many of the gentlemen at the congress there are quite charming.'

'I like doctors very much,' said Mrs Freer; 'my father was a doctor. But they don't marry the daughters of marquises.'

'I don't believe Jackson wants to marry that one.'

'Very possibly not – people are such asses,' said Dexter Freer. 'But he will have to decide. I wish you would find out, by the way; you can if you will.'

'I will ask him – up at the congress; I can do that. I suppose he has got to marry some one,' Sidney Feeder added, in a moment, 'and she may be a nice girl.'

'She is said to be charming.'

'Very well, then; it won't hurt him. I must say, however, I am not sure I like all that about her family.'

'What I told you? It's all to their honour and glory.'

'Are they quite on the square? It's like those people in Thackeray.'

'Oh, if Thackeray could have done this!' Mrs Freer exclaimed, with a good deal of expression.

'You mean all this scene?' asked the young man.

'No; the marriage of a British noblewoman and an American doctor. It would have been a subject for Thackeray.'

'You see you do want it, my dear,' said Dexter Freer quietly.

'I want it as a story, but I don't want it for Doctor Lemon.'

'Does he call himself "Doctor" still?' Mr Freer asked of young Feeder.

'I suppose he does; I call him so. Of course he doesn't practise. But once a doctor, always a doctor.'

'That's doctrine for Lady Barb!'

Sidney Feeder stared. 'Hasn't she got a title too? What would she expect him to be? President of the United States? He's a man of real ability; he might have stood at the head of his profession. When I think of that, I want to swear. What did his father want to go and make all that money for?'

'It must certainly be odd to them to see a "medical man" with six or eight millions,' Mr Freer observed.

'They use the same term as the Choctaws,' said his wife.

'Why, some of their own physicians make immense fortunes,' Sidney Feeder declared.

'Couldn't he be made a baronet by the Queen?' This suggestion came from Mrs Freer.

'Yes, then he would be aristocratic,' said the young man. 'But I don't see why he should want to marry over here; it seems to me to be going out of his way. However, if he is happy, I don't care. I like him very much; he has got lots of ability. If it hadn't been for his father he would have made a splendid doctor. But, as I say, he takes a great interest in medical science, and I guess he means to promote it all he can – with his fortune. He will always be doing something in the way of research. He thinks we *do* know something, and he is bound we shall know more. I hope she won't prevent him, the young marchioness – is that her rank? And I hope they are really good people. He ought to be very useful. I should want to know a good deal about the family I was going to marry into.'

'He looked to me, as he rode there, as if he knew a good deal about the Clements,' Dexter Freer said, rising, as his wife suggested that they ought to be going; 'and he looked to me pleased with the knowledge. There they come, down on the other side. Will you walk away with us, or will you stay?'

'Stop him and ask him, and then come and tell us – in Jermyn Street.' This was Mrs Freer's parting injunction to Sidney Feeder.

'He ought to come himself – tell him that,' her husband added.

'Well, I guess I'll stay,' said the young man, as his companions merged themselves in the crowd that now was tending toward the gates. He went and stood by the barrier, and saw Doctor Lemon and his friends pull up at the entrance to the Row, where they apparently prepared to separate. The separation took some time, and Sidney Feeder became interested. Lord Canterville and his younger daughter lingered to talk with two gentlemen, also mounted, who looked a good deal at the legs of Lady Agatha's horse. Jackson Lemon and Lady Barberina were face to face, very near each other, and she, leaning forward a little, stroked the overlapping neck of his glossy bay. At a distance he appeared to be talking, and she to be listening and saying nothing. 'Oh yes, he's making love to her,' thought Sidney Feeder. Suddenly her father turned away, to leave the Park, and she joined him and disappeared, while Doctor Lemon came up on the left again, as if for a final gallop. He had not gone far before he perceived his *confrère*, who awaited him at the rail; and he repeated the gesture which Lady Barberina had spoken of as a kissing of his hand, though it must be added that, to his friend's eyes, it had not quite that significance. When he reached the point where Feeder stood he pulled up.

'If I had known you were coming here I would have given you a mount,' he said. There was not in his person that irradiation of wealth and distinction which made Lord Canterville glow like a picture; but as he sat there with his little legs stuck out, he looked very bright and sharp and happy, wearing in his degree the aspect of one of Fortune's favourites. He had a thin, keen, delicate face, a nose very carefully finished, a rapid eye, a trifle hard in expression, and a small moustache, a good deal cultivated. He was not striking, but he was very positive, and it was easy to see that he was full of purpose.

'How many horses have you got – about forty?' his compatriot inquired, in response to his greeting.

'About five hundred,' said Jackson Lemon.

'Did you mount your friends – the three you were riding with?'

'Mount them? They have got the best horses in England.'

'Did they sell you this one?' Sidney Feeder continued in the same humorous strain.

'What do you think of him?' said his friend, not deigning to answer this question.

'He's an awful old screw; I wonder he can carry you.'

'Where did you get your hat?' asked Doctor Lemon, in return.

'I got it in New York. What's the matter with it?'

'It's very beautiful; I wish I had bought one like it.'

'The head's the thing – not the hat. I don't mean yours, but mine. There is something very deep in your question; I must think it over.'

'Don't – don't,' said Jackson Lemon; 'you will never get to the bottom of it. Are you having a good time?'

'A glorious time. Have you been up to-day?'

'Up among the doctors? No; I have had a lot of things to do.'

'We had a very interesting discussion. I made a few remarks.'

'You ought to have told me. What were they about?'

'About the intermarriage of races, from the point of view – '

And Sidney Feeder paused a moment, occupied with the attempt to scratch the nose of his friend's horse.

'From the point of view of the progeny, I suppose?'

'Not at all; from the point of view of the old friends.'

'Damn the old friends!' Doctor Lemon exclaimed, with jocular crudity.

'Is it true that you are going to marry a young marchioness?'

The face of the young man in the saddle became just a trifle rigid, and his firm eyes fixed themselves on Doctor Feeder.

'Who has told you that?'

'Mr and Mrs Freer, whom I met just now.'

'Mr and Mrs Freer be hanged! And who told them?'

'Ever so many people; I don't know who.'

'Gad, how things are tattled!' cried Jackson Lemon, with some asperity.

'I can see it's true, by the way you say that.'

'Do Freer and his wife believe it?' Jackson Lemon went on impatiently.

'They want you to go and see them; you can judge for yourself.'

'I will go and see them, and tell them to mind their own business.'

'In Jermyn Street; but I forget the number. I am sorry the marchioness isn't American,' Sidney Feeder continued.

'If I should marry her, she would be,' said his friend. 'But I don't see what difference it can make to you.'

'Why, she'll look down on the profession; and I don't like that from your wife.'

'That will touch me more than you.'

'Then it *is* true?' cried Feeder, more seriously looking up at his friend.

'She won't look down; I will answer for that.'

'You won't care; you are out of it all now.'

'No, I am not; I mean to do a great deal of work.'

'I will believe that when I see it,' said Sidney Feeder, who was by no means perfectly incredulous, but who thought it salutary to take that tone. 'I am not sure that you have any right to work – you oughtn't to have everything; you ought to leave the field to us. You must pay the penalty of being so rich.

You would have been celebrated if you had continued to practise – more celebrated than any one. But you won't be now – you can't be. Some one else will be, in your place.'

Jackson Lemon listened to this, but without meeting the eyes of the speaker; not, however, as if he were avoiding them, but as if the long stretch of the Ride, now less and less obstructed, invited him and made his companion's talk a little retarding. Nevertheless, he answered, deliberately and kindly enough: 'I hope it will be you'; and he bowed to a lady who rode past.

'Very likely it will. I hope I make you feel badly – that's what I'm trying to do.'

'Oh, awfully!' cried Jackson Lemon; 'all the more that I am not in the least engaged.'

'Well, that's good. Won't you come up to-morrow?' Doctor Feeder went on.

'I'll try, my dear fellow; I can't be sure. By-by!'

'Oh, you're lost anyway!' cried Sidney Feeder, as the other started away.

2

IT WAS Lady Marmaduke, the wife of Sir Henry Marmaduke, who had introduced Jackson Lemon to Lady Beauchemin; after which Lady Beauchemin had made him acquainted with her mother and sisters. Lady Marmaduke was also transatlantic; she had been for her conjugal baronet the most permanent consequence of a tour in the United States. At present, at the end of ten years, she knew her London as she had never known her New York, so that it had been easy for her to be, as she called herself, Jackson Lemon's social godmother. She had views with regard to his career, and these views fitted into a social scheme which, if our space permitted, I should be glad to lay before the reader in its magnitude. She wished to add an arch or two to the bridge on which she had effected her transit from America, and it was her belief that Jackson Lemon might furnish the materials.

This bridge, as yet a somewhat sketchy and rickety structure, she saw (in the future) boldly stretching from one solid pillar to another. It would have to go both ways, for reciprocity was the keynote of Lady Marmaduke's plan. It was her belief that an ultimate fusion was inevitable, and that those who were the first to understand the situation would gain the most. The first time Jackson Lemon had dined with her, he met Lady Beauchemin, who was her intimate friend. Lady Beauchemin was remarkably gracious; she asked him to come and see her as if she really meant it. He presented himself, and in her drawing-room met her mother, who happened to be calling at the same moment. Lady Canterville, not less friendly than her daughter, invited him down to Pasterns for Easter week; and before a month had passed it seemed to him that, though he was not what he would have called intimate at any house in London, the door of the house of Clement opened to him pretty often. This was a considerable good fortune, for it always opened upon a charming picture. The inmates were a blooming and beautiful race, and their interior had an aspect of the ripest comfort. It was not the splendour of New York (as New York had lately begun to appear to the young man), but a splendour in which there was an unpurchasable ingredient of age. He himself had a great deal of money, and money was good, even when it was new; but old money was the best. Even after he learned that Lord Canterville's fortune was more ancient than abundant, it was still the mellowness of the golden element that struck him. It was Lady Beauchemin who had told him that her father was not rich; having told him, besides this, many surprising things – things that were surprising in themselves or surprising on her lips. This struck him afresh later that evening – the day he met Sidney Feeder in the Park. He dined out, in the company of Lady Beauchemin, and afterward, as she was alone – her husband had gone down to listen to a debate – she offered to 'take him on'. She was going to several places, and he must be going to some of them. They compared notes, and it was settled that they should proceed together to the Trumpingtons', whither, also, it appeared at eleven o'clock that all in the world was going, the approach to the house being choked for half a mile with carriages. It was a close, muggy night; Lady

Beauchemin's chariot, in its place in the rank, stood still for long periods. In his corner beside her, through the open window, Jackson Lemon, rather hot, rather oppressed, looked out on the moist, greasy pavement, over which was flung, a considerable distance up and down, the flare of a public-house. Lady Beauchemin, however, was not impatient, for she had a purpose in her mind, and now she could say what she wished.

'Do you really love her?' That was the first thing she said.

'Well, I guess so,' Jackson Lemon answered, as if he did not recognise the obligation to be serious.

Lady Beauchemin looked at him a moment in silence; he felt her gaze, and turning his eyes, saw her face, partly shadowed, with the aid of a street-lamp. She was not so pretty as Lady Barberina; her countenance had a certain sharpness; her hair, very light in colour and wonderfully frizzled, almost covered her eyes, the expression of which, however, together with that of her pointed nose, and the glitter of several diamonds, emerged from the gloom. 'You don't seem to know. I never saw a man in such an odd state,' she presently remarked.

'You push me a little too much; I must have time to think of it,' the young man went on. 'You know in my country they allow us plenty of time.' He had several little oddities of expression, of which he was perfectly conscious, and which he found convenient, for they protected him in a society in which a lonely American was rather exposed; they gave him the advantage which corresponded with certain drawbacks. He had very few natural Americanisms, but the occasional use of one, discreetly chosen, made him appear simpler than he really was, and he had his reasons for wishing this result. He was not simple; he was subtle, circumspect, shrewd, and perfectly aware that he might make mistakes. There was a danger of his making a mistake at present – a mistake which would be immensely grave. He was determined only to succeed. It is true that for a great success he would take a certain risk; but the risk was to be considered, and he gained time while he multiplied his guesses and talked about his country.

'You may take ten years if you like,' said Lady Beauchemin. 'I am in no hurry whatever to make you my brother-in-law. Only you must remember that you spoke to me first.'

'What did I say?'

'You told me that Barberina was the finest girl you had seen in England.'

'Oh, I am willing to stand by that; I like her type.'

'I should think you might!'

'I like her very much – with all her peculiarities.'

'What do you mean by her peculiarities?'

'Well, she has some peculiar ideas,' said Jackson Lemon, in a tone of the sweetest reasonableness; 'and she has a peculiar way of speaking.'

'Ah, you can't expect us to speak as well as you!' cried Lady Beauchemin.

'I don't know why not; you do some things much better.'

'We have our own ways, at any rate, and we think them the best in the world. One of them is not to let a gentleman devote himself to a girl for three or four months without some sense of responsibility. If you don't wish to marry my sister you ought to go away.'

'I ought never to have come,' said Jackson Lemon.

'I can scarcely agree to that; for I should have lost the pleasure of knowing you.'

'It would have spared you this duty, which you dislike very much.'

'Asking you about your intentions? I don't dislike it at all; it amuses me extremely.'

'Should you like your sister to marry me?' asked Jackson Lemon, with great simplicity.

If he expected to take Lady Beauchemin by surprise he was disappointed; for she was perfectly prepared to commit herself. 'I should like it very much. I think English and American society ought to be but one – I mean the best of each – a great whole.'

'Will you allow me to ask whether Lady Marmaduke suggested that to you?'

'We have often talked of it.'

'Oh yes, that's her aim.'

'Well, it's my aim too. I think there's a great deal to be done.'

'And you would like me to do it?'

'To begin it, precisely. Don't you think we ought to see more of each other? – I mean the best in each country.'

Jackson Lemon was silent a moment. 'I am afraid I haven't any general ideas. If I should marry an English girl it wouldn't be for the good of the species.'

'Well, we want to be mixed a little; that I am sure of,' Lady Beauchemin said.

'You certainly got that from Lady Marmaduke.'

'It's too tiresome, your not consenting to be serious! But my father will make you so,' Lady Beauchemin went on. 'I may as well let you know that he intends in a day or two to ask you your intentions. That's all I wished to say to you. I think you ought to be prepared.'

'I am much obliged to you; Lord Canterville will do quite right.'

There was, to Lady Beauchemin, something really unfathomable in this little American doctor, whom she had taken up on grounds of large policy, and who, though he was assumed to have sunk the medical character, was neither handsome nor distinguished, but only immensely rich and quite original, for he was not insignificant. It was unfathomable, to begin with, that a medical man should be so rich, or that so rich a man should be medical; it was even, to an eye which was always gratified by suitability, rather irritating. Jackson Lemon himself could have explained it better than any one else, but this was an explanation that one could scarcely ask for. There were other things; his cool acceptance of certain situations; his general indisposition to explain; his way of taking refuge in jokes which at times had not even the merit of being American; his way, too, of appearing to be a suitor without being an aspirant. Lady Beauchemin, however, was, like Jackson Lemon, prepared to run a certain risk. His reserves made him slippery; but that was only when one pressed. She flattered herself that she could handle people lightly. 'My father will be sure to act with perfect tact,' she said; 'of course, if you shouldn't care to be questioned, you can go out of town.' She had the air of really wishing to make everything easy for him.

'I don't want to go out of town; I am enjoying it far too much here,' her companion answered. 'And wouldn't your father have a right to ask me what I meant by that?'

Lady Beauchemin hesitated; she was slightly perplexed. But

in a moment she exclaimed: 'He is incapable of saying anything vulgar!'

She had not really answered his inquiry, and he was conscious of that; but he was quite ready to say to her, a little later, as he guided her steps from the brougham to the strip of carpet which, between a somewhat rickety border of striped cloth and a double row of waiting footmen, policemen and dingy amateurs of both sexes, stretched from the curbstone to the portal of the Trumpingtons, 'Of course I shall not wait for Lord Canterville to speak to me.'

He had been expecting some such announcement as this from Lady Beauchemin, and he judged that her father would do no more than his duty. He knew that he ought to be prepared with an answer to Lord Canterville, and he wondered at himself for not yet having come to the point. Sidney Feeder's question in the Park had made him feel rather pointless; it was the first allusion that had been made to his possible marriage, except on the part of Lady Beauchemin. None of his own people were in London; he was perfectly independent, and even if his mother had been within reach he could not have consulted her on the subject. He loved her dearly, better than any one; but she was not a woman to consult, for she approved of whatever he did; it was her standard. He was careful not to be too serious when he talked with Lady Beauchemin; but he was very serious indeed as he thought over the matter within himself, which he did even among the diversions of the next half-hour, while he squeezed obliquely and slowly through the crush in Mrs Trumpington's drawing-room. At the end of the half-hour he came away, and at the door he found Lady Beauchemin, from whom he had separated on entering the house, and who, this time with a companion of her own sex, was awaiting her carriage and still 'going on'. He gave her his arm into the street, and as she stepped into the vehicle she repeated that she wished he would go out of town for a few days.

'Who, then, would tell me what to do?' he asked, for answer, looking at her through the window.

She might tell him what to do, but he felt free, all the same; and he was determined this should continue. To prove it to himself he jumped into a hansom and drove back to Brook

Street, to his hotel, instead of proceeding to a bright-windowed house in Portland Place, where he knew that after midnight he should find Lady Canterville and her daughters. There had been a reference to the subject between Lady Barberina and himself during their ride, and she would probably expect him; but it made him taste his liberty not to go, and he liked to taste his liberty. He was aware that to taste it in perfection he ought to go to bed; but he did not go to bed, he did not even take off his hat. He walked up and down his sitting-room, with his head surmounted by this ornament, a good deal tipped back, and his hands in his pockets. There were a good many cards stuck into the frame of the mirror, over his chimney-piece, and every time he passed the place he seemed to see what was written on one of them – the name of the mistress of the house in Portland Place, his own name, and, in the lower left-hand corner, the words: 'A small Dance'. Of course, now, he must make up his mind; he would make it up to the next day: that was what he said to himself as he walked up and down; and according to his decision he would speak to Lord Canterville or he would take the night-express to Paris. It was better meanwhile that he should not see Lady Barberina. It was vivid to him, as he paused occasionally, looking vaguely at that card in the chimney-glass, that he had come pretty far; and he had come so far because he was under the charm – yes, he was in love with Lady Barb. There was no doubt whatever of that; he had a faculty for diagnosis, and he knew perfectly well what was the matter with him. He wasted no time in musing upon the mystery of this passion, in wondering whether he might not have escaped it by a little vigilance at first, or whether it would die out if he should go away. He accepted it frankly, for the sake of the pleasure it gave him – the girl was the delight of his eyes – and confined himself to considering whether such a marriage would square with his general situation. This would not at all necessarily follow from the fact that he was in love; too many other things would come in between. The most important of these was the change, not only of the geographical, but of the social, standpoint for his wife, and a certain readjustment that it would involve in his own relation to things. He was not inclined to readjustments, and there was no reason why he should be; his own position was in most respects so advantageous. But the girl tempted him almost irresistibly, satisfying his imagination both as a lover and as a student of the human organism; she was so blooming, so complete, of a type so rarely encountered in that degree of perfection. Jackson Lemon was not an Anglo-maniac, but he admired the physical conditions of the English – their complexion, their temperament, their tissue; and Lady Barberina struck him, in flexible, virginal form, as a wonderful compendium of these elements. There was something simple and robust in her beauty; it had the quietness of an old Greek statue, without the vulgarity of the modern simper or of contemporary prettiness. Her head was antique; and though her conversation was quite of the present period, Jackson Lemon had said to himself that there was sure to be in her soul a certain primitive sincerity which would match with her facial mould. He saw her as she might be in the future, the beautiful mother of beautiful children, in whom the look of race should be conspicuous. He should like his children to have the look of race, and he was not unaware that he must take his precautions accordingly. A great many people had it in England; and it was a pleasure to him to see it, especially as no one had it so unmistakably as the second daughter of Lord Canterville. It would be a great luxury to call such a woman one's own; nothing could be more evident than that, because it made no difference that she was not strikingly clever. Striking cleverness was not part of harmonious form and the English complexion; it was associated with the modern simper, which was a result of modern nerves. If Jackson Lemon had wanted a nervous wife, of course he could have found her at home; but this tall, fair girl, whose character, like her figure, appeared mainly to have been formed by riding across country, was differently put together. All the same, would it suit his book, as they said in London, to marry her and transport her to New York? He came back to this question; came back to it with a persistency which, had she been admitted to a view of it, would have tried the patience of Lady Beauchemin. She had been irritated, more than once, at his appearing to attach himself so exclusively to this horn of the dilemma – as if it could possibly fail to be a good thing for a little American doctor to marry the daughter of an English peer. It would have been more becoming, in her ladyship's eyes, that he should take that for granted a little more, and the consent of her ladyship's – of their ladyships' – family a little less. They looked at the matter so differently! Jackson Lemon was conscious that if he should marry Lady Barberina Clement it would be because it suited him, and not because it suited his possible sisters-in-law. He believed that he acted in all things by his own will – an organ for which he had the highest respect.

It would have seemed, however, that on this occasion it was not working very regularly, for though he had come home to go to bed, the stroke of half-past twelve saw him jump, not into his couch, but in a hansom which the whistle of the porter had summoned to the door of his hotel, and in which he rattled off to Portland Place. Here he found – in a very large house – an assembly of three hundred people, and a band of music concealed in a bower of azaleas. Lady Canterville had not arrived; he wandered through the rooms and assured himself of that. He also discovered a very good conservatory, where there were banks and pyramids of azaleas. He watched the top of the staircase, but it was a long time before he saw what he was looking for, and his impatience at last was extreme. The reward, however, when it came, was all that he could have desired. It was a little smile from Lady Barberina, who stood behind her mother while the latter extended her finger-tips to the hostess. The entrance of this charming woman, with her beautiful daughters – always a noticeable incident – was effected with a certain brilliancy, and just now it was agreeable to Jackson Lemon to think that it concerned him more than any one else in the house. Tall, dazzling, indifferent, looking about her as if she saw very little, Lady Barberina was certainly a figure round which a young man's fancy might revolve. She was very quiet and simple, had little manner and little movement; but her detachment was not a vulgar art. She appeared to efface herself, to wait till, in the natural course, she should be attended to; and in this there was evidently no exaggeration, for she was too proud not to have perfect confidence. Her sister, smaller, slighter, with a little surprised smile, which seemed to say that in her extreme innocence she was yet prepared for anything, having heard, indirectly, such extraordinary things about society, was much more impatient and more expressive, and projected across a threshold the pretty radiance of her eyes and teeth before her mother's name was announced. Lady Canterville was thought by many persons to be very superior to her daughters; she had kept even more beauty than she had given them; and it was a beauty which had been called intellectual. She had extraordinary sweetness, without any definite professions; her manner was mild almost to tenderness; there was even a kind of pity in it. Moreover, her features were perfect, and nothing could be more gently gracious than a way she had of speaking, or rather, of listening, to people, with her head inclined a little to one side. Jackson Lemon liked her very much, and she had certainly been most kind to him. He approached Lady Barberina as soon as he could do so without an appearance of precipitation, and said to her that he hoped very much she would not dance. He was a master of the art which flourishes in New York above every other, and he had guided her through a dozen waltzes with a skill which, as she felt, left absolutely nothing to be desired. But dancing was not his business to-night. She smiled a little at the expression of his hope.

'That is what mamma has brought us here for,' she said; 'she doesn't like it if we don't dance.'

'How does she know whether she likes it or not? You have always danced.'

'Once I didn't,' said Lady Barberina.

He told her that, at any rate, he would settle it with her mother, and persuaded her to wander with him into the conservatory, where there were coloured lights suspended among the plants, and a vault of verdure overhead. In comparison with the other rooms the conservatory was dusky and remote. But they were not alone; half a dozen other couples were in possession. The gloom was rosy with the slopes of azalea, and suffused with mitigated music, which made it possible to talk without consideration of one's neighbours. Nevertheless, though it was only in looking back on the scene later that Lady Barberina perceived this, these dispersed couples were talking very softly. She did not look at them; it seemed to her that, virtually, she was alone with Jackson Lemon. She said something about conservatories, about the fragrance of the air;

for all answer to which he asked her, as he stood there before her, a question by which she might have been exceedingly startled.

'How do people who marry in England ever know each other before marriage? They have no chance.'

'I am sure I don't know,' said Lady Barberina; 'I never was married.'

'It's very different in my country. There a man may see much of a girl; he may come and see her, he may be constantly alone with her. I wish you allowed that over here.'

Lady Barberina suddenly examined the less ornamental side of her fan, as if it had never occurred to her before to look at it. 'It must be so very odd, America,' she murmured at last.

'Well, I guess in that matter we are right; over here it's a leap in the dark.'

'I am sure I don't know,' said the girl. She had folded her fan; she stretched out her arm mechanically and plucked a sprig of azalea.

'I guess it doesn't signify, after all,' Jackson Lemon remarked. 'They say that love is blind at the best.' His keen young face was bent upon hers; his thumbs were in the pockets of his trousers; he smiled a little, showing his fine teeth. She said nothing, but only pulled her azalea to pieces. She was usually so quiet that this small movement looked restless.

'This is the first time I have seen you in the least without a lot of people,' he went on.

'Yes, it's very tiresome,' she said.

'I have been sick of it; I didn't want to come here to-night.'

She had not met his eyes, though she knew they were seeking her own. But now she looked at him a moment. She had never objected to his appearance, and in this respect she had no repugnance to overcome. She liked a man to be tall and handsome, and Jackson Lemon was neither; but when she was sixteen, and as tall herself as she was to be at twenty, she had been in love (for three weeks) with one of her cousins, a little fellow in the Hussars, who was shorter even than the American, shorter consequently than herself. This proved that distinction might be independent of stature – not that she ever reasoned it out. Jackson Lemon's facial spareness, his bright little eye, which seemed always to be measuring things, struck her as original, and she thought them very cutting, which would do very well for a husband of hers. As she made this reflection, of course it never occurred to her that she herself might be cut; she was not a sacrificial lamb. She perceived that his features expressed a mind – a mind that would be rather effective. She would never have taken him for a doctor; though, indeed, when all was said, that was very negative and didn't account for the way he imposed himself.

'Why, then, did you come?' she asked, in answer to his last speech.

'Because it seems to me after all better to see you in this way than not to see you at all; I want to know you better.'

'I don't think I ought to stay here,' said Lady Barberina, looking round her.

'Don't go till I have told you I love you,' murmured the young man.

She made no exclamation, indulged in no start; he could not see even that she changed colour. She took his request with a noble simplicity, with her head erect and her eyes lowered.

'I don't think you have a right to tell me that.'

'Why not?' Jackson Lemon demanded. 'I wish to claim the right; I wish you to give it to me.'

'I can't – I don't know you. You have said it yourself.'

'Can't you have a little faith? That will help us to know each other better. It's disgusting, the want of opportunity; even at Pasterns I could scarcely get a walk with you. But I have the greatest faith in you. I feel that I love you, and I couldn't do more than that at the end of six months. I love your beauty – I love you from head to foot. Don't move, please don't move.' He lowered his tone; but it went straight to her ear, and it must be believed that it had a certain eloquence. For himself, after he had heard himself say these words, all his being was in a glow. It was a luxury to speak to her of her beauty; it brought him nearer to her than he had ever been. But the colour had come into her face, and it seemed to remind him that her beauty was not all. 'Everything about you is sweet and noble,' he went on; 'everything is dear to me. I am sure you are good. I don't know what you think of me; I asked Lady Beauchemin to tell me, and she told me to judge for myself. Well, then, I judge you like me. Haven't I a right to assume that till the contrary is proved? May I speak to your father? That's what I want to know. I have been waiting; but now what should I wait for longer? I want to be able to tell him that you have given me some hope. I suppose I ought to speak to him first. I meant to, to-morrow, but meanwhile, to-night, I thought I would just put this in. In my country it wouldn't matter particularly. You must see all that over there for yourself. If you should tell me not to speak to your father, I wouldn't; I would wait. But I like better to ask your leave to speak to him than to ask his to speak to you.'

His voice had sunk almost to a whisper; but, though it trembled, his emotion gave it peculiar intensity. He had the same attitude, his thumbs in his trousers, his attentive head, his smile, which was a matter of course; no one would have imagined what he was saying. She had listened without moving, and at the end she raised her eyes. They rested on his a moment, and he remembered, a good while later, the look which passed her lids.

'You may say anything that you please to my father, but I don't wish to hear any more. You have said too much, considering how little idea you have given me before.'

'I was watching you,' said Jackson Lemon.

Lady Barberina held her head higher, looking straight at him. Then, quite seriously, 'I don't like to be watched,' she remarked.

'You shouldn't be so beautiful, then. Won't you give me a word of hope?' he added.

'I have never supposed I should marry a foreigner,' said Lady Barberina.

'Do you call me a foreigner?'

'I think your ideas are very different, and your country is different; you have told me so yourself.'

'I should like to show it to you; I would make you like it.'

'I am not sure what you would make me do,' said Lady Barberina, very honestly.

'Nothing that you don't want.'

'I am sure you would try,' she declared, with a smile.

'Well,' said Jackson Lemon, 'after all, I am trying now.'

To this she simply replied she must go to her mother, and he was obliged to lead her out of the conservatory. Lady

Canterville was not immediately found, so that he had time to murmur as they went. 'Now that I have spoken, I am very happy.'

'Perhaps you are happy too soon,' said the girl.

'Ah, don't say that, Lady Barb.'

'Of course I must think of it.'

'Of course you must!' said Jackson Lemon. 'I will speak to your father to-morrow.'

'I can't fancy what he will say.'

'How can he dislike me?' the young man asked, in a tone which Lady Beauchemin, if she had heard him, would have been forced to attribute to his general affectation of the jocose. What Lady Beauchemin's sister thought of it is not recorded; but there is perhaps a clue to her opinion in the answer she made him after a moment's silence: 'Really, you know, you *are* a foreigner!' With this she turned her back upon him, for she was already in her mother's hands. Jackson Lemon said a few words to Lady Canterville; they were chiefly about its being very hot. She gave him her vague, sweet attention, as if he were saying something ingenious of which she missed the point. He could see that she was thinking of the doings of her daughter Agatha, whose attitude toward the contemporary young man was wanting in the perception of differences – a madness without method; she was evidently not occupied with Lady Barberina, who was more to be trusted. This young woman never met her suitor's eyes again; she let her own rest, rather ostentatiously, upon other objects. At last he was going away without a glance from her. Lady Canterville had asked him to come to lunch on the morrow, and he had said he would do so if she would promise him he should see his lordship. 'I can't pay you another visit until I have had some talk with him,' he said.

'I don't see why not; but if I speak to him I dare say he will be at home,' she answered.

'It will be worth his while!'

Jackson Lemon left the house reflecting that as he had never proposed to a girl before he could not be expected to know how women demean themselves in this emergency. He had heard, indeed, that Lady Barb had had no end of offers; and though he thought it probable that the number was exaggerated, as it

always is, it was to be supposed that her way of appearing
suddenly to have dropped him was but the usual behaviour of
the occasion.

3

AT HER mother's the next day she was absent from luncheon,
and Lady Canterville mentioned to him (he didn't ask) that she
had gone to see a dear old great-aunt, who was also her
godmother, and who lived at Roehampton. Lord Canterville
was not present, but our young man was informed by his hostess
that he had promised her he would come in exactly at three
o'clock. Jackson Lemon lunched with Lady Canterville and the
children, who appeared in force at this repast, all the younger
girls being present, and two little boys, the juniors of the two
sons who were in their teens. Jackson, who was very fond of
children, and thought these absolutely the finest in the world –
magnificent specimens of a magnificent brood, such as it would
be so satisfactory in future days to see about his own knee –
Jackson felt that he was being treated as one of the family, but
was not frightened by what he supposed the privilege to imply.
Lady Canterville betrayed no consciousness whatever of his
having mooted the question of becoming her son-in-law, and he
believed that her eldest daughter had not told her of their talk
the night before. This idea gave him pleasure; he liked to think
that Lady Barb was judging him for herself. Perhaps, indeed, she
was taking counsel of the old lady at Roehampton: he believed
that he was the sort of lover of whom a godmother would
approve. Godmothers in his mind were mainly associated with
fairy-tales (he had had no baptismal sponsors of his own); and
that point of view would be favourable to a young man with a
great deal of gold who had suddenly arrived from a foreign
country – an apparition, surely, sufficiently elfish. He made up
his mind that he should like Lady Canterville as a mother-
in-law; she would be too well-bred to meddle. Her husband

came in at three o'clock, just after they had left the table, and said to Jackson Lemon that it was very good in him to have waited.

'I haven't waited,' Jackson replied, with his watch in his hand; 'you are punctual to the minute.'

I know not how Lord Canterville may have judged his young friend, but Jackson Lemon had been told more than once in his life that he was a very good fellow, but rather too literal. After he had lighted a cigarette in his lordship's 'den', a large brown apartment on the ground-floor, which partook at once of the nature of an office and of that of a harness-room (it could not have been called in any degree a library), he went straight to the point in these terms: 'Well now, Lord Canterville, I feel as if I ought to let you know without more delay that I am in love with Lady Barb, and that I should like to marry her.' So he spoke, puffing his cigarette, with his conscious but unextenuating eye fixed on his host.

No man, as I have intimated, bore better being looked at than this noble personage; he seemed to bloom in the envious warmth of human contemplation, and never appeared so faultless as when he was most exposed. 'My dear fellow, my dear fellow,' he murmured, almost in disparagement, stroking his ambrosial beard from before the empty fireplace. He lifted his eyebrows, but he looked perfectly good-natured.

'Are you surprised, sir?' Jackson Lemon asked.

'Why, I suppose any one is surprised at a man wanting one of his children. He sometimes feels the weight of that sort of thing so much, you know. He wonders what the devil another man wants of them.' And Lord Canterville laughed pleasantly out of the copious fringe of his lips.

'I only want one of them,' said Jackson Lemon, laughing too, but with a lighter organ.

'Polygamy would be rather good for the parents. However, Louisa told me the other night that she thought you were looking the way you speak of.'

'Yes, I told Lady Beauchemin that I love Lady Barb, and she seemed to think it was natural.'

'Oh yes, I suppose there's no want of nature in it! But, my dear fellow, I really don't know what to say.'

'Of course you'll have to think of it.' Jackson Lemon, in saying this, felt that he was making the most liberal concession to the point of view of his interlocutor; being perfectly aware that in his own country it was not left much to the parents to think of.

'I shall have to talk it over with my wife.'

'Lady Canterville has been very kind to me; I hope she will continue.'

'My dear fellow, we are excellent friends. No one could appreciate you more than Lady Canterville. Of course we can only consider such a question on the – a – highest grounds. You would never want to marry without knowing, as it were, exactly what you are doing. I, on my side, naturally, you know, am bound to do the best I can for my own child. At the same time, of course, we don't want to spend our time in – a – walking round the horse. We want to keep to the main line.' It was settled between them after a little that the main line was that Jackson Lemon knew to a certainty the state of his affections and was in a position to pretend to the hand of a young lady who, Lord Canterville might say – of course, you know, without any swagger – had a right to expect to do well, as the women call it.

'I should think she had,' Jackson Lemon said, 'she's a beautiful type.'

Lord Canterville stared a moment. 'She is a clever, well-grown girl, and she takes her fences like a grasshopper. Does she know all this, by the way?' he added.

'Oh yes, I told her last night.'

Again Lord Canterville had the air, unusual with him, of returning his companion's scrutiny. 'I am not sure that you ought to have done that, you know.'

'I couldn't have spoken to you first – I couldn't,' said Jackson Lemon. 'I meant to, but it stuck in my crop.'

'They don't in your country, I guess,' his lordship returned, smiling.

'Well, not as a general thing; however, I find it very pleasant to discuss with you now.' And in truth it was very pleasant. Nothing could be easier, friendlier, more informal, than Lord Canterville's manner, which implied all sorts of equality, especially that of age and fortune, and made Jackson Lemon feel at the end of three minutes almost as if he too were a beautifully preserved and somewhat straitened nobleman of sixty, with the views of a man of the world about his own marriage. The young American perceived that Lord Canterville waived the point of his having spoken first to the girl herself, and saw in this indulgence a just concession to the ardour of young affection. For Lord Canterville seemed perfectly to appreciate the sentimental side – at least so far as it was embodied in his visitor – when he said, without deprecation: 'Did she give you any encouragement?'

'Well, she didn't box my ears. She told me that she would think of it, but that I must speak to you. But, naturally, I shouldn't have said what I did to her if I hadn't made up my mind during the last fortnight that I am not disagreeable to her.'

'Ah, my dear young man, women are odd cattle!' Lord Canterville exclaimed, rather unexpectedly. 'But of course you know all that,' he added in an instant; 'you take the general risk.'

'I am perfectly willing to take the general risk; the particular risk is small.'

'Well, upon my honour I don't really know my girls. You see a man's time, in England, is tremendously taken up; but I dare say it's the same in your country. Their mother knows them – I think I had better send for their mother. If you don't mind I'll just suggest that she join us here.'

'I'm rather afraid of you both together, but if it will settle it any quicker –' said Jackson Lemon. Lord Canterville rang the bell, and, when a servant appeared, despatched him with a message to her ladyship. While they were waiting, the young man remembered that it was in his power to give a more definite account of his pecuniary basis. He had simply said before that he was abundantly able to marry; he shrank from putting himself forward as a billionaire. He had a fine taste, and he wished to appeal to Lord Canterville primarily as a gentleman. But now that he had to make a double impression, he bethought himself of his millions, for millions were always impressive. 'I think it only fair to let you know that my fortune is really very considerable,' he remarked.

'Yes, I dare say you are beastly rich,' said Lord Canterville.

'I have about seven millions.'

'Seven millions?'

'I count in dollars; upwards of a million and a half sterling.'

Lord Canterville looked at him from head to foot, with an air of cheerful resignation to a form of grossness which threatened to become common. Then he said, with a touch of that inconsequence of which he had already given a glimpse: 'What the deuce, then, possessed you to turn doctor?'

Jackson Lemon coloured a little, hesitated, and then replied, quickly: 'Because I had the talent for it.'

'Of course, I don't for a moment doubt of your ability; but don't you find it rather a bore?'

'I don't practise much. I am rather ashamed to say that.'

'Ah, well, of course, in your country it's different. I dare say you've got a door-plate, eh?'

'Oh yes, and a tin sign tied to the balcony!' said Jackson Lemon, smiling.

'What did your father say to it?'

'To my going into medicine? He said he would be hanged if he'd take any of my doses. He didn't think I should succeed; he wanted me to go into the house.'

'Into the House – a –' said Lord Canterville, hesitating a little. 'Into your Congress – yes, exactly.'

'Ah, no, not so bad as that. Into the store,' Jackson Lemon replied, in the candid tone in which he expressed himself when, for reasons of his own, he wished to be perfectly national.

Lord Canterville stared, not venturing, even for the moment, to hazard an interpretation; and before a solution had presented itself Lady Canterville came into the room.

'My dear, I thought we had better see you. Do you know he wants to marry our second girl?' It was in these simple terms that her husband acquainted her with the question.

Lady Canterville expressed neither surprise nor elation; she simply stood there, smiling, with her head a little inclined to the side, with all her customaary graciousness. Her charming eyes rested on those of Jackson Lemon, and though they seemed to show that she had to think a little of so serious a proposition, his own discovered in them none of the coldness of calculation. 'Are you talking about Barberina?' she asked in a moment, as if her thoughts had been far away.

Of course they were talking about Barberina, and Jackson Lemon repeated to her ladyship what he had said to the girl's father. He had thought it all over, and his mind was quite made up. Moreover, he had spoken to Lady Barb.

'Did she tell you that, my dear?' asked Lord Canterville, while he lighted another cigar.

She gave no heed to this inquiry, which had been vague and accidental on his lordship's part, but simply said to Jackson Lemon that the thing was very serious, and that they had better sit down for a moment. In an instant he was near her on the sofa on which she had placed herself, still smiling and looking up at her husband with an air of general meditation, in which a sweet compassion for every one concerned was apparent.

'Barberina has told me nothing,' she said, after a little.

'That proves she cares for me!' Jackson Lemon exclaimed eagerly.

Lady Canterville looked as if she thought this almost too ingenious, almost professional; but her husband said cheerfully, jovially: 'Ah, well, if she cares for you, I don't object.'

This was a little ambiguous; but before Jackson Lemon had time to look into it, Lady Canterville asked gently: 'Should you expect her to live in America?'

'Oh, yes; that's my home, you know.'

'Shouldn't you be living sometimes in England?'

'Oh, yes, we'll come over and see you.' The young man was in love, he wanted to marry, he wanted to be genial, and to commend himself to the parents of Lady Barb; at the same time it was in his nature not to accept conditions, save in so far as they exactly suited him, to tie himself, or, as they said in New York, to give himself away. In any transaction he preferred his own terms to those of any one else. Therefore, the moment Lady Canterville gave signs of wishing to extract a promise, he was on his guard.

'She'll find it very different; perhaps she won't like it,' her ladyship suggested.

'If she likes me, she'll marry my country,' said Jackson Lemon, with decision.

'He tells me he has got a plate on his door,' Lord Canterville remarked humorously.

'We must talk to her, of course; we must understand how she feels,' said his wife, looking more serious than she had done as yet.

'Please don't discourage her, Lady Canterville,' the young man begged, 'and give me a chance to talk to her a little more myself. You haven't given me much chance, you know.'

'We don't offer our daughters to people, Mr. Lemon,' Lady Canterville was always gentle, but now she was a little majestic.

'She isn't like some women in London, you know,' said Jackson Lemon's host, who seemed to remember that to a discussion of such importance he ought from time to time to contribute a word of wisdom. And Jackson Lemon, certainly, if the idea had been presented to him, would have said that, No, decidedly, Lady Barberina had not been thrown at him.

'Of course not,' he declared, in answer to her mother's remark. 'But, you know, you mustn't refuse them too much, either; you mustn't make a poor fellow wait too long. I admire her, I love her, more than I can say; I give you my word of honour for that.'

'He seems to think that settles it,' said Lord Canterville, smiling down at the young American, very indulgently, from his place before the cold chimney-piece.

'Of course that's what we desire, Philip,' her ladyship returned, very nobly.

'Lady Barb believes it; I am sure she does!' Jackson Lemon exclaimed. 'Why should I pretend to be in love with her if I am not?'

Lady Canterville received this inquiry in silence, and her husband, with just the least air in the world of repressed impatience, began to walk up and down the room. He was a man of many engagements, and he had been closeted for more than a quarter of an hour with the young American doctor. 'Do you imagine you should come often to England?' Lady Canterville demanded, with a certain abruptness, returning to that important point.

'I'm afraid I can't tell you that; of course we shall do whatever seems best.' He was prepared to suppose they should cross the Atlantic every summer: that prospect was by no means dis-pleasing to him; but he was not prepared to give any such pledge to Lady Canterville, especially as he did not believe it would really be necessary. It was in his mind, not as an overt pretension, but as a tacit implication, that he should treat with Barberina's parents on a footing of perfect equality; and there would somehow be nothing equal if he should begin to enter into engagements which didn't belong to the essence of the matter. They were to give their daughter, and he was to take her: in this arrangement there would be as much on one side as on the other. But beyond this he had nothing to ask of them; there was nothing he wished them to promise, and his own pledges, therefore, would have no equivalent. Whenever his wife should wish it, she should come over and see her people. Her home was to be in New York; but he was tacitly conscious that on the question of absences he should be very liberal. Nevertheless, there was something in the very grain of his character which forbade that he should commit himself at present in respect to times and dates.

Lady Canterville looked at her husband, but her husband was not attentive; he was taking a peep at his watch. In a moment, however, he threw out a remark to the effect that he thought it a capital thing that the two countries should become more united, and there was nothing that would bring it about better than a few of the best people on both sides pairing off together. The English, indeed, had begun it; a lot of fellows had brought over a lot of pretty girls, and it was quite fair play that the Americans should take their pick. They were all one race, after all; and why shouldn't they make one society – the best on both sides, of course? Jackson Lemon smiled as he recognised Lady Marmaduke's philosophy, and he was pleased to think that Lady Beauchemin had some influence with her father; for he was sure the old gentleman (as he mentally designated his host) had got all this from her, though he expressed himself less happily than the cleverest of his daughters. Our hero had no objection to make to it, especially if there was anything in it that would really help his case. But it was not in the least on these high grounds that he had sought the hand of Lady Barb. He wanted her not in order that her people and his (the best on both sides!) should make one society; he wanted her simply because he wanted her. Lady Canterville smiled; but she seemed to have another thought.

'I quite appreciate what my husband says; but I don't see why poor Barb should be the one to begin.'

'I dare say she'll like it,' said Lord Canterville, as if he were attempting a short cut. 'They say you spoil your women awfully.'

'She's not one of their women yet,' her ladyship remarked, in the sweetest tone in the world; and then she added, without Jackson Lemon's knowing exactly what she meant, 'It seems so strange.'

He was a little irritated; and perhaps these simple words added to the feeling. There had been no positive opposition to his suit, and Lord and Lady Canterville were most kind; but he felt that they held back a little, and though he had not expected them to throw themselves on his neck, he was rather disappointed, his pride was touched. Why should they hesitate? He considered himself such a good *parti*. It was not so much the old gentleman, it was Lady Canterville. As he saw the old gentleman look, covertly, a second time at his watch, he could have believed he would have been glad to settle the matter on the spot. Lady Canterville seemed to wish her daughter's lover to come forward more, to give certain assurances and guarantees. He felt that he was ready to say or do anything that was a matter of proper form; but he couldn't take the tone of trying to purchase her ladyship's consent, penetrated as he was with the conviction that such a man as he could be trusted to care for his wife rather more than an impecunious British peer and *his* wife could be supposed (with the lights he had acquired in English society) to care even for the handsomest of a dozen children. It was a mistake on Lady Canterville's part not to recognise that. He humoured her mistake to the extent of saying, just a little drily, 'My wife shall certainly have everything she wants.'

'He tells me he is disgustingly rich,' Lord Canterville added, pausing before their companion with his hands in his pockets.

'I am glad to hear it; but it isn't so much that,' she answered, sinking back a little on her sofa. If it was not that, she did not say what it was, though she had looked for a moment as if she were going to. She only raised her eyes to her husband's face, as if to ask for inspiration. I know not whether she found it, but in a moment she said to Jackson Lemon, seeming to imply that it was quite another point: 'Do you expect to continue your profession?'

He had no such intention, so far as his profession meant getting up at three o'clock in the morning to assuage the ills of humanity; but here, as before, the touch of such a question instantly stiffened him. 'Oh, my profession! I am rather ashamed of that matter. I have neglected my work so much, I don't know what I shall be able to do, once I am really settled at home.'

Lady Canterville received these remarks in silence; fixing her eyes again upon her husband's face. But this nobleman was really not helpful; still with his hands in his pockets, save when he needed to remove his cigar from his lips, he went and looked out of the window. 'Of course we know you don't practise, and when you're a married man you will have less time even than now. But I should really like to know if they call you Doctor over there.'

'Oh yes, universally. We are nearly as fond of titles as your people.'

'I don't call that a title.'

'It's not so good as duke or marquis, I admit; but we have to take what we have got.'

'Oh, bother, what does it signify?' Lord Canterville demanded, from his place at the window. 'I used to have a horse named Doctor, and a devilish good one too.'

'You may call me bishop, if you like,' said Jackson Lemon, laughing.

Lady Canterville looked grave, as if she did not enjoy this pleasantry. 'I don't care for any titles,' she observed; 'I don't see why a gentleman shouldn't be called Mr.'

It suddenly appeared to Jackson Lemon that there was something helpless, confused, and even slightly comical, in the position of this noble and amiable lady. The impression made him feel kindly; he too, like Lord Canterville, had begun to long for a short cut. He relaxed a moment, and leaning toward his hostess, with a smile and his hands on his little knees, he said softly, 'It seems to me a question of no importance; all I desire is that you should call me your son-in-law.'

Lady Canterville gave him her hand, and he pressed it almost affectionately. Then she got up, remarking that before anything was decided she must see her daughter, she must learn from her own lips the state of her feelings. 'I don't like at all her not having spoken to me already,' she added.

'Where has she gone – to Roehampton? I dare say she has told it all to her godmother,' said Lord Canterville.

'She won't have much to tell, poor girl!' Jackson Lemon exclaimed. 'I must really insist upon seeing with more freedom the person I wish to marry.'

'You shall have all the freedom you want, in two or three days,' said Lady Canterville. She smiled with all her sweetness; she appeared to have accepted him, and yet still to be making tacit assumptions. 'Are there not certain things to be talked of first?'

'Certain things, dear lady?'

Lady Canterville looked at her husband, and though he was still at his window, this time he felt it in her silence, and had to come away and speak. 'Oh, she means settlements, and that kind of thing.' This was an allusion which came with a much better grace from him.

Jackson Lemon looked from one of his companions to the other; he coloured a little, and gave a smile that was perhaps a trifle fixed. 'Settlements? We don't make them in the United States. You may be sure I shall make a proper provision for my wife.'

'My dear fellow, over here – in our class, you know, it's the custom,' said Lord Canterville, with a richer brightness in his face at the thought that the discussion was over.

'I have my own ideas,' Jackson answered, smiling.

'It seems to me it's a question for the solicitors to discuss,' Lady Canterville suggested.

'They may discuss it as much as they please,' said Jackson Lemon, with a laugh. He thought he saw his solicitors discussing it! He had indeed his own ideas. He opened the door for Lady Canterville, and the three passed out of the room together, walking into the hall in a silence in which there was just a tinge of awkwardness. A note had been struck which grated and scratched a little. A pair of brilliant footmen, at their approach, rose from a bench to a great altitude, and stood there like sentinels presenting arms. Jackson Lemon stopped, looking for a moment into the interior of his hat, which he had in his hand.

Then, raising his keen eyes, he fixed them a moment on those of Lady Canterville, addressing her, instinctively, rather than her husband. 'I guess you and Lord Canterville had better leave it to me!'

'We have our traditions, Mr. Lemon,' said her ladyship, with nobleness. 'I imagine you don't know —' she murmured.

Lord Canterville laid his hand on the young man's shoulder. 'My dear boy, those fellows will settle it in three minutes.'

'Very likely they will!' said Jackson Lemon. Then he asked of Lady Canterville when he might see Lady Barb.

She hesitated a moment, in her gracious way. 'I will write you a note.'

One of the tall footmen, at the end of the impressive vista, had opened wide the portals, as if even he were aware of the dignity to which the little visitor had virtually been raised. But Jackson lingered a moment; he was visibly unsatisfied, though apparently so little unconscious that he was unsatisfying. 'I don't think you understand me.'

'Your ideas are certainly different,' said Lady Canterville.

'If the girl understands you, that's enough!' Lord Canterville exclaimed in a jovial, detached, irrelevant way.

'May not *she* write to me?' Jackson asked of her mother. 'I certainly must write to her, you know, if you won't let me see her.'

'Oh yes, you may write to her, Mr Lemon.'

There was a point for a moment in the look that he gave Lady Canterville, while he said to himself that if it were necessary he would transmit his notes through the old lady at Roehampton. 'All right, good-bye; you know what I want, at any rate.' Then, as he was going, he turned and added: 'You needn't be afraid that I won't bring her over in the hot weather!'

'In the hot weather?' Lady Canterville murmured, with vague visions of the torrid zone, while the young American quitted the house with the sense that he had made great concessions.

His host and hostess passed into a small morning-room, and (Lord Canterville having taken up his hat and stick to go out again) stood there a moment, face to face.

'It's clear enough he wants her,' said his lordship, in a summary manner.

'There's something so odd about him,' Lady Canterville answered. 'Fancy his speaking so about settlements!'

'You had better give him his head; he'll go much quieter.'

'He's so obstinate – very obstinate; it's easy to see that. And he seems to think a girl in your daughter's position can be married from one day to the other – with a ring and a new frock – like a housemaid.'

'Well, of course, over there, that's the kind of thing. But he seems really to have a most extraordinary fortune; and every one does say their women have *carte blanche*.'

'*Carte blanche* is not what Barb wishes; she wishes a settlement. She wants a definite income; she wants to be safe.'

Lord Canterville stared a moment. 'Has she told you so? I thought you said –' And then he stopped. 'I beg your pardon,' he added.

Lady Canterville gave no explanation of her inconsistency. She went on to remark that American fortunes were notoriously insecure; one heard of nothing else; they melted away like smoke. It was their duty to their child to demand that something should be fixed.

'He has a million and a half sterling,' said Lord Canterville. 'I can't make out what he does with it.'

'She ought to have something very handsome,' his wife remarked.

'Well, my dear, you must settle it: you must consider it; you must send for Hilary. Only take care you don't put him off; it may be a very good opening, you know. There is a great deal to be done out there; I believe in all that,' Lord Canterville went on, in the tone of a conscientious parent.

'There is no doubt that he *is* a doctor – in those places,' said Lady Canterville, musingly.

'He may be a pedlar for all I care.'

'If they should go out, I think Agatha might go with them,' her ladyship continued, in the same tone, a little disconnectedly.

'You may send them all out if you like. Good-bye!' And Lord Canterville kissed his wife.

But she detained him a moment, with her hand on his arm. 'Don't you think he is very much in love?'

'Oh yes, he's very bad; but he's a clever little beggar.'

'She likes him very much,' Lady Canterville announced, rather formally, as they separated.

4

JACKSON LEMON had said to Sidney Feeder in the Park that he would call on Mr and Mrs Freer; but three weeks elapsed before he knocked at their door in Jermyn Street. In the meantime he had met them at dinner, and Mrs Freer had told him that she hoped very much he would find time to come and see her. She had not reproached him, nor shaken her finger at him; and her clemency, which was calculated, and very characteristic of her, touched him so much (for he was in fault; she was one of his mother's oldest and best friends), that he very soon presented himself. It was a fine Sunday afternoon, rather late, and the region of Jermyn Street looked forsaken and inanimate; the native dulness of the landscape appeared in all its purity. Mrs Freer, however, was at home, resting on a lodging-house sofa – an angular couch, draped in faded chintz – before she went to dress for dinner. She made the young man very welcome; she told him she had been thinking of him a great deal; she had wished to have a chance to talk with him. He immediately perceived what she had in mind, and then he remembered that Sidney Feeder had told him what it was that Mr and Mrs Freer took upon themselves to say. This had provoked him at the time, but he had forgotten it afterward; partly because he became aware, that same evening, that he did wish to marry the 'young marchioness', and partly because since then he had had much greater annoyances. Yes, the poor young man, so conscious of liberal intentions, of a large way of looking at the future, had had much to irritate and disgust him. He had seen the mistress of his affections but three or four times, and he had received letters from Mr Hilary, Lord Canterville's solicitor, asking him, in terms the most obsequious, it is true, to designate some gentleman of the law with whom the preliminaries of his

marriage to Lady Barberina Clement might be arranged. He had
given Mr Hilary the name of such a functionary, but he had
written by the same post to his own solicitor (for whose services
in other matters he had had much occasion, Jackson Lemon
being distinctly contentious), instructing him that he was at
liberty to meet Mr Hilary, but not at liberty to entertain any
proposals as to this odious English idea of a settlement. If
marrying Jackson Lemon were not settlement enough, then Lord
and Lady Canterville had better alter their point of view. It was
quite out of the question that he should alter his. It would
perhaps be difficult to explain the strong aversion that he
entertained to the introduction into his prospective union of this
harsh diplomatic element; it was as if they mistrusted him,
suspected him; as if his hands were to be tied, so that he could
not handle his own fortune as he thought best. It was not the
idea of parting with his money that displeased him, for he
flattered himself that he had plans of expenditure for his wife
beyond even the imagination of her distinguished parents. It
struck him even that they were fools not to have perceived that
they should make a much better thing of it by leaving him
perfectly free. This intervention of the solicitor was a nasty little
English tradition – totally at variance with the large spirit of
American habits – to which he would not submit. It was not his
way to submit when he disapproved: why should he change his
way on this occasion, when the matter lay so near him? These
reflections, and a hundred more, had flowed freely through his
mind for several days before he called in Jermyn Street, and they
had engendered a lively indignation and a really bitter sense of
wrong. As may be imagined, they had infused a certain
awkwardness into his relations with the house of Canterville, and
it may be said of these relations that they were for the moment
virtually suspended. His first interview with Lady Barb, after his
conference with the old couple, as he called her august elders,
had been as tender as he could have desired. Lady Canterville, at
the end of three days, had sent him an invitation – five words on
a card – asking him to dine with them to-morrow, quite *en
famille*. This had been the only formal intimation that his
engagement to Lady Barb was recognised; for even at the family
banquet, which included half a dozen outsiders, there had been

no allusion on the part either of his host or his hostess to the subject of their conversation in Lord Canterville's den. The only allusion was a wandering ray, once or twice, in Lady Barberina's eyes. When, however, after dinner, she strolled away with him into the music-room, which was lighted and empty, to play for him something out of *Carmen*, of which he had spoken at table, and when the young couple were allowed to enjoy for upwards of an hour, unmolested, the comparative privacy of this rich apartment, he felt that Lady Canterville definitely counted upon him. She didn't believe in any serious difficulties. Neither did he, then; and that was why it was a nuisance there should be a vain appearance of them. The arrangements, he supposed Lady Canterville would have said, were pending, and indeed they were; for he had already given orders in Bond Street for the setting of an extraordinary number of diamonds. Lady Barb, at any rate, during that hour he spent with her, had had nothing to say about arrangements; and it had been an hour of pure satisfaction. She had seated herself at the piano and had played perpetually, in a soft incoherent manner, while he leaned over the instrument, very close to her, and said everything that came into his head. She was very bright and serene, and she looked at him as if she liked him very much.

This was all he expected of her, for it did not belong to the cast of her beauty to betray a vulgar infatuation. That beauty was more delightful to him than ever; and there was a softness about her which seemed to say to him that from this moment she was quite his own. He felt more than ever the value of such a possession; it came over him more than ever that it had taken a great social outlay to produce such a mixture. Simple and girlish as she was, and not particularly quick in the give and take of conversation, she seemed to him to have a part of the history of England in her blood; she was a *résumé* of generations of privileged people, and of centuries of rich country-life. Between these two, of course, there was no allusion to the question which had been put into the hands of Mr Hilary, and the last thing that occurred to Jackson Lemon was that Lady Barb had views as to his settling a fortune upon her before their marriage. It may appear singular, but he had not asked himself whether his money operated upon her in any degree as a bribe; and this was because,

instinctively, he felt that such a speculation was idle, – the point
was not to be ascertained, – and because he was willing to
assume that it was agreeable to her that she should continue to
live in luxury. It was eminently agreeable to him that he might
enable her to do so. He was acquainted with the mingled
character of human motives, and he was glad that he was rich
enough to pretend to the hand of a young woman who, for the
best of reasons, would be very expensive. After that happy hour
in the music-room he had ridden with her twice; but he had not
found her otherwise accessible. She had let him know, the
second time they rode, that Lady Canterville had directed her to
make, for the moment, no further appointment with him; and
on his presenting himself, more than once at the house, he
had been told that neither the mother nor the daughter was at
home; it had been added that Lady Barberina was staying at
Roehampton. On giving him that information in the Park, Lady
Barb had looked at him with a mute reproach – there was
always a certain superior dumbness in her eyes – as if he were
exposing her to an annoyance that she ought to be spared; as if
he were taking an eccentric line on a question that all well-bred
people treated in the conventional way. His induction from this
was not that she wished to be secure about his money, but that,
like a dutiful English daughter, she received her opinions (on
points that were indifferent to her) ready-made from a mamma
whose fallibility had never been exposed. He knew by this that
his solicitor had answered Mr Hilary's letter, and that Lady
Canterville's coolness was the fruit of this correspondence. The
effect of it was not in the least to make him come round, as he
phrased it; he had not the smallest intention of doing that. Lady
Canterville had spoken of the traditions of her family; but he had
no need to go to his family for his own. They resided within
himself; anything that he had definitely made up his mind to,
acquired in an hour a kind of legendary force. Meanwhile, he
was in the detestable position of not knowing whether or no he
were engaged. He wrote to Lady Barb to inquire – it being so
strange that she should not receive him; and she answered in a
very pretty little letter, which had to his mind a sort of bygone
quality, an old-fashioned freshness, as if it might have been
written in the last century by Clarissa or Amelia: she answered

that she did not in the least understand the situation; that, of course, she would never give him up; that her mother had said that there were the best reasons for their not going too fast; that, thank God, she was yet young, and could wait as long as he would; but that she begged he wouldn't write her anything about money-matters, as she could never comprehend them. Jackson felt that he was in no danger whatever of making this last mistake; he only noted how Lady Barb thought it natural that there should be a discussion; and this made it vivid to him afresh that he had got hold of a daughter of the Crusaders. His ingenious mind could appreciate this hereditary assumption perfectly, at the same time that, to light his own footsteps, it remained entirely modern. He believed − or he thought he believed − that in the end he should marry Barberina Clement on his own terms; but in the interval there was a sensible indignity in being challenged and checked. One effect of it, indeed, was to make him desire the girl more keenly. When she was not before his eyes in the flesh, she hovered before him as an image; and this image had reasons of its own for being a radiant picture. There were moments, however, when he wearied of looking at it; it was so impalpable and thankless, and then Jackson Lemon, for the first time in his life, was melancholy. He felt alone in London, and very much out of it, in spite of all the acquaintances he had made, and the bills he had paid; he felt the need of a greater intimacy than any he had formed (save, of course, in the case of Lady Barb). He wanted to vent his disgust, to relieve himself, from the American point of view. He felt that in engaging in a contest with the great house of Canterville he was, after all, rather single. That singleness was, of course, in a great measure an inspiration; but it pinched him a little at moments. Then he wished his mother had been in London, for he used to talk of his affairs a great deal with this delightful parent, who had a soothing way of advising him in the sense he liked best. He had even gone so far as to wish he had never laid eyes on Lady Barb and had fallen in love with some trans-atlantic maiden of a similar composition. He presently came back, of course, to the knowledge that in the United States there was − and there could be − nothing similar to Lady Barb; for was it not precisely as a product of the English climate and the

British constitution that he valued her? He had relieved himself, from his American point of view, by speaking his mind to Lady Beauchemin, who confessed that she was very much vexed with her parents. She agreed with him that they had made a great mistake; they ought to have left him free; and she expressed her confidence that that freedom would be for her family, as it were, like the silence of the sage, golden. He must excuse them; he must remember that what was asked of him had been their custom for centuries. She did not mention her authority as to the origin of customs, but she assured him that she would say three words to her father and mother which would make it all right. Jackson answered that customs were all very well, but that intelligent people recognised, when they saw it, the right occasion for departing from them; and with this he awaited the result of Lady Beauchemin's remonstrance. It had not as yet been perceptible, and it must be said that this charming woman was herself much bothered. When, on her venturing to say to her mother that she thought a wrong line had been taken with regard to her sister's *prétendant*, Lady Canterville had replied that Mr Lemon's unwillingness to settle anything was in itself a proof of what they had feared, the unstable nature of his fortune (for it was useless to talk – this gracious lady could be very decided – there could be no serious reason but that one): on meeting this argument, as I say, Jackson's protectress felt considerably baffled. It was perhaps true, as her mother said, that if they didn't insist upon proper guarantees Barberina might be left in a few years with nothing but the stars and stripes (this odd phrase was a quotation from Mr Lemon) to cover her. Lady Beauchemin tried to reason it out with Lady Marmaduke; but these were complications unforeseen by Lady Marmaduke in her project of an Anglo-American society. She was obliged to confess that Mr Lemon's fortune could not have the solidity of long-established things; it was a very new fortune indeed. His father had made the greater part of it all in a lump, a few years before his death, in the extraordinary way in which people made money in America; that, of course, was why the son had those singular professional attributes. He had begun to study to be a doctor very young, before his expectations were so great. Then he had found he was very clever, and very fond of it; and he had

kept on, because, after all, in America, where there were no
country-gentlemen, a young man had to have something to do,
don't you know? And Lady Marmaduke, like an enlightened
woman, intimated that in such a case she thought it much better
taste not to try to sink anything. 'Because, in America, don't you
see,' she reasoned, 'you can't sink it – nothing *will* sink.
Everything is floating about – in the newspapers.' And she tried
to console her friend by remarking that if Mr Lemon's fortune
was precarious, it was at all events so big. That was just the
trouble for Lady Beauchemin; it was so big, and yet they were
going to lose it. He was as obstinate as a mule; she was sure he
would never come round. Lady Marmaduke declared that he
would come round; she even offered to bet a dozen pair of *gants
de Suède* on it; and she added that this consummation lay quite
in the hands of Barberina. Lady Beauchemin promised herself to
converse with her sister; for it was not for nothing that she
herself had felt the international contagion.

Jackson Lemon, to dissipate his chagrin, had returned to the
sessions of the medical congress, where, inevitably, he had fallen
into the hands of Sidney Feeder, who enjoyed in this disinterested assembly a high popularity. It was Doctor Feeder's
earnest desire that his old friend should share it, which was all
the more easy as the medical congress was really, as the young
physician observed, a perpetual symposium. Jackson Lemon
entertained the whole body – entertained it profusely, and in a
manner befitting one of the patrons of science rather than its
humbler votaries; but these dissipations only made him forget
for a moment that his relations with the house of Canterville
were anomalous. His great difficulty punctually came back to
him, and Sidney Feeder saw it stamped upon his brow. Jackson
Lemon with his acute inclination to open himself, was on the
point, more than once, of taking the sympathetic Sidney into his
confidence. His friend gave him easy opportunity; he asked him
what it was he was thinking of all the time, and whether the
young marchioness had concluded she couldn't swallow a
doctor. These forms of speech were displeasing to Jackson
Lemon, whose fastidiousness was nothing new; but it was for
even deeper reasons that he said to himself that, for such
complicated cases as his, there was no assistance in Sidney Feeder.

To understand his situation one must know the world; and the child of Cincinnati didn't know the world – at least the world with which his friend was now concerned.

'Is there a hitch in your marriage? Just tell me that,' Sidney Feeder had said, taking everything for granted, in a manner which was in itself a proof of great innocence. It is true he had added that he supposed he had no business to ask; but he had been anxious about it ever since hearing from Mr and Mrs Freer that the British aristocracy was down on the medical profession. 'Do they want you to give it up? Is that what the hitch is about? Don't desert your colours, Jackson. The elimination of pain, the mitigation of misery, constitute surely the noblest profession in the world.'

'My dear fellow, you don't know what you are talking about,' Jackson observed, for answer to this. 'I haven't told any one I was going to be married; still less have I told any one that any one objected to my profession. I should like to see them do it. I have got out of the swim to-day, but I don't regard myself as the sort of person that people object to. And I do expect to do something, yet.'

'Come home, then, and do it. And excuse me if I say that the facilities for getting married are much greater over there.'

'You don't seem to have found them very great.'

'I have never had time. Wait till my next vacation, and you will see.'

'The facilities over there are too great. Nothing is good but what is difficult,' said Jackson Lemon, in a tone of artificial sententiousness that quite tormented his interlocutor.

'Well, they have got their backs up, I can see that. I'm glad you like it. Only if they despise your profession, what will they say to that of your friends? If they think you are queer, what would they think of me?' asked Sidney Feeder, the turn of whose mind was not, as a general thing, in the least sarcastic, but who was pushed to this sharpness by a conviction that (in spite of declarations which seemed half an admission and half a denial) his friend was suffering himself to be bothered for the sake of a good which might be obtained elsewhere without bother. It had come over him that the bother was of an unworthy kind.

'My dear fellow, all that is idiotic.' That had been Jackson

Lemon's reply; but it expressed but a portion of his thoughts. The rest was inexpressible, or almost; being connected with a sentiment of rage at its having struck even so genial a mind as Sidney Feeder's that, in proposing to marry a daughter of the highest civilisation, he was going out of his way – departing from his natural line. Was he then so ignoble, so pledged to inferior things, that when he saw a girl who (putting aside the fact that she had not genius, which was rare, and which, though he prized rarity, he didn't want) seemed to him the most complete feminine nature he had known, he was to think himself too different, too incongruous, to mate with her? He would mate with whom he chose; that was the upshot of Jackson Lemon's reflections. Several days elapsed, during which everybody – even the pure-minded, like Sidney Feeder – seemed to him very abject.

I relate all this to show why it was that in going to see Mrs Freer he was prepared much less to be angry with people who, like the Dexter Freers, a month before, had given it out that he was engaged to a peer's daughter, than to resent the insinuation that there were obstacles to such a prospect. He sat with Mrs Freer alone for half an hour in the sabbatical stillness of Jermyn Street. Her husband had gone for a walk in the Park; he always walked in the Park on Sunday. All the world might have been there, and Jackson and Mrs Freer in sole possession of the district of St James's. This perhaps had something to do with making him at last rather confidential; the influences were conciliatory, persuasive. Mrs Freer was extremely sympathetic; she treated him like a person she had known from the age of ten; asked his leave to continue recumbant; talked a great deal about his mother; and seemed almost for a while to perform the kindly functions of that lady. It had been wise of her from the first not to allude, even indirectly, to his having neglected so long to call; her silence on this point was in the best taste. Jackson Lemon had forgotten that it was a habit with her, and indeed a high accomplishment, never to reproach people with these omissions. You might have left her alone for two years, her greeting was always the same; she was never either too delighted to see you or not delighted enough. After a while, however, he perceived that her silence had been to a certain extent a reference; she appeared to take for granted that he devoted all his hours to a certain young lady. It came over him for a moment that his country people took a great deal for granted; but when Mrs Freer, rather abruptly, sitting up on her sofa, said to him, half simply, half solemnly, 'And now, my dear Jackson, I want you to tell me something!' – he perceived that after all she didn't pretend to know more about the impending matter than he himself did. In the course of a quarter of an hour – so appreciatively she listened – he had told her a good deal about it. It was the first time he had said so much to any one, and the process relieved him even more than he would have supposed. It made certain things clear to him, by bringing them to a point – above all, the fact that he had been wronged. He made no allusion whatever to its being out of the usual way that, as an American doctor, he should sue for the hand of a marquis's daughter; and this reserve was not voluntary, it was quite unconscious. His mind was too full of the offensive conduct of the Cantervilles, and the sordid side of their want of confidence. He could not imagine that while he talked to Mrs Freer – and it amazed him afterward that he should have chattered so; he could account for it only by the state of his nerves – she should be thinking only of the strangeness of the situation he sketched for her. She thought Americans as good as other people, but she didn't see where, in American life, the daughter of a marquis would, as she phrased it, work in. To take a simple instance, – they coursed through Mrs Freer's mind with extraordinary speed – would she not always expect to go in to dinner first? As a novelty, over there, they might like to see her do it, at first; there might be even a pressure for places for the spectacle. But with the increase of every kind of sophistication that was taking place in America, the humorous view to which she would owe her safety might not continue to be taken; and then where would Lady Barberina be? This was but a small instance; but Mrs Freer's vivid imagination – much as she lived in Europe, she knew her native land so well – saw a host of others massing themselves behind it. The consequence of all of which was that after listening to him in the most engaging silence, she raised her clasped hands, pressed them against her breast, lowered her voice to a tone of entreaty, and, with her perpetual little smile, uttered three words; 'My dear Jackson, don't – don't – don't.'

'Don't what?' he asked, staring.

'Don't neglect the chance you have of getting out of it; it would never do.'

He knew what she meant by his chance of getting out of it; in his many meditations he had, of course, not overlooked that. The ground the old couple had taken about settlements (and the fact that Lady Beauchemin had not come back to him to tell him, as she promised, that she had moved them, proved how firmly they were rooted) would have offered an all-sufficient pretext to a man who should have repented of his advances. Jackson Lemon knew that; but he knew at the same time that he had not repented. The old couple's want of imagination did not in the least alter the fact that Barberina was, as he had told her father, a beautiful type. Therefore he simply said to Mrs Freer that he didn't in the least wish to get out of it; he was as much in it as ever, and he intended to remain there. But what did she mean, he inquired in a moment, by her statement that it would never do? Why wouldn't it do? Mrs Freer replied by another inquiry – Should he really like her to tell him? It wouldn't do, because Lady Barb would not be satisfied with her place at dinner. She would not be content – in a society of commoners – with any but the best; and the best she could not expect (and it was to be supposed that he did not expect her) always to have.

'What do you mean by commoners?' Jackson Lemon demanded, looking very serious.

'I mean you, and me, and my poor husband, and Dr Feeder,' said Mrs Freer.

'I don't see how there can be commoners where there are not lords. It is the lord that makes the commoner; and *vice versa*.'

'Won't a lady do as well? Lady Barberina – a single English girl – can make a million inferiors.'

'She will be, before anything else, my wife; and she will not talk about inferiors any more than I do. I never do; it's very vulgar.'

'I don't know what she'll talk about, my dear Jackson, but she will think; and her thoughts won't be pleasant – I mean for others. Do you expect to sink her to your own rank?'

Jackson Lemon's bright little eyes were fixed more brightly

than ever upon his hostess. 'I don't understand you; and I don't think you understand yourself.' This was not absolutely candid, for he did understand Mrs Freer to a certain extent; it has been related that, before he asked Lady Barb's hand of her parents, there had been moments when he himself was not very sure that the flower of the British aristocracy would flourish in American soil. But an intimation from another person that it was beyond his power to pass off his wife – whether she were the daughter of a peer or of a shoemaker – set all his blood on fire. It quenched on the instant his own perception of difficulties of detail, and made him feel only that he was dishonoured – he, the heir of all the ages – by such insinuations. It was his belief – though he had never before had occasion to put it forward – that his position, one of the best in the world, was one of those positions that make everything possible. He had had the best education the age could offer, for if he had rather wasted his time at Harvard, where he entered very young, he had, as he believed, been tremendously serious at Heidelberg and at Vienna. He had devoted himself to one of the noblest pro-fessions – a profession recognised as such everywhere but in England – and he had inherited a fortune far beyond the expectation of his earlier years, the years when he cultivated habits of work which alone – or rather in combination with talents that he neither exaggerated nor minimised – would have conduced to distinction. He was one of the most fortunate inhabitants of an immense, fresh, rich country, a country whose future was admitted to be incalculable, and he moved with perfect ease in a society in which he was not overshadowed by others. It seemed to him, therefore, beneath his dignity to wonder whether he could afford, socially speaking, to marry according to his taste. Jackson Lemon pretended to be strong; and what was the use of being strong if you were not prepared to undertake things that timid people might find difficult? It was his plan to marry the woman he liked, and not be afraid of her afterward. The effect of Mrs Freer's doubt of his success was to represent to him that his own character would not cover his wife's; she couldn't have made him feel otherwise if she had told him that he was marrying beneath him, and would have to ask for indulgence. 'I don't believe you know how much I think that any woman who marries me will be doing very well,' he added, directly.

'I am very sure of that; but it isn't so simple – one's being an American,' Mrs Freer rejoined, with a little philosophic sigh.

'It's whatever one chooses to make it.'

'Well, you'll make it what no one has done yet, if you take that young lady to America and make her happy there.'

'Do you think it's such a very dreadful place?'

'No, indeed; but she will.'

Jackson Lemon got up from his chair, and took up his hat and stick. He had actually turned a little pale, with the force of his emotion; it had made him really quiver that his marriage to Lady Barberina should be looked at as too high a flight. He stood a moment leaning against the mantlepiece, and very much tempted to say to Mrs Freer that she was a vulgar-minded old woman. But he said something that was really more to the point: 'You forget that she will have her consolations.'

'Don't go away, or I shall think I have offended you. You can't console a wounded marchioness.'

'How will she be wounded? People will be charming to her.'

'They will be charming to her – charming to her!' These words fell from the lips of Dexter Freer, who had opened the door of the room and stood with the knob in his hand, putting himself into relation to his wife's talk with their visitor. This was accomplished in an instant. 'Of course I know whom you mean.' he said, while he exchanged greetings with Jackson Lemon. 'My wife and I – of course you know we are great busybodies – have talked of your affair, and we differ about it completely: she sees only the dangers and I see the advantages.'

'By the advantages he means the fun for us,' Mrs Freer remarked, settling her sofa-cushions.

Jackson looked with a certain sharp blankness from one of these disinterested judges to the other; and even yet they did not perceive how their misdirected familiarities wrought upon him. It was hardly more agreeable to him to know that the husband wished to see Lady Barb in America, than to know that the wife had a dread of such a vision; for there was that in Dexter Freer's face which seemed to say that the thing would take place somehow for the benefit of the spectators. 'I think you both see too much – a great deal too much,' he answered, rather coldly.

'My dear young man, at my age I can take certain liberties,' said Dexter Freer. 'Do it – I beseech you to do it: it has never been done before.' And then, as if Jackson's glance had challenged this last assertion, he went on: 'Never, I assure you, this particular thing. Young female members of the British aristocracy have married coachmen and fishmongers, and all that sort of thing: but they have never married you and me.'

'They certainly haven't married you,' said Mrs Freer.

'I am much obliged to you for your advice.' It may be thought that Jackson Lemon took himself rather seriously: and indeed I am afraid that if he had not done so there would have been no occasion for my writing this little history. But it made him almost sick to hear his engagement spoken of as a curious and ambiguous phenomenon. He might have his own ideas about it – one always had about one's engagement; but the ideas that appeared to have peopled the imagination of his friends ended by kindling a little hot spot in each of his cheeks. 'I would rather not talk any more about my little plans,' he added to Dexter Freer. 'I have been saying all sorts of absurd things to Mrs Freer.'

'They have been most interesting', that lady declared. 'You have been very stupidly treated.'

'May she tell me when you go?' her husband asked of the young man.

'I am going now; she may tell you whatever she likes.'

'I am afraid we have displeased you,' said Mrs Freer; 'I have said too much what I think. You must excuse me, it's all for your mother.'

'It's she whom I want Lady Barberina to see!' Jackson Lemon exclaimed, with the inconsequence of filial affection.

'Deary me!' murmured Mrs Freer.

'We shall go back to America to see how you get on,' her husband said; 'and if you succeed, it will be a great precedent.'

'Oh, I shall succeed!' And with this he took his departure. He walked away with the quick step of a man labouring under a certain excitement; walked up to Piccadilly and down past Hyde Park Corner. It relieved him to traverse these distances, for he was thinking hard, under the influence of irritation; and

locomotion helped him to think. Certain suggestions that had
been made him in the last half hour rankled in his mind, all the
more that they seemed to have a kind of representative value, to
be an echo of the common voice. If his prospects wore that face
to Mrs Freer, they would probably wear it to others; and he felt
a sudden need of showing such others that they took a pitiful
measure of his position. Jackson Lemon walked and walked till
he found himself on the highway of Hammersmith. I have
represented him as a young man of much strength of purpose,
and I may appear to undermine this plea when I relate that he
wrote that evening to his solicitor that Mr Hilary was to be
informed that he would agree to any proposals for settlements
that Mr Hilary should make. Jackson's strength of purpose was
shown in his deciding to marry Lady Barberina on any terms. It
seemed to him, under the influence of his desire to prove that he
was not afraid – so odious was the imputation – that terms of
any kind were very superficial things. What was fundamental,
and of the essence of the matter, would be to marry Lady Barb
and carry everything out.

5

'ON SUNDAYS, now, you might be at home,' Jackson Lemon
said to his wife in the following month of March, more than six
months after his marriage.

'Are the people any nicer on Sundays than they are on other
days?' Lady Barberina replied, from the depths of her chair,
without looking up from a stiff little book.

He hesitated a single instant before answering: 'I don't know
whether they are, but I think they might be.'

'I am as nice as I know how to be. You must take me as I am.
You knew when you married me that I was not an American.'

Jackson Lemon stood before the fire, towards which his wife's
face was turned and her feet were extended; stood there some
time, with his hands behind him and his eyes dropped a little

obliquely upon the bent head and richly-draped figure of Lady Barberina. It may be said without delay that he was irritated, and it may be added that he had a double cause. He felt himself to be on the verge of the first crisis that had occurred between himself and his wife – the reader will perceive that it had occurred rather promptly – and he was annoyed at his annoyance. A glimpse of his state of mind before his marriage has been given to the reader, who will remember that at that period Jackson Lemon somehow regarded himself as lifted above possibilities of irritation. When one was strong, one was not irritable; and a union with a kind of goddess would of course be an element of strength. Lady Barb was a goddess still, and Jackson Lemon admired his wife as much as the day he led her to the altar; but I am not sure that he felt so strong.

'How do you know what people are?' he said in a moment. 'You have seen so few; you are perpetually denying yourself. If you should leave New York to-morrow you would know wonderfully little about it.'

'It's all the same,' said Lady Barb; 'the people are all exactly alike.'

'How can you tell? You never see them.'

'Didn't I go out every night for the first two months we were here?'

'It was only to about a dozen houses – always the same; people, moreover, you had already met in London. You have got no general impressions.'

'That's just what I have got; I had them before I came. Every one is just the same; they have the same names – just the same manners.'

Again, for an instant, Jackson Lemon hesitated; then he said, in that apparently artless tone of which mention has already been made, and which he sometimes used in London during his wooing: 'Don't you like it over here?'

Lady Barb raised her eyes from her book. 'Did you expect me to like it?'

'I hoped you would, of course, I think I told you so.'

'I don't remember. You said very little about it; you seemed to make a kind of mystery. I knew, of course, you expected me to live here, but I didn't know you expected me to like it.'

'You thought I asked of you the sacrifice, as it were.'

'I am sure I don't know,' said Lady Barb. She got up from her chair and tossed the volume she had been reading into the empty seat. 'I recommend you to read that book,' she added.

'Is it interesting?'

'It's an American novel.'

'I never read novels.'

'You had better look at that one; it will show you the kind of people you want me to know.'

'I have no doubt it's very vulgar,' said Jackson Lemon; 'I don't see why you read it.'

'What else can I do? I can't always be riding in the Park; I hate the Park,' Lady Barb remarked.

'It's quite as good as your own,' said her husband.

She glanced at him with a certain quickness, her eyebrows slightly lifted. 'Do you mean the park at Pasterns?'

'No; I mean the park in London.'

'I don't care about London. One was only in London a few weeks.'

'I suppose you miss the country,' said Jackson Lemon. It was his idea of life that he should not be afraid of anything, not be afraid, in any situation, of knowing the worst that was to be known about it; and the demon of a courage with which discretion was not properly commingled prompted him to take soundings which were perhaps not absolutely necessary for safety, and yet which revealed unmistakable rocks. It was useless to know about rocks if he couldn't avoid them; the only thing was to trust to the wind.

'I don't know what I miss, I think I miss everything!' This was his wife's answer to his too curious inquiry. It was not peevish for that is not the tone of a goddess; but it expressed a good deal – a good deal more than Lady Barb, who was rarely eloquent, had expressed before. Nevertheless, though his question had been precipitate, Jackson Lemon said to himself that he might take his time to think over what his wife's little speech contained; he could not help seeing that the future would give him abundant opportunity for that. He was in no hurry to ask himself whether poor Mrs Freer, in Jermyn Street, might not, after all, have been right in saying that, in regard to marrying the product of an English caste, it was not so simple to be an American doctor – might avail little even, in such a case, to be the heir of all the ages. The transition was complicated, but in his bright mind it was rapid, from the brush of a momentary contact with such ideas to certain considerations which led him to say, after an instant, to his wife, 'Should you like to go down into Connecticut?'

'Into Connecticut?'

'That's one of our States; it's about as large as Ireland. I'll take you there if you like.'

'What does one do there?'

'We can try and get some hunting.'

'You and I alone?'

'Perhaps we can get a party to join us.'

'The people in the State?'

'Yes; we might propose it to them.'

'The tradespeople in the towns?'

'Very true; they will have to mind their shops,' said Jackson Lemon. 'But we might hunt alone.'

'Are there any foxes?'

'No; but there are a few old cows.'

Lady Barb had already perceived that her husband took it into his head once in a while to laugh at her and she was aware that the present occasion was neither worse nor better than some others. She didn't mind it particularly now, though in England it would have disgusted her; she had the consciousness of virtue – an immense comfort – and flattered herself that she had learned the lesson of an altered standard of fitness; there were, moreover, so many more disagreeable things in America than being laughed at by one's husband. But she pretended to mind it, because it made him stop, and above all it stopped discussion, which with Jackson was so often jocular, and none the less tiresome for that. 'I only want to be left alone,' she said, in answer – though, indeed, it had not the manner of an answer – to his speech about the cows. With this she wandered away to one of the windows which looked out on the Fifth Avenue. She was very fond of these windows, and she had taken a great fancy to the Fifth Avenue, which, in the high-pitched winter weather, when everything sparkled, was a spectacle full of novelty. It will be seen that she was not wholly unjust to her adoptive country: she found it delightful to look out of the window. This was a pleasure she had enjoyed in London only in the most furtive manner: it was not the kind of thing that girls did in England. Besides, in London, in Hill Street, there was nothing particular to see; but in the Fifth Avenue everything and every one went by, and observation was made consistent with dignity by the masses of brocade and lace in which the windows were draped, which, somehow, would not have been tidy in England, and which made an ambush without concealing the brilliant day. Hundreds of women – the curious women of New York, who were unlike any that Lady Barb had hitherto seen – passed the house every hour, and her ladyship was infinitely entertained and mystified by the sight of their clothes. She spent a good deal more time than she was aware of in this amusement; and if she had been addicted to returning upon herself, or asking herself for an account of her conduct – an inquiry which she did not, indeed, completely neglect, but treated very cursorily – it would have made her smile sadly to think what she appeared mainly to have come to America for, conscious though she was that her tastes were very simple, and that so long as she didn't hunt, it didn't much matter what she did.

Her husband turned about to the fire, giving a push with his foot to a log that had fallen out of its place. Then he said – and the connection with the words she had just uttered was apparent enough – 'You really must be at home on Sundays, you know. I used to like that so much in London. All the best women here do it. You had better begin to-day. I am going to see my mother; if I meet any one I will tell them to come.'

'Tell them not to talk so much,' said Lady Barb, among her lace curtains.

'Ah, my dear,' her husband replied, 'it isn't every one that has your concision!' And he went and stood behind her in the window, putting his arm round her waist. It was as much of a satisfaction to him as it had been six months before, at the time the solicitors were settling the matter, that this flower of an ancient stem should be worn upon his own breast; he still thought its fragrance a thing quite apart, and it was as clear as day to him that his wife was the handsomest woman in New

York. He had begun, after their arrival, by telling her this very often; but the assurance brought no colour to her cheek, no light to her eyes; to be the handsomest woman in New York evidently did not seem to her a position in life. Moreover, the reader may be informed that, oddly enough, Lady Barb did not particularly believe this assertion. There were some very pretty women in New York, and without in the least wishing to be like them – she had seen no woman in America whom she desired to resemble – she envied some of their elements. It is probable that her own finest points were those of which she was most unconscious. But her husband was aware of all of them; nothing could exceed the minuteness of his appreciation of his wife. It was a sign of this that after he had stood behind her a moment he kissed her very tenderly. 'Have you any message for my mother?' he asked.

'Please give her my love. And you might take her that book.'
'What book?'
'That nasty one I have been reading.'
'Oh, bother your books,' said Jackson Lemon, with a certain irritation, as he went out of the room.

There had been a good many things in her life in New York that cost Lady Barb an effort; but sending her love to her mother-in-law was not one of these. She liked Mrs Lemon better than any one she had seen in America; she was the only person who seemed to Lady Barb really simple, as she understood that quality. Many people had struck her as homely and rustic, and many others as pretentious and vulgar; but in Jackson's mother she had found the golden mean of a simplicity which, as she would have said, was really nice. Her sister, Lady Agatha, was even fonder of Mrs Lemon; but then Lady Agatha had taken the most extraordinary fancy to every one and everything, and talked as if America were the most delightful country in the world. She was having a lovely time (she already spoke the most beautiful American), and had been, during the winter that was just drawing to a close, the most prominent girl in New York. She had gone out at first with her sister; but for some weeks past Lady Barb had let so many occasions pass, that Agatha threw herself into the arms of Mrs Lemon, who found her extra-ordinarily quaint and amusing and was delighted to take her into society. Mrs Lemon, as an old woman, had given up such vanities; but she only wanted a motive, and in her good nature she ordered a dozen new caps and sat smiling against the wall while her little English maid, on polished floors, to the sound of music, cultivated the American step as well as the American tone. There was no trouble, in New York, about going out, and the winter was not half over before the little English maid found herself an accomplished diner, rolling about, without any chaperon at all, to banquets where she could count upon a bouquet at her plate. She had had a great deal of correspondence with her mother on this point, and Lady Canterville at last withdrew her protest, which in the meantime had been perfectly useless. It was ultimately Lady Canterville's feeling that if she had married the handsomest of her daughters to an American doctor, she might let another become a professional *raconteuse* (Agatha had written to her that she was expected to talk so much), strange as such a destiny seemed for a girl of nineteen. Mrs Lemon was even a much simpler woman than Lady Barberina thought her; for she had not noticed that Lady Agatha danced much oftener with Herman Longstraw than with any one else. Jackson Lemon, though he went little to balls, had discovered this truth, and he looked slightly preoccupied when, after he had sat five minutes with his mother on the Sunday afternoon through which I have invited the reader to trace so much more than (I am afraid) is easily apparent of the progress of this simple story, he learned that his sister-in-law was entertaining Mr Longstraw in the library. He had called half an hour before, and she had taken him into the other room to show him the seal of the Cantervilles, which she had fastened to one of her numerous trinkets (she was adorned with a hundred bangles and chains), and the proper exhibition of which required a taper and a stick of wax. Apparently he was examining it very carefully, for they had been absent a good while. Mrs Lemon's simplicity was further shown by the fact that she had not measured their absence; it was only when Jackson questioned her that she remembered.

Herman Longstraw was a young Californian who had turned up in New York the winter before, and who travelled on his moustache, as they were understood to say in his native State.

This moustache, and some of the accompanying features, were very ornamental; several ladies in New York had been known to declare that they were as beautiful as a dream. Taken in connection with his tall stature, his familiar good-nature, and his remarkable Western vocabulary, they constituted his only social capital; for of the two great divisions, the rich Californians and the poor Californians, it was well known to which he belonged. Jackson Lemon looked at him as a slightly mitigated cowboy, and was somewhat vexed at his dear mother, though he was aware that she could scarcely figure to herself what an effect such an accent as that would produce in the halls of Canterville. He had no desire whatever to play a trick on the house to which he was allied, and knew perfectly that Lady Agatha had not been sent to America to become entangled with a Californian of the wrong denomination. He had been perfectly willing to bring her; he thought, a little vindictively, that this would operate as a hint to her parents as to what he might have been inclined to do if they had not sent Mr Hilary after him. Herman Longstraw, according to the legend, had been a trapper, a squatter, a miner, a pioneer – had been everything that one could be in the romantic parts of America, and had accumulated masses of experience before the age of thirty. He had shot bears in the Rockies and buffaloes on the plains; and it was even believed that he had brought down animals of a still more dangerous kind, among the haunts of men. There had been a story that he owned a cattle-ranch in Arizona; but a later and apparently more authentic version of it, though it represented him as looking after the cattle, did not depict him as their proprietor. Many of the stories told about him were false; but there is no doubt that his moustache, his good-nature and his accent were genuine. He danced very badly; but Lady Agatha had frankly told several persons that that was nothing new to her; and she liked (this, however, she did not tell) Mr Herman Longstraw. What she enjoyed in America was the revelation of freedom; and there was no such proof of freedom as conversation with a gentleman who dressed in skins when he was not in New York, and who, in his usual pursuits, carried his life (as well as that of other people) in his hand. A gentleman whom she had sat next to at a dinner in the early part of her stay in New York, remarked to her that the

United States were the paradise of women and mechanics; and this had seemed to her at the time very abstract, for she was not conscious, as yet, of belonging to either class. In England she had been only a girl; and the principal idea connected with that was simply that, for one's misfortune, one was not a boy. But presently she perceived that New York was a paradise; and this helped her to know that she must be one of the people mentioned in the axiom of her neighbour – people who could do whatever they wanted, had a voice in everything, and made their taste and their ideas felt. She saw that it was great fun to be a woman in America, and that this was the best way to enjoy the New York winter – the wonderful, brilliant New York winter, the queer, long-shaped, glittering city, the heterogeneous hours, among which you couldn't tell the morning from the afternoon or the night from either of them, the perpetual liberties and walks, the rushings-out and the droppings-in, the intimacies, the endearments, the comicalities, the sleigh-bells, the cutters, the sunsets on the snow, the ice-parties in the frosty clearness, the bright, hot, velvety houses, the bouquets, the bonbons, the little cakes, the big cakes, the irrepressible inspirations of shopping, the innumerable luncheons and dinners that were offered to youth and innocence, the quantities of chatter of quantities of girls, the perpetual motion of the German, the suppers at restaurants after the play, the way in which life was pervaded by Delmonico and Delmonico by the sense that though one's hunting was lost and this so different, it was almost as good – and in all, through all, a kind of suffusion of bright, loud, friendly sound, which was very local, but very human.

Lady Agatha at present was staying, for a little change, with Mrs Lemon, and such adventures as that were part of the pleasure of her American season. The house was too close; but physically the girl could bear anything, and it was all she had to complain of; for Mrs Lemon, as we know, thought her a bonnie little damsel, and had none of the old-world scruples in regard to spoiling young people to which Lady Agatha now perceived that she herself, in the past, had been unduly sacrificed. In her own way – it was not at all her sister's way – she liked to be of importance; and this was assuredly the case when she saw that Mrs Lemon had apparently nothing in the world to do (after spending a part of the morning with her servants) but invent little distractions (many of them of the edible sort) for her guest. She appeared to have certain friends, but she had no society to speak of, and the people who came into her house came principally to see Lady Agatha. This, as we have seen, was strikingly the case with Herman Longstraw. The whole situation gave Lady Agatha a great feeling of success – success of a new and unexpected kind. Of course, in England, she had been born successful, in a manner, in coming into the world in one of the most beautiful rooms at Pasterns; but her present triumph was achieved more by her own effort (not that she had tried very hard) and by her merit. It was not so much what she said (for she could never say half as much as the girls in New York), as the spirit of enjoyment that played in her fresh young face, with its pointless curves, and shone in her grey English eyes. She enjoyed everything, even the street-cars, of which she made liberal use; and more than everything she enjoyed Mr Longstraw and his talk about buffaloes and bears. Mrs Lemon promised to be very careful, as soon as her son had begun to warn her; and this time she had a certain understanding of what she promised. She thought people ought to make the matches they liked; she had given proof of this in her late behaviour to Jackson, whose own union was, in her opinion, marked with all the arbitrariness of pure love. Nevertheless, she could see that Herman Longstraw would probably be thought rough in England; and it was not simply that he was so inferior to Jackson, for, after all, certain things were not to be expected. Jackson Lemon was not oppressed with his mother-in-law having taken his precautions against such a danger; but he was aware that he should give Lady Canterville a permanent advantage over him if, while she was in America, her daughter Agatha should attach herself to a mere moustache.

It was not always, as I have hinted, that Mrs Lemon entered completely into the views of her son, though in form she never failed to subscribe to them devoutly. She had never yet, for instance, apprehended his reason for marrying Lady Barberina Clement. This was a great secret, and Mrs Lemon was determined that no one should ever know it. For herself, she was sure that, to the end of time, she should not discover Jackson's reason.

She could never ask about it, for that of course would betray her. From the first she had told him she was delighted; there being no need of asking for explanation then, as the young lady herself, when she should come to know her, would explain. But the young lady had not yet explained; and after this, evidently, she never would. She was very tall, very handsome, she answered exactly to Mrs Lemon's prefigurement of the daughter of a lord, and she wore her clothes, which were peculiar, but, to her, remarkably becoming, very well. But she did not elucidate; we know ourselves that there was very little that was explanatory about Lady Barb. So Mrs Lemon continued to wonder, to ask herself, 'Why that one, more than so many others, who would have been more natural?' The choice appeared to her, as I have said, very arbitrary. She found Lady Barb very different from other girls she had known, and this led her almost immediately to feel sorry for her daughter-in-law. She said to herself that Barb was to be pitied if she found her husband's people as peculiar as his mother found *her*; for the result of that would be to make her very lonesome. Lady Agatha was different, because she seemed to keep nothing back; you saw all there was of her, and she was evidently not home-sick. Mrs Lemon could see that Barberina was ravaged by this last passion and was too proud to show it. She even had a glimpse of the ultimate truth; namely, that Jackson's wife had not the comfort of crying, because that would have amounted to a confession that she had been idiotic enough to believe in advance that, in an American town, in the society of doctors, she should escape such pangs. Mrs Lemon treated her with the greatest gentleness – all the gentleness that was due to a young woman who was in the unfortunate position of having been married one couldn't tell why. The world, to Mrs Lemon's view, contained two great departments – that of persons, and that of things; and she believed that you must take an interest either in one or the other. The incomprehensible thing in Lady Barb was that she cared for neither side of the show. Her house apparently inspired her with no curiosity and no enthusiasm, though it had been thought magnificent enough to be described in successive columns of the American newspapers; and she never spoke of her furniture or her domestics, though she had a prodigious supply of such possessions. She was the same with regard to her acquaintance, which was immense, inasmuch as every one in the place had called on her. Mrs Lemon was the least critical woman in the world; but it had sometimes exasperated her just a little that her daughter-in-law should receive every one in New York in exactly the same way. There were differences, Mrs Lemon knew, and some of them were of the highest importance: but poor Lady Barb appeared never to suspect them. She accepted every one and everything, and asked no questions. She had no curiosity about her fellow-citizens, and as she never assumed it for a moment, she gave Mrs Lemon no opportunity to enlighten her. Lady Barb was a person with whom you could do nothing unless she gave you an opening; and nothing would have been more difficult than to enlighten her against her will. Of course she picked up a little knowledge; but she confounded and transposed American attributes in the most extraordinary way. She had a way of calling every one Doctor; and Mrs Lemon could scarcely convince her that this distinction was too precious to be so freely bestowed. She had once said to her mother-in-law that in New York there was nothing to know people by, their names were so very monotonous; and Mrs Lemon had entered into this enough to see that there was something that stood out a good deal in Barberina's own prefix. It is probable that during her short stay in New York complete justice was not done Lady Barb; she never got credit, for instance, for repressing her annoyance at the aridity of the social nomenclature, which seemed to her hideous. That little speech to her mother was the most reckless sign she gave of it; and there were few things that contributed more to the good conscience she habitually enjoyed, than her self-control on this particular point.

Jackson Lemon was making some researches, just now, which took up a great deal of his time; and, for the rest, he passed his hours abundantly with his wife. For the last three months, therefore, he had seen his mother scarcely more than once a week. In spite of researches, in spite of medical societies, where Jackson, to her knowledge, read papers, Lady Barb had more of her husband's company than she had counted upon at the time she married. She had never known a married pair to be so much together as she and Jackson; he appeared to expect her to sit with

him in the library in the morning. He had none of the occu-
pations of gentlemen and noblemen in England, for the element
of politics appeared to be as absent as the hunting. There were
politics in Washington, she had been told, and even at Albany,
and Jackson had proposed to introduce her to these cities; but the
proposal, made to her once at dinner before several people, had
excited such cries of horror that it fell dead on the spot. 'We
don't want you to see anything of that kind,' one of the ladies
had said, and Jackson had appeared to be discouraged – that is if,
in regard to Jackson, one could really tell.

'Pray, what is it you want me to see?' Lady Barb had asked
on this occasion.

'Well, New York; and Boston, if you want to very much –
but not otherwise; and Niagara; and, more than anything,
Newport.'

Lady Barb was tired of their eternal Newport; she had heard
of it a thousand times, and felt already as if she had lived there
half her life; she was sure, moreover, that she should hate it. This
is perhaps as near as she came to having a lively conviction on
any American subject. She asked herself whether she was then to
spend her life in the Fifth Avenue, with alternations of a city of
villas (she detested villas), and wondered whether that was all the
great American country had to offer her. There were times
when she thought that she should like the backwoods, and that
the Far West might be a resource; for she had analysed her
feelings just deep enough to discover that when she had –
hesitating a good deal – turned over the question of marrying
Jackson Lemon, it was not in the least of American barbarism
that she was afraid; her dread was of American civilisation. She
believed the little lady I have just quoted was a goose; but that
did not make New York any more interesting. It would be
reckless to say that she suffered from an overdose of Jackson's
company, because she had a view of the fact that he was much
her most important social resource. She could talk to him about
England; about her own England, and he understood more or
less what she wished to say, when she wished to say anything,
which was not frequent. There were plenty of other people who
talked about England; but with them the range of allusion was
always the hotels, of which she knew nothing, and the shops,

and the opera, and the photographs: they had a mania for photographs. There were other people who were always wanting her to tell them about Pasterns, and the manner of life there, and the parties; but if there was one thing Lady Barb disliked more than another, it was describing Pasterns. She had always lived with people who knew, of themselves, what such a place would be, without demanding these pictorial efforts, proper only, as she vaguely felt, to persons belonging to the classes whose trade was the arts of expression. Lady Barb, of course, had never gone into it; but she knew that in her own class the business was not to express, but to enjoy; not to represent, but to be represented – though, indeed, this latter liability might convey offence; for it may be noted that even for an aristocrat Jackson Lemon's wife was aristocratic.

Lady Agatha and her visitor came back from the library in course of time, and Jackson Lemon felt it his duty to be rather cold to Herman Longstraw. It was not clear to him what sort of a husband his sister-in-law would do well to look for in America – if there were to be any question of husbands; but as to this he was not bound to be definite, provided he should rule out Mr Longstraw. This gentleman, however, was not given to perceive shades of manner; he had little observation, but very great confidence.

'I think you had better come home with me,' Jackson said to Lady Agatha; 'I guess you have stayed here long enough.'

'Don't let him say that, Mrs Lemon!' the girl cried. 'I like being with you so very much.'

'I try to make it pleasant,' said Mrs Lemon. 'I should really miss you now; but perhaps it's your mother's wish.' If it was a question of defending her guest from ineligible suitors, Mrs Lemon felt, of course, that her son was more competent than she; though she had a lurking kindness for Herman Longstraw, and a vague idea that he was a gallant, genial specimen of young America.

'Oh, mamma wouldn't see any difference!' Lady Agatha exclaimed, looking at Jackson with pleading blue eyes. 'Mamma wants me to see every one; you know she does. That's what she sent me to America for; she knew it was not like England. She wouldn't like it if I didn't sometimes stay with people; she always wanted us to stay at other houses. And she knows all about you, Mrs Lemon, and she likes you immensely. She sent you a message the other day, and I am afraid I forgot to give it you – to thank you for being so kind to me and taking such a lot of trouble. Really she did, but I forgot it. If she wants me to see as much as possible of America, it's much better I should be here than always with Barb – it's much less like one's own country. I mean it's much nicer – for a girl,' said Lady Agatha, affectionately, to Mrs Lemon, who began also to look at Jackson with a kind of tender argumentativeness.

'If you want the genuine thing, you ought to come out on the plains,' Mr Longstraw interposed, with smiling sincerity. 'I guess that was your mother's idea. Why don't you all come out?' He had been looking intently at Lady Agatha while the remarks I have just repeated succeeded each other on her lips – looking at her with a kind of fascinated approbation, for all the world as if he had been a slightly slow-witted English gentleman and the girl had been a flower of the West – a flower that knew how to talk. He made no secret of the fact that Lady Agatha's voice was music to him, his ear being much more susceptible than his own inflections would have indicated. To Lady Agatha those inflections were not displeasing, partly because, like Mr Herman himself, in general, she had not a perception of shades; and partly because it never occurred to her to compare them with any other tones. He seemed to her to speak a foreign language altogether – a romantic dialect, through which the most comical meanings gleamed here and there.

'I should like it above all things,' she said, in answer to his last observation.

'The scenery's superior to anything round here,' Mr Longstraw went on.

Mrs Lemon, as we know, was the softest of women; but, as an old New Yorker, she had no patience with some of the new fashions. Chief among these was the perpetual reference, which had become common only within a few years, to the outlying parts of the country, the States and Territories of which children, in her time, used to learn the names, in their order, at school, but which no one ever thought of going to or talking about. Such places, in Mrs Lemon's opinion, belonged to the geography-books, or at most to the literature of newspapers, but not to society nor to conversation; and the change – which, so far as it lay in people's talk, she thought at bottom a mere affectation – threatened to make her native land appear vulgar and vague. For this amiable daughter of Manhattan, the normal existence of man, and, still more, of woman, had been 'located', as she would have said, between Trinity Church and the beautiful Reservoir at the top of the Fifth Avenue – monuments of which she was personally proud; and if we could look into the deeper parts of her mind, I am afraid we should discover there an impression that both the countries of Europe and the remainder of her own continent were equally far from the centre and the light.

'Well, scenery isn't everything,' she remarked, mildly, to Mr Longstraw; 'and if Lady Agatha should wish to see anything of that kind, all she has got to do is to take the boat up the Hudson.'

Mrs Lemon's recognition of this river, I should say, was all that it need have been; she thought that it existed for the purpose of supplying New Yorkers with poetical feelings, helping them to face comfortably occasions like the present, and, in general, meet foreigners with confidence – part of the oddity of foreigners being their conceit about their own places.

'That's a good idea, Lady Agatha; let's take the boat,' said Mr Longstraw. 'I've had great times on the boats.'

Lady Agatha looked at her cavalier a little with those singular, charming eyes of hers – eyes of which it was impossible to say, at any moment, whether they were the shyest or the frankest in the world; and she was not aware, while this contemplation lasted, that her brother-in-law was observing her. He was thinking of certain things while he did so, of things he had heard about the English; who still, in spite of his having married into a family of that nation, appeared to him very much through the medium of hearsay. They were more passionate than the Americans, and they did things that would never have been expected; though they seemed steadier and less excitable, there was much social evidence to show that they were more impulsive.

'It's so very kind of you to propose that', Lady Agatha said in a moment to Mrs Lemon. 'I think I have never been in a

ship – except, of course, coming from England. I am sure
mamma would wish me to see the Hudson. We used to go in
immensely for boating in England.'

'Did you boat in a ship?' Herman Longstraw asked, showing
his teeth hilariously, and pulling his moustaches.

'Lots of my mother's people have been in the navy.' Lady
Agatha perceived vaguely and good-naturedly that she had said
something which the odd Americans thought odd, and that she
must justify herself. Her standard of oddity was getting
dreadfully dislocated.

'I really think you had better come back to us,' said Jackson;
'your sister is very lonely without you.'

'She is much more lonely with me. We are perpetually having
differences. Barb is dreadfully vexed because I like America,
instead of – instead of – ' And Lady Agatha paused a moment;
for it just occurred to her that this might be a betrayal.

'Instead of what?' Jackson Lemon inquired.

'Instead of perpetually wanting to go to England, as she does',
she went on, only giving her phrase a little softer turn; for she
felt the next moment that her sister could have nothing to hide,
and must, of course, have the courage of her opinions. 'Of
course England's best, but I dare say I like to be bad,' said Lady
Agatha, artlessly.

'Oh, there's no doubt you are awfully bad!' Mr Longstraw
exclaimed, with joyous eagerness. Of course he could not know
that what she had principally in mind was an exchange of
opinions that had taken place between her sister and herself just
before she came to stay with Mrs Lemon. This incident, of
which Longstraw was the occasion, might indeed have been
called a discussion, for it had carried them quite into the realms
of the abstract. Lady Barb had said she didn't see how Agatha
could look at such a creature as that – an odious, familiar, vulgar
being, who had not about him the rudiments of a gentleman.
Lady Agatha had replied that Mr Longstraw was familiar and
rough, and that he had a twang, and thought it amusing to talk
of her as 'the Princess'; but that he was a gentleman for all that,
and that at any rate he was tremendous fun. Her sister to this had
rejoined that if he was rough and familiar he couldn't be a
gentleman, inasmuch as that was just what a gentleman

meant – a man who was civil, and well-bred, and well-born. Lady Agatha had argued that this was just where she differed; that a man might perfectly be a gentleman, and yet be rough, and even ignorant, so long as he was really nice. The only thing was that he should be really nice, which was the case with Mr Longstraw, who, moreover, was quite extraordinarily civil – as civil as a man could be. And then Lady Agatha made the strongest point she had ever made in her life (she had never been so inspired) in saying that Mr Longstraw was rough, perhaps, but not rude – a distinction altogether wasted on her sister, who declared that she had not come to America, of all places, to learn what a gentleman was. The discussion, in short, had been lively. I know not whether it was the tonic effect on them, too, of the fine winter weather, or, on the other hand, that of Lady Barb's being bored and having nothing else to do; but Lord Canterville's daughters went into the question with the moral earnestness of a pair of Bostonians. It was part of Lady Agatha's view of her admirer that he, after all, much resembled other tall people, with smiling eyes and moustaches, who had ridden a good deal in rough countries, and whom she had seen in other places. If he was more familiar, he was also more alert; still, the difference was not in himself, but in the way she saw him – the way she saw everybody in America. If she should see the others in the same way, no doubt they would be quite the same; and Lady Agatha sighed a little over the possibilities of life; for this peculiar way, especially regarded in connection with gentlemen, had become very pleasant to her.

She had betrayed her sister more than she thought, even though Jackson Lemon did not particularly show it in the tone in which he said: 'Of course she knows that she is going to see your mother in the summer.' His tone, rather, was that of irritation at the repetition of a familiar idea.

'Oh, it isn't only mamma,' replied Lady Agatha.

'I know she likes a cool house,' said Mrs Lemon, suggestively.

'When she goes, you had better bid her good-bye,' the girl went on.

'Of course I shall bid her good-bye,' said Mrs Lemon, to whom, apparently, this remark was addressed.

'I shall never bid you good-bye, Princess,' Herman Longstraw interposed. 'I can tell you that you never will see the last of me.'

'Oh, it doesn't matter about me, for I shall come back; but if Barb once gets to England she will never come back.'

'Oh, my dear child,' murmured Mrs Lemon, addressing Lady Agatha, but looking at her son.

Jackson looked at the ceiling, at the floor; above all, he looked very conscious.

'I hope you don't mind my saying that, Jackson dear,' Lady Agatha said to him, for she was very fond of her brother-in-law.

'Ah, well, then, she shan't go, then,' he remarked, after a moment, with a dry little laugh.

'But you promised mamma, you know,' said the girl, with the confidence of her affection.

Jackson looked at her with an eye which expressed none even of his very moderate hilarity. 'Your mother, then, must bring her back.'

'Get some of your navy people to supply an ironclad!' cried Mr Longstraw.

'It would be very pleasant if the Marchioness could come over,' said Mrs Lemon.

'Oh, she would hate it more than poor Barb,' Lady Agatha quickly replied. It did not suit her mood at all to see a marchioness inserted into the field of her vision.

'Doesn't she feel interested, from what you have told her?' Herman Longstraw asked of Lady Agatha. But Jackson Lemon did not heed his sister-in-law's answers; he was thinking of something else. He said nothing more, however, about the subject of his thought, and before ten minutes were over he took his departure, having, meanwhile, neglected also to revert to the question of Lady Agatha's bringing her visit to his mother to a close. It was not to speak to him of this (for, as we know, she wished to keep the girl, and somehow could not bring herself to be afraid of Herman Longstraw) that when Jackson took leave she went with him to the door of the house, detaining him a little, while she stood on the steps, as people had always done in New York in her time, though it was another of the new fashions she did not like, not to come out of the parlour. She placed her hand on his arm to keep him on the 'stoop', and looked up and down into the brilliant afternoon and the beautiful city – its chocolate-coloured houses, so extraordinarily smooth – in which it seemed to her that even the most fastidious people ought to be glad to live. It was useless to attempt to conceal it; her son's marriage had made a difference, had put up a kind of barrier. It had brought with it a problem much more difficult than his old problem of how to make his mother feel that she was still, as she had been in his childhood, the dispenser of his rewards. The old problem had been easily solved; the new one was a visible preoccupation. Mrs Lemon felt that her daughter-in-law did not take her seriously; and that was a part of the barrier. Even if Barberina liked her better than any one else, this was mostly because she liked every one else so little. Mrs Lemon had not a grain of resentment in her nature; and it was not to feed a sense of wrong that she permitted herself to criticise her son's wife. She could not help feeling that his marriage was not altogether fortunate if his wife didn't take his mother seriously. She knew she was not otherwise remarkable than as being his mother; but that position, which was no merit of hers (the merit was all Jackson's, in being her son), seemed to her one which, familiar as Lady Barb appeared to have been in England with positions of various kinds, would naturally strike the girl as a very high one, to be accepted as freely as a fine morning. If she didn't think of his mother as an indivisible part of him, perhaps she didn't think of other things either; and Mrs Lemon vaguely felt that, remarkable as Jackson was, he was made up of parts, and that it would never do that these parts should depreciate one by one, for there was no knowing what that might end in. She feared that things were rather cold for him at home when he had to explain so much to his wife – explain to her, for instance, all the sources of happiness that were to be found in New York. This struck her as a new kind of problem altogether for a husband. She had never thought of matrimony without a community of feeling in regard to religion and country; one took those great conditions for granted, just as one assumed that one's food was to be cooked; and if Jackson should have to discuss them with his wife, he might, in spite of his great abilities, be carried into regions where he would get entangled and embroiled – from which, even, possibly, he would not come back at all. Mrs Lemon had a horror of losing him in some way; and this fear was in her eyes as she stood on the steps of her house, and after she had glanced up and down the street, looked at him a moment in silence. He simply kissed her again, and said she would take cold.

'I am not afraid of that, I have a shawl!' Mrs Lemon, who was very small and very fair, with pointed features and an elaborate cap, passed her life in a shawl, and owed to this habit her reputation for being an invalid – an idea which she scorned, naturally enough, inasmuch as it was precisely her shawl that (as she believed) kept her from being one. 'Is it true Barberina won't come back?' she asked of her son.

'I don't know that we shall ever find out; I don't know that I shall take her to England.'

'Didn't you promise, dear?'

'I don't know that I promised; not absolutely.'

'But you wouldn't keep her here against her will?' said Mrs Lemon, inconsequently.

'I guess she'll get used to it,' Jackson answered, with a lightness he did not altogether feel.

Mrs Lemon looked up and down the street again, and gave a little sigh. 'What a pity she isn't American!' She did not mean this as a reproach, a hint of what might have been; it was simply embarrassment resolved into speech.

'She couldn't have been American,' said Jackson, with decision.

'Couldn't she, dear?' Mrs Lemon spoke with a kind of respect; she felt that there were imperceptible reasons in this.

'It was just as she is that I wanted her,' Jackson added.

'Even if she won't come back?' his mother asked, with a certain wonder.

'Oh, she has got to come back!' Jackson said, going down the steps.

6

LADY BARB, after this, did not decline to see her New York acquaintances on Sunday afternoons, though she refused for the present to enter into a project of her husband's, who thought it would be a pleasant thing that she should entertain his friends on the evening of that day. Like all good Americans, Jackson Lemon devoted much consideration to the great question how, in his native land, society should be brought into being. It seemed to him that it would help the good cause, for which so many Americans are ready to lay down their lives, if his wife should, as he jocularly called it, open a saloon. He believed, or he tried to believe, the *salon* now possible in New York, on condition of its being reserved entirely for adults; and in having taken a wife out of a country in which social traditions were rich and ancient, he had done something towards qualifying his own house – so splendidly qualified in all strictly material respects – to be the scene of such an effort. A charming woman, accustomed only to the best in each country, as Lady Beauchemin said, what might she not achieve by being at home (to the elder generation) in an easy, early, inspiring, comprehensive way, on the evening in the week on which worldly engagements were least numerous? He laid this philosophy before Lady Barb, in pursuance of a theory that if she disliked New York on a short acquaintance, she could not fail to like it on a long one. Jackson Lemon believed in the New York mind – not so much, indeed, in its literary, artistic, or political achievements, as in its general quickness and nascent adaptability. He clung to this belief, for it was a very important piece of material in the structure that he was attempting to rear. The New York mind would throw its glamour over Lady Barb if she would only give it a chance; for it was exceedingly bright, entertaining, and sympathetic. If she would only have a *salon*, where this charming organ might expand, and where she might inhale its fragrance in the most convenient and luxurious way, without, as it were, getting up from her chair; if she would only just try this graceful, good-natured experiment (which would make every one like *her* so much too), he was sure that all the wrinkles in the gilded scroll of his fate would be smoothed out. But Lady Barb did not rise at all to his conception, and had not the least curiosity about the New York mind. She thought it would be extremely disagreeable to have a lot of people tumbling in on Sunday evening without being invited; and altogether her husband's sketch of the Anglo-American saloon seemed to suggest familiarity, high-pitched talk (she had already made a remark to him about 'screeching women'), and exaggerated laughter. She did not tell him – for this, somehow, it was not in her power to express, and, strangely enough, he never completely guessed it – that she was singularly deficient in any natural, or indeed acquired, understanding of what a saloon might be. She had never seen one, and for the most part she never thought of things she had not seen. She had seen great dinners, and balls, and meets, and runs, and races; she had seen garden-parties, and a lot of people, mainly women (who, however, didn't screech), at dull, stuffy teas, and distinguished companies collected in splendid castles; but all this gave her no idea of a tradition of conversation, of a social agreement that the continuity of talk, its accumulations from season to season, should not be lost. Conversation, in Lady Barb's experience, had never been continuous; in such a case it would surely have been a bore. It had been occasional and fragmentary, a trifle jerky, with allusions that were never explained: it had a dread of detail; it seldom pursued anything very far, or kept hold of it very long.

There was something else that she did not say to her husband in reference to his visions of hospitality, which was, that if she should open a saloon (she had taken up the joke as well, for Lady Barb was eminently good-natured), Mrs Vanderdecken would straightway open another, and Mrs Vanderdecken's would be the more successful of the two. This lady, for reasons that Lady Barb had not yet explored, was supposed to be the great personage in New York; there were legends of her husband's family having behind them a fabulous antiquity. When this was alluded to, it was spoken of as something incalculable, and lost in the dimness of time. Mrs Vanderdecken was young, pretty, clever, absurdly pretentious (Lady Barb thought), and had a wonderfully artistic house. Ambition, also, was expressed in every rustle of her garments; and if she was the first person in America (this had an immense sound), it was plain that she intended to remain so. It was not till after she had been several months in New York that it came over Lady Barb that this brilliant, bristling native had flung down the glove; and when the idea presented itself, lighted up by an incident which I have no space to relate, she simply blushed a little (for Mrs Vanderdecken), and held her tongue. She had not come to America to bandy words about precedence with such a woman as that. She had ceased to think about it much (of course one thought about it in England); but an instinct of self-preservation led her not to expose herself to occasions on which her claim might be tested. This, at bottom, had much to do with her having, very soon after the first flush of the honours paid her on her arrival, and which seemed to her rather grossly overdone, taken the line of scarcely going out. 'They can't keep *that* up!' she had said to herself; and, in short, she would stay at home. She had a feeling that whenever she should go forth she would meet Mrs Vanderdecken, who would withhold, or deny, or contest something – poor Lady Barb could never imagine what. She did not try to, and gave little thought to all this; for she was not prone to confess to herself fears, especially fears from which terror was absent. But, as I have said, it abode within her as a presentiment that if she should set up a drawing-room in the foreign style (it was curious, in New York, how they tried to be foreign), Mrs Vanderdecken would be beforehand with her. The continuity of conversation, oh! that idea she would certainly have; there was no one so continuous as Mrs Vanderdecken. Lady Barb, as I have related, did not give her husband the surprise of telling him of these thoughts, though she had given him some other surprises. He would have been very much astonished, and perhaps, after a bit, a little encouraged, at finding that she was liable to this particular form of irritation.

On the Sunday afternoon she was visible; and on one of these occasions, going into her drawing-room late, he found her entertaining two ladies and a gentleman. The gentleman was

Sidney Feeder, and one of the ladies was Mrs Vanderdecken, whose ostensible relations with Lady Barb were of the most cordial nature. If she intended to crush her (as two or three persons, not conspicuous for a narrow accuracy, gave out that she privately declared), Mrs Vanderdecken wished at least to study the weak points of the invader, to penetrate herself with the character of the English girl. Lady Barb, indeed, appeared to have a mysterious fascination for the representative of the American patriciate. Mrs Vanderdecken could not take her eyes off her victim; and whatever might be her estimate of her importance, she at least could not let her alone. 'Why does she come to see me?' poor Lady Barb asked herself. 'I am sure I don't want to see her; she has done enough for civility long ago.' Mrs Vanderdecken had her own reasons; and one of them was simply the pleasure of looking at the Doctor's wife, as she habitually called the daughter of the Cantervilles. She was not guilty of the folly of depreciating this lady's appearance, and professed an unbounded admiration for it, defending it on many occasions against superficial people who said there were fifty women in New York that were handsomer. Whatever might have been Lady Barb's weak points, they were not the curve of her cheek and chin, the setting of her head on her throat, or the quietness of her deep eyes, which were as beautiful as if they had been blank, like those of antique busts. 'The head is enchanting – perfectly enchanting,' Mrs Vanderdecken used to say irrelevantly, as if there were only one head in the place. She always used to ask about the Doctor; and that was another reason why she came. She brought up the Doctor at every turn; asked if he were often called up at night; found it the greatest of luxuries, in a word, to address Lady Barb as the wife of a medical man, more or less *au courant* of her husband's patients. The other lady, on this Sunday afternoon, was a certain little Mrs Chew, whose clothes looked so new that she had the air of a walking advertisement issued by a great shop, and who was always asking Lady Barb about England, which Mrs Vanderdecken never did. The latter visitor conversed with Lady Barb on a purely American basis, with that continuity (on her own side) of which mention has already been made, while Mrs Chew engaged Sidney Feeder on topics equally local. Lady Barb liked Sidney Feeder; she only hated his name, which was constantly in her ears during the half-hour the ladies sat with her, Mrs Chew having the habit, which annoyed Lady Barb, of repeating perpetually the appellation of her interlocutor.

Lady Barb's relations with Mrs Vanderdecken consisted mainly in wondering, while she talked, what she wanted of her, and in looking, with her sculptured eyes, at her visitor's clothes, in which there was always much to examine. 'Oh, Doctor Feeder!' 'Now, Doctor Feeder!' 'Well, Doctor Feeder,' – these exclamations, on the lips of Mrs Chew, were an undertone in Lady Barb's consciousness. When I say that she liked her husband's *confrère*, as he used to call himself, I mean that she smiled at him when he came, and gave him her hand, and asked him if he would have some tea. There was nothing nasty (as they said in London) in Lady Barb, and she would have been incapable of inflicting a deliberate snub upon a man who had the air of standing up so squarely to any work that he might have in hand. But she had nothing to say to Sidney Feeder. He apparently had the art of making her shy, more shy than usual; for she was always a little so; she discouraged him, discouraged him completely. He was not a man who wanted drawing out, there was nothing of that in him, he was remarkably copious; but Lady Barb appeared unable to follow him, and half the time, evidently, did not know what he was saying. He tried to adapt his conversation to her needs; but when he spoke of the world, of what was going on in society, she was more at sea even than when he spoke of hospitals and laboratories, and the health of the city, and the progress of science. She appeared, indeed, after her first smile, when he came in, which was always charming, scarcely to see him, looking past him, and above him, and below him, and everywhere but at him, until he got up to go again, when she gave him another smile, as expressive of pleasure and a casual acquaintance as that with which she had greeted his entry; it seemed to imply that they had been having delightful talk for an hour. He wondered what the deuce Jackson Lemon could find interesting in such a woman, and he believed that his perverse, though gifted colleague, was not destined to feel that she illuminated his life. He pitied Jackson, he saw that Lady Barb, in New York, would neither assimilate nor be assimilated;

and yet he was afraid to betray his incredulity, thinking it might be depressing to poor Lemon to show him how his marriage – now so dreadfully irrevocable – struck others. Sidney Feeder was a man of a strenuous conscience, and he did his duty overmuch by his old friend and his wife, from the simple fear that he should not do it enough. In order not to appear to neglect them, he called upon Lady Barb heroically, in spite of pressing engagements, week after week, enjoying his virtue himself as little as he made it fruitful for his hostess, who wondered at last what she had done to deserve these visitations. She spoke of them to her husband, who wondered also what poor Sidney had in his head, and yet was unable, of course, to hint to him that he need not think it necessary to come so often. Between Doctor Feeder's wish not to let Jackson see that his marriage had made a difference, and Jackson's hesitation to reveal to Sidney that his standard of friendship was too high, Lady Barb passed a good many of those numerous hours during which she asked herself if she had come to America for that. Very little had ever passed between her and her husband on the subject of Sidney Feeder; for an instinct told her that if they were ever to have scenes, she must choose the occasion well; and this odd person was not an occasion. Jackson had tacitly admitted that his friend Feeder was anything she chose to think him; he was not a man to be guilty, in a discussion, of the disloyalty of damning him with praise that was faint. If Lady Agatha had usually been with her sister, Doctor Feeder would have been better entertained; for the younger of the English visitors prided herself, after several months of New York, on understanding everything that was said, and catching every allusion, it mattered not from what lips it fell. But Lady Agatha was never at home; she had learned how to describe herself perfectly by the time she wrote to her mother that she was always 'on the go'. None of the innumerable victims of old-world tyranny who have fled to the United States as to a land of freedom, have ever offered more lavish incense to that goddess than this emancipated London *débutante*. She had enrolled herself in an amiable band which was known by the humorous name of 'the Tearers' – a dozen young ladies of aggreeable appearance, high spirits and good wind, whose most general characteristic was that, when wanted, they were to be sought anywhere in the world but under the roof that was supposed to shelter them. They were never at home; and when Sidney Feeder, as sometimes happened, met Lady Agatha at other houses, she was in the hands of the irrepressible Longstraw. She had come back to her sister, but Mr Longstraw had followed her to the door. As to passing it, he had received direct discouragement from her brother-in-law; but he could at least hang about and wait for her. It may be confided to the reader, at the risk of diminishing the effect of the only incident which in the course of this very level narrative may startle him, that he never had to wait very long.

When Jackson Lemon came in, his wife's visitors were on the point of leaving her; and he did not ask even Sidney Feeder to remain, for he had something particular to say to Lady Barb.

'I haven't asked you half what I wanted – I have been talking so much to Doctor Feeder,' the dressy Mrs Chew said, holding the hand of her hostess in one of her own, and toying with one of Lady Barb's ribbons with the other.

'I don't think I have anything to tell you; I think I have told people everything,' Lady Barb answered, rather wearily.

'You haven't told *me* much!' Mrs Vanderdecken said, smiling brightly.

'What could one tell you? – you know everything,' Jackson Lemon interposed.

'Ah, no; there are some things that are great mysteries for me,' the lady returned. 'I hope you are coming to me on the 17th,' she added, to Lady Barb.

'On the 17th? I think we are going somewhere.'

'Do go to Mrs Vanderdecken's,' said Mrs Chew; 'you will see the cream of the cream.'

'Oh, gracious!' Mrs Vanderdecken exclaimed.

'Well, I don't care; she will, won't she, Doctor Feeder? – the very pick of American society.' Mrs Chew stuck to her point.

'Well, I have no doubt Lady Barb will have a good time,' said Sidney Feeder. 'I'm afraid you miss the bran,' he went on, with irrelevant jocosity, to Lady Barb. He always tried the jocose when other elements had failed.

'The bran?' asked Lady Barb, staring.

'Where you used to ride, in the Park.'

'My dear fellow, you speak as if it were the circus,' Jackson Lemon said, smiling; 'I haven't married a mountebank!'

'Well, they put some stuff on the road,' Sidney Feeder explained, not holding much to his joke.

'You must miss a great many things,' said Mrs Chew, tenderly.

'I don't see what,' Mrs Vanderdecken remarked, 'except the fogs and the Queen. New York is getting more and more like London. It's a pity, you ought to have known us thirty years ago.'

'You are the queen, here,' said Jackson Lemon; 'but I don't know what you know about thirty years ago.'

'Do you think she doesn't go back? – she goes back to the last century!' cried Mrs Chew.

'I dare say I should have liked that,' said Lady Barb; 'but I can't imagine.' And she looked at her husband – a look she often had – as if she vaguely wished him to do something.

He was not called upon, however, to take any violent steps, for Mrs Chew said: 'Well, Lady Barberina, good-bye'; and Mrs Vanderdecken smiled in silence at her hostess, and addressed a farewell, accompanied very audibly with his title, to her host; and Sidney Feeder made a joke about stepping on the trains of the ladies' dresses as he accompanied them to the door. Mrs Chew had always a great deal to say at the last; she talked till she was in the street, and then she did not cease. But at the end of five minutes Jackson Lemon was alone with his wife; and then he told her a piece of news. He prefaced it, however, by an inquiry as he came back from the hall.

'Where is Agatha, my dear?'

'I haven't the least idea. In the streets somewhere, I suppose.'

'I think you ought to know a little more.'

'How can I know about things here? I have given her up; I can do nothing with her, I don't care what she does.'

'She ought to go back to England,' Jackson Lemon said, after a pause.

'She ought never to have come.'

'It was not my proposal, God knows!' Jackson answered, rather sharply.

'Mamma could never know what it really is,' said his wife.

'No, it has not been as yet what your mother supposed! Herman Longstraw wants to marry her. He has made me a formal proposal. I met him half an hour ago in Madison Avenue, and he asked me to come with him into the Columbia Club. There, in the billiard-room, which to-day is empty, he opened himself – thinking evidently that in laying the matter before me he was behaving with extraordinary propriety. He tells me he is dying of love, and that she is perfectly willing to go and live in Arizona.'

'So she is,' said Lady Barb. 'And what did you tell him?'

'I told him that I was sure it would never do, and that at any rate I could have nothing to say to it. I told him explicitly, in short, what I had told him virtually before. I said that we should send Agatha straight back to England, and that if they have the courage they must themselves broach the question over there.'

'When shall you send her back?' asked Lady Barb.

'Immediately; by the very first steamer.'

'Alone, like an American girl?'

'Don't be rough, Barb,' said Jackson Lemon. 'I shall easily find some people; lots of people are sailing now.'

'I must take her myself,' Lady Barb declared in a moment. 'I brought her out, and I must restore her to my mother's hands.'

Jackson Lemon had expected this, and he believed he was prepared for it. But when it came he found his preparation was not complete; for he had no answer to make – none, at least, that seemed to him to go to the point. During these last weeks it had come over him, with a quiet, irresistible, unmerciful force, that Mrs Dexter Freer had been right when she said to him, that Sunday afternoon in Jermyn Street, the summer before, that he would find it was not so simple to be an American. Such an identity was complicated, in just the measure that she had foretold, by the difficulty of domesticating one's wife. The difficulty was not dissipated by his having taken a high tone about it; it pinched him from morning till night, like a misfitting shoe. His high tone had given him courage when he took the great step; but he began to perceive that the highest tone in the world cannot change the nature of things. His ears tingled when he reflected that if the Dexter Freers, whom he had thought alike ignoble in their hopes and their fears, had been by ill-luck spending the winter in New York, they would have found his predicament as entertaining as they could desire. Drop by drop the conviction had entered his mind – the first drop had come in the form of a word from Lady Agatha – that if his wife should return to England she would never again cross the Atlantic to the West. That word from Lady Agatha had been the touch from the outside, at which, often, one's fears crystallise. What she would do, how she would resist – this he was not yet prepared to tell himself; but he felt, every time he looked at her, that this beautiful woman whom he had adored was filled with a dumb, insuperable, ineradicable purpose. He knew that if she should plant herself, no power on earth would move her; and her blooming, antique beauty, and the general loftiness of her breeding, came to seem to him – rapidly – but the magnificent expression of a dense, patient, imperturbable obstinacy. She was not light, she was not supple, and after six months of marriage he had made up his mind that she was not clever; but nevertheless she would elude him. She had married him, she had come into his fortune and his consideration – for who was she, after all? Jackson Lemon was once so angry as to ask himself, reminding himself that in England Lady Claras and Lady Florences were as thick as blackberries – but she would have nothing to do, if she could help it, with his country. She had gone in to dinner first in every house in the place, but this had not satisfied her. It *had* been simple to be an American, in this sense that no one else in New York had made any difficulties; the difficulties had sprung from her peculiar feelings, which were after all what he had married her for, thinking they would be a fine temperamental heritage for his brood. So they would, doubtless, in the coming years, after the brood should have appeared; but meanwhile they interfered with the best heritage of all – the nationality of his possible children. Lady Barb would do nothing violent; he was tolerably certain of that. She would not return to England without his consent; only, when she should return, it would be once for all. His only possible line, then, was not to take her back – a position replete with difficulties, because, of course, he had, in a manner, given his word, while she had given no word at all, beyond the general promise she had murmured at the altar. She had been general, but he had been specific; the settlements he had made were a part of that. His difficulties were such as he could not directly face. He must tack in approaching so uncertain a coast. He said to Lady Barb presently that it would be very inconvenient for him to leave New York at that moment: she must remember that their plans had been laid for a later departure. He could not think of letting her make the voyage without him, and, on the other hand, they must pack her sister off without delay. He would therefore make instant inquiry for a chaperon, and he relieved his irritation by expressing considerable disgust at Herman Langstraw.

Lady Barb did not trouble herself to denounce this gentleman; her manner was that of having for a long time expected the worst. She simply remarked dryly, after having listened to her husband for some minutes in silence: 'I would as lief she should marry Doctor Feeder!'

The day after this, Jackson Lemon closeted himself for an hour with Lady Agatha, taking great pains to set forth to her the reasons why she should not unite herself with her Californian. Jackson was kind, he was affectionate; he kissed her and put his arm round her waist, he reminded her that he and she were the best of friends, and that she had always been awfully nice to him; therefore he counted upon her. She would break her mother's heart, she would deserve her father's curse, and she would get him, Jackson, into a pickle from which no human power could ever disembroil him. Lady Agatha listened and cried, and returned his kiss very affectionately, and admitted that her father and mother would never consent to such a marriage; and when he told her that he had made arrangements for her to sail for Liverpool (with some charming people) the next day but one, she embraced him again and assured him that she could never thank him enough for all the trouble he had taken about her. He flattered himself that he had convinced, and in some degree comforted her, and reflected with complacency that even should his wife take it into her head, Barberina would never get ready to embark for her native land between a Monday and a Wednesday. The next morning Lady Agatha did not appear at breakfast; but as she usually rose very late, her absence excited no alarm. She had not rung her bell, and she was supposed still to be sleeping. But she had never yet slept later than midday; and as this hour approached her sister went to her room. Lady Barb then discovered that she had left the house at seven o'clock in the morning, and had gone to meet Herman Longstraw at a neighbouring corner. A little note on the table explained it very succinctly, and put beyond the power of Jackson Lemon and his wife to doubt that by the time this news reached them their wayward sister had been united to the man of her preference as closely as the laws of the State of New York could bind her. Her little note set forth that as she knew she should never be permitted to marry him, she had determined to marry him without permission, and that directly after the ceremony, which would be of the simplest kind, they were to take a train for the far West. Our history is concerned only with the remote consequences of this incident, which made, of course, a great deal of trouble for Jackson Lemon. He went to the far West in pursuit of the fugitives, and overtook them in California; but he had not the audacity to propose to them to separate, as it was easy for him to see that Herman Longstraw was at least as well married as himself. Lady Agatha was already popular in the new States, where the history of her elopement, emblazoned in enormous capitals, was circulated in a thousand newspapers. This question of the newspapers had been for Jackson Lemon one of the most definite results of his sister-in-law's *coup de tête*. His first thought had been of the public prints, and his first exclamation a prayer that they should not get hold of the story. But they did get hold of it, and they treated the affair with their customary energy and eloquence. Lady Barb never saw them; but an affectionate friend of the family, travelling at that time in the United States, made a parcel of some of the leading journals, and sent them to Lord Canterville. This missive elicited from her ladyship a letter addressed to Jackson Lemon which shook the young man's position to the base. The phials of an unnameable vulgarity had been opened upon the house of Canterville, and his mother-in-law demanded that in compensation for the affronts and injuries that were being heaped upon her family, and bereaved and dishonoured as she was, she should at least be allowed to look on the face of her other daughter. 'I suppose you will not, for very pity, be deaf to such a prayer as that,' said

Lady Barb; and though shrinking from recording a second act of weakness on the part of a man who had such pretensions to be strong, I must relate that poor Jackson, who blushed dreadfully over the newspapers, and felt afresh, as he read them, the force of Mrs Freer's terrible axiom – poor Jackson paid a visit to the office of the Cunarders. He said to himself afterward that it was the newspapers that had done it; he could not bear to appear to be on their side; they made it so hard to deny that the country was vulgar, at a time when one was in such need of all one's arguments. Lady Barb, before sailing, definitely refused to mention any week or month as the date of their pre-arranged return to New York. Very many weeks and months have elapsed since then, and she gives no sign of coming back. She will never fix a date. She is much missed by Mrs Vanderdecken, who still alludes to her – still says the line of the shoulders was superb; putting the statement, pensively, in the past tense. Lady Beauchemin and Lady Marmaduke are much disconcerted; the international project has not, in their view, received an impetus.

Jackson Lemon has a house in London, and he rides in the park with his wife, who is as beautiful as the day, and a year ago presented him with a little girl, with features that Jackson already scans for the look of race – whether in hope or fear, to-day, is more than my muse has revealed. He has occasional scenes with Lady Barb, during which the look of race is very visible in her own countenance; but they never terminate in a visit to the Cunarders. He is exceedingly restless, and is constantly crossing to the Continent; but he returns with a certain abruptness, for he cannot bear to meet the Dexter Freers, and they seem to pervade the more comfortable parts of Europe. He dodges them in every town. Sidney Feeder feels very badly about him; it is months since Jackson has sent him any 'results'. The excellent fellow goes very often, in a consolatory spirit, to see Mrs Lemon; but he has not yet been able to answer her standing question: 'Why that girl more than another?' Lady Agatha Longstraw and her husband arrived a year ago in England, and Mr Longstraw's personality had immense success during the last London season. It is not exactly known what they live on, though it is perfectly known that he is looking for something to do. Meanwhile it is as good as known that Jackson Lemon supports them.

BROOKSMITH

JAMES recorded in his notebook in 1884 the provenance of this story, deriving from an anecdote told him by his friend Mrs James Rogerson. It concerned another friend, Mrs Duncan Stewart, and her lady's maid, Past, who had been with her for many years until Mrs Stewart's recent death. James wrote:

She had to find a new place of course, on Mrs. S's death, to relapse into ordinary service. Her sorrow, the way she felt the change, and the way she expressed it to Mrs. R. 'Ah yes, ma'am, you have lost your mother, and it's a great grief, but what is your loss to mine?' (She was devoted to Mrs. D.S.) 'You continue to see good society, to live with clever, cultivated people: but I fall again into my own class, I shall never see such company – hear such talk – again. She was so good to me that I lived *with* her, as it were; and nothing will ever make up to me again for the loss of her conversation. Common, vulgar people now: that's my lot for the future!' Represent this – the refined nature of the little plain, quiet woman – her appreciation – and the way her new conditions sicken her, with a denouement if possible. Represent first, of course, her life with the old lady – figure of old Mrs. D.S. (modified) – her interior – her talk. Mrs. R.'s relations with her servants. 'My child – my dear child'.[1]

James did not write the story until 1891, and it appeared on 2nd May that year simultaneously in *Black and White* (a new London illustrated weekly) and *Harper's Weekly*. His limit was 7,000 words, which he found 'a very tight squeeze'.[2] *Brooksmith* first appeared in book form in *The Lesson of the Master and other stories* (1892).

---

1. *The Complete Notebooks* (1987), pp 28–9.
2. Ibid, p 56.

BROOKSMITH

WE ARE scattered now, the friends of the late Mr Oliver
Offord; but whenever we chance to meet I think we are
conscious of a certain esoteric respect for each other. 'Yes, you
too have been in Arcadia,' we seem not too grumpily to allow.
When I pass the house in Mansfield Street I remember that
Arcadia was there. I don't know who has it now, and I don't
want to know; it's enough to be so sure that if I should ring the
bell there would be no such luck for me as that Brooksmith
should open the door. Mr Offord, the most agreeable, the most
lovable of bachelors, was a retired diplomatist, living on his
pension, confined by his infirmities to his fireside and delighted
to be found there any afternoon in the year by such visitors as
Brooksmith allowed to come up. Brooksmith was his butler and
his most intimate friend, to whom we all stood, or I should say
sat, in the same relation in which the subject of the sovereign
finds himself to the prime minister. By having been for years, in
foreign lands, the most delightful Englishman any one had ever
known, Mr Offord had, in my opinion, rendered signal service
to his country. But I suppose he had been too much liked – liked
even by those who didn't like *it* – so that as people of that sort
never get titles or dotations for the horrid things they have *not*
done, his principal reward was simply that we went to see him.

Oh, we went perpetually, and it was not our fault if he was
not overwhelmed with this particular honour. Any visitor who
came once came again – to come merely once was a slight
which nobody, I am sure, had ever put upon him. His circle,
therefore, was essentially composed of *habitués*, who were
habitués for each other as well as for him, as those of a happy
salon should be. I remember vividly every element of the place,
down to the intensely Londonish look of the grey opposite
houses, in the gap of the white curtains of the high windows,
and the exact spot where, on a particular afternoon, I put down

my tea-cup for Brooksmith, lingering an instant, to gather it up as if he were plucking a flower. Mr Offord's drawing-room was indeed Brooksmith's garden, his pruned and tended human *parterre*, and if we all flourished there and grew well in our places it was largely owing to his supervision.

Many persons have heard much, though most have doubtless seen little, of the famous institution of the *salon*, and many are born to the depression of knowing that this finest flower of social life refuses to bloom where the English tongue is spoken. The explanation is usually that our women have not the skill to cultivate it – the art to direct, between suggestive shores, the course of the stream of talk. My affectionate, my pious memory of Mr Offord contradicts this induction only, I fear, more insidiously to confirm it. The very sallow and slightly smoked drawing-room in which he spent so large a portion of the last years of his life certainly deserved the distinguished name; but on the other hand it could not be said at all to owe its stamp to the soft pressure of the indispensable sex. The dear man had indeed been capable of one of those sacrifices to which women are deemed peculiarly apt; he had recognised (under the influence, in some degree, it is true, of physical infirmity), that if you wished people to find you at home you must manage not to be out. He had in short accepted the fact which many dabblers in the social art are slow to learn, that you must really, as they say, take a line and that the only way to be at home is to stay at home. Finally his own fireside had become a summary of his habits. Why should he ever have left it? – since this would have been leaving what was notoriously pleasantest in London, the compact charmed cluster (thinning away indeed into casual couples), round the fine old last century chimney-piece which, with the exception of the remarkable collection of miniatures, was the best thing the place contained. Mr Offord was not rich; he had nothing but his pension and the use for life of the somewhat superannuated house.

When I am reminded by some uncomfortable contrast of to-day how perfectly we were all handled there I ask myself once more what had been the secret of such perfection. One had taken it for granted at the time, for anything that is supremely good produces more acceptance than surprise. I felt we were all happy, but I didn't consider how our happiness was managed. And yet there were questions to be asked, questions that strike me as singularly obvious now that there is nobody to answer them. Mr Offord had solved the insoluble; he had, without feminine help (save in the sense that ladies were dying to come to him and he saved the lives of several), established a *salon*; but I might have guessed that there was a method in his madness – a law in his success. He had not hit it off by a mere fluke. There was an art in it all, and how was the art so hidden? Who, indeed, if it came to that, was the occult artist? Launching this inquiry the other day, I had already got hold of the tail of my reply. I was helped by the very wonder of some of the conditions that came back to me – those that used to seem as natural as sunshine in a fine climate.

How was it, for instance, that we never were a crowd, never either too many or too few, always the right people *with* the right people (there must really have been no wrong people at all), always coming and going, never sticking fast nor over-staying, yet never popping in or out with an indecorous familiarity? How was it that we all sat where we wanted and moved when we wanted and met whom we wanted and escaped whom we wanted; joining, according to the accident of inclination, the general circle or falling in with a single talker on a convenient sofa? Why were all the sofas so convenient, the accidents so happy, the talkers so ready, the listeners so willing, the subjects presented to you in a rotation as quickly fore-ordained as the courses at dinner? A dearth of topics would have been as unheard of as a lapse in the service. These speculations couldn't fail to lead me to the fundamental truth that Brooksmith had been somehow at the bottom of the mystery. If he had not established the *salon* at least he had carried it on. Brooksmith, in short, was the artist!

We felt this, covertly, at the time, without formulating it, and were conscious, as an ordered and prosperous community, of his evenhanded justice, untainted with flunkeyism. He had none of that vulgarity – his touch was infinitely fine. The delicacy of it was clear to me on the first occasion my eyes rested, as they were so often to rest again, on the domestic revealed, in the turbid light of the street, by the opening of the house-door. I saw on the spot that though he had plenty of school he carried it without arrogance – he had remained articulate and human. *L'Ecole Anglaise*, Mr Offord used to call him, laughing, when, later, it happened more than once that we had some conversation about him. But I remember accusing Mr Offord of not doing him quite ideal justice. That he was not one of the giants of the school, however, my old friend, who really understood him perfectly and was devoted to him, as I shall show, quite admitted; which doubtless poor Brooksmith had himself felt, to his cost, when his value in the market was originally determined. The utility of his class in general is estimated by the foot and the inch, and poor Brooksmith had only about five feet two to put into circulation. He acknowledged the inadequacy of this provision, and I am sure was penetrated with the everlasting fitness of the relation between service and stature. If *he* had been Mr Offord he certainly would have found Brooksmith wanting, and indeed the laxity of his employer on this score was one of many things which he had had to condone and to which he had at last indulgently adapted himself.

I remember the old man's saying to me: 'Oh, my servants, if they can live with me a fortnight they can live with me for ever. But it's the first fortnight that tries 'em.' It was in the first fortnight, for instance, that Brooksmith had had to learn that he was exposed to being addressed as 'my dear fellow' and 'my poor child.' Strange and deep must such a probation have been to him, and he doubtless emerged from it tempered and purified. This was written to a certain extent in his appearance; in his spare, brisk little person, in his cloistered white face and extraordinarily polished hair, which told of responsibility, looked as if it were kept up to the same high standard as the plate; in his small, clear, anxious eyes, even in the permitted, though not exactly encouraged tuft on his chin. 'He thinks me rather mad, but I've broken him in, and now he likes the place, he likes the company,' said the old man. I embraced this fully after I had become aware that Brooksmith's main characteristic was a deep and shy refinement, though I remember I was rather puzzled when, on another occasion, Mr Offord remarked: 'What he likes is the talk – mingling in the conversation.' I was conscious that I had never seen Brooksmith permit himself this freedom, but I guessed in a moment that what Mr Offord alluded to was a participation more intense than any speech could have represented – that of being perpetually present on a hundred legitimate pretexts, errands, necessities, and breathing the very atmosphere of criticism, the famous criticism of life. 'Quite an education, sir, isn't it, sir?' he said to me one day at the foot of the stairs, when he was letting me out; and I have always remembered the words and the tone as the first sign of the quickening drama of poor Brooksmith's fate. It was indeed an education, but to what was this sensitive young man of thirty-five, of the servile class, being educated?

Practically and inevitably, for the time, to companionship, to the perpetual, the even exaggerated reference and appeal of a person brought to dependence by his time of life and his infirmities and always addicted moreover (this was the exaggeration) to the art of giving you pleasure by letting you do things for him. There were certain things Mr Offord was capable of pretending he liked you to do, even when he didn't, if he thought *you* liked them. If it happened that you didn't either (this was rare, but it might be), of course there were cross-purposes; but Brooksmith was there to prevent their going very far. This was precisely the way he acted as moderator: he averted misunderstandings or cleared them up. He had been capable, strange as it may appear, of acquiring for this purpose an insight into the French tongue, which was often used at Mr Offord's; for besides being habitual to most of the foreigners, and they were many, who haunted the place or arrived with letters (letters often requiring a little worried consideration, of which Brooksmith always had cognisance), it had really become the primary language of the master of the house. I don't know if all the *malentendus* were in French, but almost all the explanations were, and this didn't a bit prevent Brooksmith from following them. I know Mr Offord used to read passages to him from Montaigne and Saint-Simon, for he read perpetually when he was alone – when they were alone, I should say – and Brooksmith was always about. Perhaps you'll say no wonder Mr Offord's butler regarded him as 'rather mad.' However, if I'm not sure what he thought about Montaigne I'm convinced he admired Saint-Simon. A certain feeling for letters must have rubbed off on him from the mere handling of his master's books, which he was always carrying to and fro and putting back in their places.

I often noticed that if an anecdote or a quotation, much more a lively discussion, was going forward, he would, if busy with the fire or the curtains, the lamp or the tea, find a pretext for remaining in the room till the point should be reached. If his purpose was to catch it you were not discreet to call him off, and I shall never forget a look, a hard, stony stare (I caught it in its passage), which, one day when there were a good many people in the room, he fastened upon the footman who was helping him in the service and who, in an undertone, had asked him some irrelevant question. It was the only manifestation of harshness that I ever observed on Brooksmith's part, and at first I wondered what was the matter. Then I became conscious that Mr Offord was relating a very curious anecdote, never before perhaps made so public, and imparted to the narrator by an eye-witness of the fact, bearing upon Lord Byron's life in Italy. Nothing would induce me to reproduce it here; but Brooksmith had been in danger of losing it. If I ever should venture to reproduce it I shall feel how much I lose in not having my fellow-auditor to refer to.

The first day Mr Offord's door was closed was therefore a dark date in contemporary history. It was raining hard and my umbrella was wet, but Brooksmith took it from me exactly as if this were a preliminary for going upstairs. I observed however that instead of putting it away he held it poised and trickling over the rug, and then I became aware that he was looking at me with deep, acknowledging eyes – his air of universal responsibility. I immediately understood; there was scarcely need of the question and the answer that passed between us. When I did understand that the old man had given up, for the first time, though only for the occasion, I exclaimed dolefully: 'What a difference it will make – and to how many people!'

'I shall be one of them, sir!' said Brooksmith; and that was the beginning of the end.

Mr Offord came down again, but the spell was broken, and the great sign of it was that the conversation was, for the first time, not directed. It wandered and stumbled, a little frightened, like a lost child – it had let go the nurse's hand. 'The worst of it

is that now we shall talk about my health – *c'est la fin de tout*,'
Mr Offord said, when he reappeared; and then I recognised what
a sign of change that would be – for he had never tolerated
anything so provincial. The talk became ours, in a word – not
his; and as ours, even when *he* talked, it could only be inferior.
In this form it was a distress to Brooksmith, whose attention
now wandered from it altogether: he had so much closer a vision
of his master's intimate conditions than our superficialities
represented. There were better hours, and he was more in and
out of the room, but I could see that he was conscious that the
great institution was falling to pieces. He seemed to wish to take
counsel with me about it, to feel responsible for its going on in
some form or other. When for the second period – the first had
lasted several days – he had to tell me that our old friend didn't
receive, I half expected to hear him say after a moment: 'Do you
think I ought to, sir, in his place?' – as he might have asked me,
with the return of autumn, if I thought he had better light the
drawing-room fire.

He had a resigned philosophic sense of what his guests – our
guests, as I came to regard them in our colloquies – would
expect. His feeling was that he wouldn't absolutely have
approved of himself as a substitute for the host; but he was so
saturated with the religion of habit that he would have made, for
our friends, the necessary sacrifice to the divinity. He would take
them on a little further, till they could look about them. I think
I saw him also mentally confronted with the opportunity to
deal – for once in his life – with some of his own dumb
preferences, his limitations of sympathy, *weeding* a little, in
prospect, and returning to a purer tradition. It was not unknown
to me that he considered that toward the end of Mr Offord's
career a certain laxity of selection had crept in.

At last it came to be the case that we all found the closed door
more often than the open one; but even when it was closed
Brooksmith managed a crack for me to squeeze through; so that
practically I never turned away without having paid a visit. The
difference simply came to be that the visit was to Brooksmith. It
took place in the hall, at the familiar foot of the stairs, and we
didn't sit down – at least Brooksmith didn't; moreover it was
devoted wholly to one topic and always had the air of being

already over − beginning, as it were, at the end. But it was always interesting − it always gave me something to think about. It is true that the subject of my meditation was ever the same − ever 'It's all very well, but what *will* become of Brooksmith?' Even my private answer to this question left me still unsatisfied. No doubt Mr Offord would provide for him, but *what* would he provide? that was the great point. He couldn't provide society; and society had become a necessity of Brooksmith's nature. I must add that he never showed a symptom of what I may call sordid solicitude − anxiety on his own account. He was rather livid and intensely grave, as befitted a man before whose eyes the 'shade of that which once was great' was passing away. He had the solemnity of a person winding up, under depressing circumstances, a long established and celebrated business; he was a kind of social executor or liquidator. But his manner seemed to testify exclusively to the uncertainty of *our* future. I couldn't in those days have afforded it − I lived in two rooms in Jermyn Street and didn't 'keep a man'; but even if my income had permitted I shouldn't have ventured to say to Brooksmith (emulating Mr Offord), 'My dear fellow, I'll take you on.' The whole tone of our intercourse was so much more an implication that it was *I* who should now want a lift. Indeed there was a tacit assurance in Brooksmith's whole attitude that he would have me on his mind.

One of the most assiduous members of our circle had been Lady Kenyon, and I remember his telling me one day that her ladyship had, in spite of her own infirmities, lately much aggravated, been in person to inquire. In answer to this I remarked that she would feel it more than any one. Brooksmith was silent a moment; at the end of which he said, in a certain tone (there is no reproducing some of his tones), 'I'll go and see her.' I went to see her myself, and I learned that he had waited upon her; but when I said to her, in the form of a joke but with a core of earnest, that when all was over some of us ought to combine, to club together to set Brooksmith up on his own account, she replied a trifle disappointingly: 'Do you mean in a public-house?' I looked at her in a way that I think Brooksmith himself would have approved, and then I answered: 'Yes, the

Offord Arms.' What I had meant, of course, was that, for the love of art itself, we ought to look to it that such a peculiar faculty and so much acquired experience should not be wasted. I really think that if we had caused a few black-edged cards to be struck off and circulated – 'Mr Brooksmith will continue to receive on the old premises from four to seven; business carried on as usual during the alterations' – the majority of us would have rallied.

Several times he took me upstairs – always by his own proposal – and our dear old friend, in bed, in a curious flowered and brocaded *casaque* which made him, especially as his head was tied up in a handkerchief to match, look, to my imagination, like the dying Voltaire, held for ten minutes a sadly shrunken little *salon*. I felt indeed each time, as if I were attending the last *coucher* of some social sovereign. He was royally whimsical about his sufferings and not at all concerned – quite as if the Constitution provided for the case – about his successor. He glided over *our* sufferings charmingly, and none of his jokes – it was a gallant abstention, some of them would have been so easy – were at our expense. Now and again, I confess, there was one at Brooksmith's, but so pathetically sociable as to make the excellent man look at me in a way that seemed to say: 'Do exchange a glance with me, or I sha'n't be able to stand it.' What he was not able to stand was not what Mr Offord said about him, but what he wasn't able to say in return. His notion of conversation, for himself, was giving you the convenience of speaking to him; and when he went to 'see' Lady Kenyon, for instance, it was to carry her the tribute of his receptive silence. Where would the speech of his betters have been if proper service had been a manifestation of sound? In that case the fundamental difference would have had to be shown by *their* dumbness, and many of them, poor things, were dumb enough without that provision. Brooksmith took an unfailing interest in the preservation of the fundamental difference; it was the thing he had most on his conscience.

What had become of it, however, when Mr Offord passed away like any inferior person – was relegated to eternal stillness like a butler upstairs? His aspect for several days after the expected event may be imagined, and the multiplication by

funereal observance of the things he didn't say. When everything was over – it was late the same day – I knocked at the
door of the house of mourning as I so often had done before. I
could never call on Mr Offord again, but I had come, literally,
to call on Brooksmith. I wanted to ask him if there was anything
I could do for him, tainted with vagueness as this inquiry could
only be. My wild dream of taking him into my own service had
died away: my service was not worth his being taken into. My
offer to him could only be to help him to find another place, and
yet there was an indelicacy, as it were, in taking for granted that
his thoughts would immediately be fixed on another. I had a
hope that he would be able to give his life a different
form – though certainly not the form, the frequent result of
such bereavements, of his setting up a little shop. That would
have been dreadful; for I should have wished to further any
enterprise that he might embark in, yet how could I have
brought myself to go and pay him shillings and take back
coppers over a counter? My visit then was simply an intended
compliment. He took it as such, gratefully and with all the tact
in the world. He knew I really couldn't help him and that I
knew he knew I couldn't; but we discussed the situation – with
a good deal of elegant generality – at the foot of the stairs, in the
hall already dismantled, where I had so often discussed other
situations with him. The executors were in possession, as was still
more apparent when he made me pass for a few minutes into
the dining-room, where various objects were muffled up for
removal.

Two definite facts, however, he had to communicate; one
being that he was to leave the house for ever that night (servants,
for some mysterious reason, seem always to depart by night),
and the other – he mentioned it only at the last, with hesitation – that he had already been informed his late master had
left him a legacy of eighty pounds. 'I'm very glad,' I said, and
Brooksmith rejoined: 'It was so like him to think of me.' This
was all that passed between us on the subject, and I know
nothing of his judgment of Mr Offord's memento. Eighty
pounds are always eighty pounds, and no one has ever left *me* an
equal sum; but, all the same, for Brooksmith, I was disappointed.
I don't know what I had expected – in short I was disappointed.

Eighty pounds might stock a little shop – a *very* little shop; but, I repeat, I couldn't bear to think of that. I asked my friend if he had been able to save a little, and he replied: 'No, sir; I have had to do things.' I didn't inquire what things he had had to do; they were his own affair, and I took his word for them as assentingly as if he had had the greatness of an ancient house to keep up; especially as there was something in his manner that seemed to convey a prospect of further sacrifice.

'I shall have to turn round a bit, sir – I shall have to look about me,' he said; and then he added, indulgently, magnanimously: 'If you should happen to hear of anything for me—.'

I couldn't let him finish; this was, in its essence, too much in the really grand manner. It would be a help to my getting him off my mind to be able to pretend I *could* find the right place, and that help he wished to give me, for it was doubtless painful to him to see me in so false a position. I interposed with a few words to the effect that I was well aware that wherever he should go, whatever he should do, he would miss our old friend terribly – miss him even more than I should, having been with him so much more. This led him to make the speech that I have always remembered as the very text of the whole episode.

'Oh, sir, it's sad for *you*, very sad, indeed, and for a great many gentlemen and ladies; that it is, sir. But for me, sir, it is, if I may say so, still graver even than that: it's just the loss of something that was everything. For me, sir,' he went on, with rising tears, 'he was just *all*, if you know what I mean, sir. You have others, sir, I daresay – not that I would have you understand me to speak of them as in any way tantamount. But you have the pleasures of society, sir; if it's only in talking about him, sir, as I daresay you do freely – for all his blessed memory has to fear from it – with gentlemen and ladies who have had the same honour. That's not for me, sir, and I have to keep my associations to myself. Mr Offord was *my* society, and now I have no more. You go back to conversation, sir, after all, and I go back to my place,' Brooksmith stammered, without exaggerated irony or dramatic bitterness, but with a flat, unstudied veracity and his hand on the knob of the street-door. He turned it to let me out and then he added: 'I just go downstairs, sir, again, and I stay there.'

'My poor child,' I replied, in my emotion, quite as Mr Offord used to speak, 'my dear fellow, leave it to me; we'll look after you, we'll all do something for you.'

'Ah, if you could give me some one *like* him! But there ain't two in the world,' said Brooksmith as we parted.

He had given me his address – the place where he would be to be heard of. For a long time I had no occasion to make use of the information; for he proved indeed, on trial, a very difficult case. In a word the people who knew him and had known Mr Offord, didn't want to take him, and yet I couldn't bear to try to thrust him among people who didn't know him. I spoke to many of our old friends about him, and I found them all governed by the odd mixture of feelings of which I myself was conscious, and disposed, further, to entertain a suspicion that he was 'spoiled,' with which I then would have nothing to do. In plain terms a certain embarrassment, a sensible awkwardness, when they thought of it, attached to the idea of using him as a menial: they had met him so often in society. Many of them would have asked him, and did ask him, or rather did ask me to ask him, to come and see them; but a mere visiting-list was not what I wanted for him. He was too short for people who were very particular; nevertheless I heard of an opening in a diplomatic household which led me to write him a note, though I was looking much less for something grand than for something human. Five days later I heard from him. The secretary's wife had decided, after keeping him waiting till then– that she couldn't take a servant out of a house in which there had not been a lady. The note had a P.S.: 'It's a good job there wasn't, sir, such a lady as some.'

A week later he came to see me and told me he was 'suited' – committed to some highly respectable people (they were something very large in the City), who lived on the Bayswater side of the Park. 'I daresay it will be rather poor, sir,' he admitted; 'but I've seen the fireworks, haven't I, sir? – it can't be fireworks *every* night. After Mansfield Street there ain't much choice.' There was a certain amount, however, it seemed; for the following year, going one day to call on a country cousin, a lady of a certain age who was spending a fortnight in town with some friends of her own, a family unknown to me and resident in Chester Square, the door of the house was opened, to my surprise and gratification, by Brooksmith in person. When I came out I had some conversation with him, from which I gathered that he had found the large City people too dull for endurance, and I guessed, though he didn't say it, that he had found them vulgar as well. I don't know what judgment he would have passed on his actual patrons if my relative had not been their friend; but under the circumstances he abstained from comment.

None was necessary, however, for before the lady in question brought her visit to a close they honoured me with an invitation to dinner, which I accepted. There was a largish party on the occasion, but I confess I thought of Brooksmith rather more than of the seated company. They required no depth of attention – they were all referable to usual, irredeemable, inevitable types. It was the world of cheerful commonplace and conscious gentility and prosperous density, a full-fed, material, insular world, a world of hideous florid plate and ponderous order and thin conversation. There was not a word said about Byron. Nothing would have induced me to look at Brooksmith in the course of the repast, and I felt suse that not even my overturning the wine would have induced him to meet my eye. We were in intellectual sympathy – we felt, as regards each other, a kind of social responsibility. In short we had been in Arcadia together, and we had both come to *this*! No wonder we were ashamed to be confronted. When he helped on my overcoat, as I was going away, we parted, for the first time since the earliest days in Mansfield Street, in silence. I thought he looked lean and wasted, and I guessed that his new place was not more 'human' than his previous one. There was plenty of beef and beer, but there was no reciprocity. The question for him to have asked before acceping the position would have been not 'How many footmen are kept?' but 'How much imagination?'

The next time I went to the house – I confess it was not very soon – I encountered his successor, a personage who evidently enjoyed the good fortune of never having quitted his natural level. Could any be higher? he seemed to ask – over the heads of three footmen and even of some visitors. He made me feel as if Brooksmith were dead; but I didn't dare to inquire – I couldn't have borne his 'I haven't the least idea, sir.' I despatched a note to the address Brooksmith had given me after Mr Offord's death, but I received no answer. Six months later, however, I was favoured with a visit from an elderly, dreary, dingy person, who introduced herself to me as Mr Brooksmith's aunt and from whom I learned that he was out of place and out of health and had allowed her to come and say to me that if I could spare half-an-hour to look in at him he would take it as a rare honour.

I went the next day – his messenger had given me a new address – and found my friend lodged in a short sordid street in Marylebone, one of those corners of London that wear the last expression of sickly meanness. The room into which I was shown was above the small establishment of a dyer and cleaner who had inflated kid gloves and discoloured shawls in his shop-front. There was a great deal of grimy infant life up and down the place, and there was a hot, moist smell within, as of the 'boiling' of dirty linen. Brooksmith sat with a blanket over his legs at a clean little window, where, from behind stiff bluish-white curtains, he could look across at a huckster's and a tinsmith's and a small greasy public-house. He had passed through an illness and was convalescent, and his mother, as well as his aunt, was in attendance on him. I liked the mother, who was bland and intensely humble, but I didn't much fancy the aunt, whom I connected, perhaps unjustly, with the opposite public-house (she seemed somehow to be greasy with the same grease), and whose furtive eye followed every movement of my hand, as if to see if it were not going into my pocket. It didn't take this direction – I couldn't, unsolicited, put myself at that sort of ease with Brooksmith. Several times the door of the room opened, and mysterious old women peeped in and shuffled back again. I don't know who they were; poor Brooksmith seemed encompassed with vague, prying, beery females.

He was vague himself, and evidently weak, and much embarrassed, and not an allusion was made between us to Mansfield Street. The vision of the *salon* of which he had been an ornament hovered before me, however, by contrast, sufficiently. He assured me that he was really getting better, and his mother remarked that he would come round if he could only get his spirits up. The aunt echoed this opinion, and I became more sure that in her own case she knew where to go for such a purpose. I'm afraid I was rather weak with my old friend, for I neglected the opportunity, so exceptionally good, to rebuke the levity which had led him to throw up honourable positions – fine, stiff, steady berths, with morning prayers, as I knew, attached to one of them – in Bayswater and Belgravia. Very likely his reasons had been profane and sentimental; he didn't want morning prayers, he wanted to be somebody's dear fellow; but I couldn't be the person to rebuke him. He shuffled these episodes out of sight – I saw that he had no wish to discuss them. I perceived further, strangely enough, that it would probably be a questionable pleasure for him to see me again: he doubted now even of my power to condone his aberrations. He didn't wish to have to explain; and his behaviour, in future, was likely to need explanation. When I bade him farewell he looked at me a moment with eyes that said everything: 'How can I talk about those exquisite years in this place, before these people, with the old women poking their heads in? It was very good of you to come to see me – it wasn't my idea; *she* brought you. We've said everything; it's over; you'll lose all patience with me, and I'd rather you shouldn't see the rest.' I sent him some money, in a letter, the next day, but I saw the rest only in the light of a barren sequel.

A whole year after my visit to him I became aware once, in dining out, that Brooksmith was one of the several servants who hovered behind our chairs. He had not opened the door of the house to me, and I had not recognised him in the cluster of retainers in the hall. This time I tried to catch his eye, but he never gave me a chance, and when he handed me a dish I could only be careful to thank him audibly. Indeed I partook of two *entrées* of which I had my doubts, subsequently converted into certainties, in order not to snub him. He looked well enough in health, but much older, and wore, in an exceptionally marked degree, the glazed and expressionless mask of the British domestic *de race*. I saw with dismay that if I had not known him I should have taken him, on the showing of his countenance, for an extravagant illustration of irresponsive servile gloom. I said to myself that he had become a reactionary, gone over to the

Philistines, thrown himself into religion, the religion of his
'place', like a foreign lady *sur le retour*. I divined moreover that
he was only engaged for the evening – he had become a mere
waiter, had joined the band of the white-waistcoated who 'go
out'. There was something pathetic in this fact, and it was a
terrible vulgarisation of Brooksmith. It was the mercenary prose
of butlerhood; he had given up the struggle for the poetry. If
reciprocity was what he had missed, where was the reciprocity
now? Only in the bottoms of the wine-glasses and the five
shillings (or whatever they get), clapped into his hand by the
permanent man. However, I supposed he had taken up a
precarious branch of his profession because after all it sent him
less downstairs. His relations with London society were more
superficial, but they were of course more various. As I went
away, on this occasion, I looked out for him eagerly among the
four or five attendants whose perpendicular persons, fluting the
walls of London passages, are supposed to lubricate the process
of departure; but he was not on duty. I asked one of the others
if he were not in the house, and received the prompt answer:
'Just left, sir. Anything I can do for you, sir?' I wanted to say
'Please give him my kind regards;' but I abstained; I didn't want
to compromise him, and I never came across him again.

   Often and often, in dining out, I looked for him, sometimes
accepting invitations on purpose to multiply the chances of my
meeting him. But always in vain; so that as I met many other
members of the casual class over and over again, I at last adopted
the theory that he always procured a list of expected guests
beforehand and kept away from the banquets which he thus
learned I was to grace. At last I gave up hope, and one day, at
the end of three years, I received another visit from his aunt. She
was drearier and dingier, almost squalid, and she was in great
tribulation and want. Her sister, Mrs Brooksmith, had been dead
a year, and three months later her nephew had disappeared. He
had always looked after her a bit – since her troubles; I never
knew what her troubles had been – and now she hadn't so much
as a petticoat to pawn. She had also a niece, to whom she had
been everything, before her troubles, but the niece had treated
her most shameful. These were details; the great and romantic
fact was Brooksmith's final evasion of his fate. He had gone out

to wait one evening, as usual, in a white waistcoat she had done up for him with her own hands, being due at a large party up Kensington way. But he had never come home again, and had never arrived at the large party, or at any party that any one could make out. No trace of him had come to light – no gleam of the white waistcoat had pierced the obscurity of his doom. This news was a sharp shock to me, for I had my ideas about his real destination. His aged relative had promptly, as she said, guessed the worst. Somehow and somewhere he had got out of the way altogether, and now I trust that, with characteristic deliberation, he is changing the plates of the immortal gods. As my depressing visitant also said, he never *had* got his spirits up. I was fortunately able to dismiss her with her own somewhat improved. But the dim ghost of poor Brooksmith is one of those that I see. He had indeed been spoiled.

IN THE CAGE

IN THE CAGE is surely *the* London story in James's canon, and in one of the prefaces to the New York Edition of his novels and tales he had this to say about it:

Its origin is written upon it large, and the idea it puts into play so abides in one of the commonest and taken-for-granted of London impressions that some such experimentally-figured situation as that of 'In the Cage' must again and again have flowered (granted the grain of observation) in generous minds. It had become for me, at any rate, an old story by the time (1898) I cast it into this particular form. The postal-telegraph office in general, and above all the small local office of one's immediate neighbourhood, scene of the transaction of so much of one's daily business, haunt of one's needs and one's duties, of one's labours and one's patiences, almost of one's rewards and one's disappointments, one's joys and one's sorrows, had ever had, to my sense, so much of London to give out, so much of its huge perpetual story to tell, that any momentary wait there seemed to take place in a strong social draught, the stiffest possible breeze of the human comedy.[1]

The story was James's first to be written in Rye, and Edel suggests that it owed something to his sense of isolation from his London friends and in particular a new dependence on the telegram. *In the Cage* was first published as a single volume, by Duckworth and Co in 1898.

1. *Novels and Tales, Volume XI* (1908), p xviii.

IN THE CAGE

IT HAD occurred to her early that in her position – that of a young person spending, in framed and wired confinement, the life of a guinea-pig or a magpie – she should know a great many persons without their recognizing the acquaintance. That made it an emotion the more lively – though singularly rare and always, even then, with opportunity still very much smothered – to see any one come in whom she knew, as she called it, outside, and who could add something to the poor identity of her function. Her function was to sit there with two young men – the other telegraphist and the counter-clerk; to mind the 'sounder', which was always going, to dole out stamps and postal-orders, weigh letters, answer stupid questions, give difficult change and, more than anything else, count words as numberless as the sands of the sea, the words of the telegrams thrust, from morning to night, through the gap left in the high lattice, across the encumbered shelf that her forearm ached with rubbing. This transparent screen fenced out or fenced in, according to the side of the narrow counter on which the human lot was cast, the duskiest corner of a shop pervaded not a little, in winter, by the poison of perpetual gas, and at all times by the presence of hams, cheese, dried fish, soap, varnish, paraffin, and other solids and fluids that she came to know perfectly by their smells without consenting to know them by their names.

The barrier that divided the little post-and-telegraph-office from the grocery was a frail structure of wood and wire; but the social, the professional separation was a gulf that fortune, by a stroke quite remarkable, had spared her the necessity of contributing at all publicly to bridge. When Mr Cocker's young men stepped over from behind the other counter to change a five-pound note – and Mr Cocker's situation, with the cream of the

'Court Guide' and the dearest furnished apartments, Simpkin's, Ladle's, Thrupp's, just around the corner, was so select that his place was quite pervaded by the crisp rustle of these emblems – she pushed out the sovereigns as if the applicant were no more to her than one of the momentary appearances in the great procession; and this perhaps all the more from the very fact of the connection – only recognized outside indeed – to which she had lent herself with ridiculous inconsequence. She recognised the others the less because she had at last so unreservedly, so irredeemably, recognized Mr Mudge. But she was a little ashamed, none the less, of having to admit to herself that Mr Mudge's removal to a higher sphere – to a more commanding position, that is, though to a much lower neighbourhood – would have been described still better as a luxury than as the simplification that she contented herself with calling it. He had, at any rate, ceased to be all day long in her eyes, and this left something a little fresh for them to rest on of a Sunday. During the three months that he had remained at Cocker's after her consent to their engagement, she had often asked herself what it was that marriage would be able to add to a familiarity so final. Opposite there, behind the counter of which his superior stature, his whiter apron, his more clustering curls and more present, too present, h's had been for a couple of years the principal orna-ment, he had moved to and fro before her as on the small sanded floor of their contracted future. She was conscious now of the improvement of not having to take her present and her future at once. They were about as much as she could manage when taken separate.

She had, none the less, to give her mind steadily to what Mr Mudge had again written her about, the idea of her applying for a transfer to an office quite similar – she couldn't yet hope for a place in a bigger – under the very roof where he was foreman, so that, dangled before her every minute of the day, he should see her, as he called it, 'hourly', and in a part, the far N.W. district, where, with her mother, she would save, on their two rooms alone, nearly three shillings. It would be far from dazzling to exchange Mayfair for Chalk Farm, and it was something of a predicament that he so kept at her; still, it was nothing to the old predicaments, those of the early times of their great misery, her

own, her mother's, and her elder sister's – the last of whom had
succumbed to all but absolute want when, as conscious,
incredulous ladies, suddenly bereaved, betrayed, overwhelmed,
they had slipped faster and faster down the steep slope at the
bottom of which she alone had rebounded. Her mother had
never rebounded any more at the bottom than on the way; had
only rumbled and grumbled down and down, making, in
respect of caps and conversation, no effort whatever, and too
often, alas! smelling of whisky.

2

IT WAS always rather quiet at Cocker's while the contingent
from Ladle's and Thrupp's and all the other great places were at
luncheon, or, as the young men used vulgarly to say, while the
animals were feeding. She had forty minutes in advance of this
to go home for her own dinner; and when she came back, and
one of the young men took his turn, there was often half an
hour during which she could pull out a bit of work or a book –
a book from the place where she borrowed novels, very greasy,
in fine print and all about the fine folks, at a ha'penny a day.
This sacred pause was one of the numerous ways in which the
establishment kept its finger on the pulse of fashion and fell into
the rhythm of the larger life. It had something to do, one day,
with the particular vividness marking the advent of a lady whose
meals were apparently irregular, yet whom she was destined, she
afterwards found, not to forget. The girl was *blasée*; nothing
could belong more, as she perfectly knew, to the intense
publicity of her profession; but she had a whimsical mind and
wonderful nerves; she was subject, in short, to sudden flickers of
antipathy and sympathy, red gleams in the grey, fitful awakings
and followings, odd caprices of curiosity. She had a friend who
had invented a new career for women – that of being in and out
of people's houses to look after the flowers. Mrs Jordan had a
manner of her own of sounding this illusion; 'the flowers,' on

her lips, were, in happy homes, as usual as the coals or the daily papers. She took charge of them, at any rate, in all the rooms, at so much a month, and people were quickly finding out what it was to make over this delicate duty to the widow of a clergyman. The widow, on her side, dilating on the initiations thus opened up to her, had been splendid to her young friend over the way she was made free of the greatest houses – the way, especially when she did the dinner-tables, set out so often for twenty, she felt that a single step more would socially, would absolutely, introduce her. On its being asked of her, then, if she circulated only in a sort of tropical solitude, with the upper servants for picturesque natives, and on her having to assent to this glance at her limitations, she had found a reply to the girl's invidious question. 'You've no imagination, my dear!' – that was because the social door might at any momemt open so wide.

Our young lady had not taken up the charge, had dealt with it good-humouredly, just because she knew so well what to think of it. It was at once one of her most cherished complaints and most secret supports that people didn't understand her, and it was accordingly a matter of indifference to her that Mrs Jordan shouldn't; even though Mrs Jordan, handed down from their early twilight of gentility and also the victim of reverses, was the only member of her circle in whom she recognized an equal. She was perfectly aware that her imaginative life was the life in which she spent most of her time; and she would have been ready, had it been at all worth while, to contend that, since her outward occupation didn't kill it, it must be strong indeed. Combinations of flowers and greenstuff, forsooth! What *she* could handle freely, she said to herself, was combinations of men and women. The only weakness in her faculty came from the positive abundance of her contact with the human herd; this was so constant, had the effect of becoming so cheap, that there were long stretches in which inspiration, divination and interest, quite dropped. The great thing was the flashes, the quick revivals, absolute accidents all, and neither to be counted on nor to be resisted. Someone had only sometimes to put in a penny for a stamp, and the whole thing was upon her. She was so absurdly constructed that these were literally the moments that made up – made up for the long stiffness of sitting there in the stocks, made up for the cunning hostility of Mr Buckton and the importunate sympathy of the counter-clerk, made up for the daily, deadly, flourishy letter from Mr Mudge, made up even for the most haunting of her worries, the rage at moments of not knowing how her mother did 'get it'.

She had surrendered herself moreover, of late, to a certain expansion of her consciousness; something that seemed perhaps vulgarly accounted for by the fact that, as the blast of the season roared louder and the waves of fashion tossed their spray further over the counter, there were more impressions to be gathered and really – for it came to that – more life to be led. Definite, at any rate, it was that by the time May was well started the kind of company she kept at Cocker's had begun to strike her as a reason – a reason she might almost put forward for a policy of procrastination. It sounded silly, of course, as yet, to plead such a motive, especially as the fascination of the place was, after all, a sort of torment. But she liked her torment; it was a torment she should miss at Chalk Farm. She was ingenious and uncandid, therefore, about leaving the breadth of London a little longer between herself and that austerity. If she had not quite the courage, in short, to say to Mr Mudge that her actual chance for a play of mind was worth, any week, the three shillings he desired to help her to save, she yet saw something happen in the course of the month that, in her heart of hearts at least, answered the subtle question. This was connected precisely with the appearance of the memorable lady.

3

SHE pushed in three bescribbled forms which the girl's hand was quick to appropriate, Mr Buckton having so frequent a perverse instinct for catching first any eye that promised the sort of entertainment with which she had her peculiar affinity. The amusements of captives are full of a desperate contrivance, and one of our young friend's ha'pennyworths had been the charming tale of *Picciola*. It was of course the law of the place that they were never to take no notice, as Mr Buckton said, whom they served; but this also never prevented, certainly on the same gentleman's own part, what he was fond of describing as the underhand game. Both her companions, for that matter, made no secret of the number of favourites they had among the ladies; sweet familiarities in spite of which she had repeatedly caught each of them in stupidities and mistakes, confusions of identity and lapses of observation that never failed to remind her how the cleverness of men ended where the cleverness of women began. 'Marguerite, Regent Street. Try on at six. All Spanish lace. Pearls. The full length.' That was the first; it had no signature. 'Lady Agnes Orme, Hyde Park Place. Impossible to-night, dining Haddon. Opera tomorrow, promised Fritz, but could do play Wednesday. Will try Haddon for Savoy, and anything in the world you like, if you can get Gussy. Sunday, Montenero. Sit Mason Monday, Tuesday. Marguerite awful. Cissy.' That was the second. The third, the girl noted when she took it, was on a foreign form: 'Everard, Hôtel Brighton, Paris. Only understand and believe. 22nd to 26th, and certainly 8th and 9th. Perhaps others. Come. Mary.'

Mary was very handsome, the handsomest woman, she felt in a moment, she had ever seen – or perhaps it was only Cissy. Perhaps it was both, for she had seen stranger things than that – ladies wiring to different persons under different names. She had seen all sorts of things and pieced together all sorts of mysteries. There had once been one – not long before – who, without winking, sent off five over five different signatures. Perhaps these represented five different friends who had asked her – all women, just as perhaps now Mary and Cissy, or one or other of them, were wiring by deputy. Sometimes she put in too much – too much of her own sense; sometimes she put in too little; and in either case this often came round to her afterwards, for she had an extraordinary way of keeping clues. When she noticed, she noticed; that was what it came to. There were days and days, there were weeks sometimes, of vacancy. This arose often from Mr Buckton's devilish and successful subterfuges for keeping her at the sounder whenever it looked as if anything might amuse; the sounder, which it was equally his business to mind, being the innermost cell of captivity, a cage within the cage, fenced off from the rest by a frame of ground glass. The counter-clerk would have played into her hands; but the counter-clerk was really reduced to idiocy by the effect of his passion for her. She flattered herself moreover, nobly, that with the unpleasant conspicuity of this passion she would never have consented to be obliged to him. The most she would ever do would be always to shove off on him whenever she could the registration of letters, a job she happened particularly to loathe. After the long stupors, at all events, there almost always suddenly would come a sharp taste of something; it was in her mouth before she knew it; it was in her mouth now.

To Cissy, to Mary, whichever it was, she found her curiosity going out with a rush, a mute effusion that floated back to her, like a returning tide, the living colour and splendour of the beautiful head, the light of eyes that seemed to reflect such utterly other things than the mean things actually before them; and, above all, the high, curt consideration of a manner that, even at bad moments, was a magnificent habit and of the very essence of the innumerable things – her beauty, her birth, her father and mother, her cousins, and all her ancestors – that its possessor couldn't have got rid of if she had wished. How did our obscure little public servant know that, for the lady of the telegrams, this was a bad moment? How did she guess all sorts of impossible things, such as, almost on the very spot, the presence of drama, at a critical stage, and the nature of the tie with the gentleman at the Hôtel Brighton? More than ever before it floated to her through the bars of the cage that this at last was the high reality, the bristling truth that she had hitherto only patched up and eked out – one of the creatures, in fine, in whom all the conditions for happiness actually met, and who, in the air they made, bloomed with an unwitting insolence. What came home to the girl was the way the insolence was tempered by something that was equally a part of the distinguished life, the custom of a flowerlike bend to the less fortunate – a dropped fragrance, a mere quick breath, but which in fact pervaded and lingered. The apparition was very young, but certainly married, and our fatigued friend had a sufficient store of mythological comparison to recognize the port of Juno. Marguerite might be 'awful', but she knew how to dress a goddess.

Pearls and Spanish lace – she herself, with assurance, could see them, and the 'full length' too, and also red velvet bows, which, disposed on the lace in a particular manner (she could have placed them with the turn of a hand) were of course to adorn the front of a black brocade that would be like a dress in a picture. However, neither Marguerite, nor Lady Agnes, nor Haddon, nor Fritz, nor Gussy was what the wearer of this garment had really come in for. She had come in for Everard – and that was doubtless not *his* true name either. If our young lady had never taken such jumps before, it was simply that she had never before been so affected. She went all the way. Mary and Cissy had been round together, in their single superb person, to see him – he must live round the corner; they had found that, in consequence of something they had come, precisely, to make up for or to have another scene about, he had gone off – gone off just on purpose to make them feel it; on which they had come together to Cocker's as to the nearest place; where they had put in the three forms partly in order not to put in the one alone. The two others, in a manner, covered it, muffled it, passed it off. Oh yes, she went all the way, and this was a specimen of how she often went. She would know the hand again any time. It was as handsome and as everything else as the woman herself. The woman herself had, on learning his flight, pushed past Everard's servant and into his room; she had written her missive at his table and with his pen. All this, every inch of it, came in the waft that she blew through and left behind her, the influence that, as I have said, lingered. And among the things the girl was sure of, happily, was that she should see her again.

4

SHE saw her, in fact, and only ten days later; but this time she was not alone, and that was exactly a part of the luck of it. Being clever enough to know through what possibilities it could range, our young lady had ever since had in her mind a dozen conflicting theories about Everard's type; as to which, the instant they came into the place, she felt the point settled with a thump that seemed somehow addressed straight to her heart. That organ literally beat faster at the approach of the gentleman who was this time with Cissy, and who, as seen from within the cage, became on the spot the happiest of the happy circumstances with which her mind had invested the friend of Fritz and Gussy. He was a very happy circumstance indeed as, with his cigarette in his lips and his broken familiar talk caught by his companion, he put down the half-dozen telegrams which it would take them together some minutes to despatch. And here it occurred, oddly enough, that if, shortly before, the girl's interest in his companion had sharpened her sense for the messages then transmitted, her immediate vision of himself had the effect, while she counted his seventy words, of preventing intelligibility. *His* words were mere numbers, they told her nothing whatever; and after he had gone she was in possession of no name, of no address, of no meaning, or nothing but a vague, sweet sound and an immense impression. He had been there but five minutes, he had smoked in her face, and, busy with his telegrams, with the tapping pencil and the conscious danger, the odious betrayal that would come from a mistake, she had had no wandering glances nor roundabout arts to spare. Yet she had taken him in; she knew everything; she had made up her mind.

He had come back from Paris; everything was re-arranged; the pair were again shoulder to shoulder in their high encounter with life, their large and complicated game. The fine, soundless pulse of this game was in the air for our young woman while they remained in the shop. While they remained? They remained all day; their presence continued and abode with her, was in everything she did till nightfall, in the thousands of other words she counted, she transmitted, in all the stamps she detached and the letters she weighed and the change she gave, equally unconscious and unerring in each of these particulars, and not, as the run on the little office thickened with the afternoon hours, looking up at a single ugly face in the long sequence, nor really hearing the stupid questions that she patiently and perfectly answered. All patience was possible now, and all questions stupid after his – all faces ugly. She had been sure she should see the lady again; and even now she should perhaps, she should probably, see her often. But for him it was totally different; she should never, never see him. She wanted it too much. There was a kind of wanting that helped – she had arrived, with her rich experience, at that generalization; and there was another kind that was fatal. It was this time the fatal kind; it would prevent.

Well, she saw him the very next day, and on the second occasion it was quite different; the sense of every syllable he despatched was fiercely distinct; she indeed felt her progressive pencil, dabbing as if with a quick caress the marks of his own, put life into every stroke. He was there a long time – had not brought his forms filled out, but worked them off in a nook on the counter; and there were other people as well – a changing, pushing cluster, with every one to mind at once and endless right change to make and information to produce. But she kept hold of him throughout; she continued, for herself, in a relation with him as close as that in which, behind the hated ground glass, Mr Buckton luckily continued with the sounder. This morning everything changed, but with a kind of dreariness too; she had to swallow the rebuff to her theory about fatal desires, which she did without confusion and indeed with absolute levity; yet if it was now flagrant that he did live close at hand – at Park Chambers – and belonged supremely to the class that wired everything, even their expensive feelings (so that, as he never wrote, his correspondence cost him weekly pounds and pounds, and he might be in and out five times a day), there was, all the same, involved in the prospect, and by reason of its positive excess of light, a perverse melancholy, almost a misery. This was rapidly to give it a place in an order of feelings on which I shall presently touch.

Meanwhile, for a month, he was very constant. Cissy, Mary, never re-appeared with him; he was always either alone or accompanied only by some gentleman who was lost in the blaze of his glory. There was another sense, however – and indeed there was more than one – in which she mostly found herself counting in the splendid creature with whom she had originally connected him. He addressed this correspondent neither as

Mary nor as Cissy; but the girl was sure of whom it was, in Eaton Square, that he was perpetually wiring to – and so irreproachably! – as Lady Bradeen. Lady Bradeen was Cissy, Lady Bradeen was Mary, Lady Bradeen was the friend of Fritz and of Gussy, the customer of Marguerite, and the close ally, in short (as was ideally right, only the girl had not yet found a descriptive term that was), of the most magnificent of men. Nothing could equal the frequency and variety of his com-munications to her ladyship but their extraordinary, their abysmal propriety. It was just the talk – so profuse sometimes that she wondered what was left for their real meetings – of the happiest people in the world. Their real meetings must have been constant, for half of it was appointments and allusions, all swimming in a sea of other allusions still, tangled in a complexity of questions that gave a wondrous image of their life. If Lady Bradeen was Juno it was all certainly Olympian. If the girl, missing the answers, her ladyship's own outpourings, sometimes wished that Cocker's had only been one of the bigger offices where telegrams arrived as well as departed, there were yet ways in which, on the whole, she pressed the romance closer by reason of the very quantity of imagination that it demanded. The days and hours of this new friend, as she came to account him, were at all events unrolled, and however much more she might have known she would still have wished to go beyond. In fact she did go beyond; she went quite far enough.

But she could none the less, even after a month, scarce have told if the gentlemen who came in with him recurred or changed; and this in spite of the fact that they too were always posting and wiring, smoking in her face and signing or not signing. The gentlemen who came in with him were nothing, at any rate, when he was there. They turned up alone at other times – then only perhaps with a dim richness of reference. He himself, absent as well as present, was all. He was very tall, very fair, and had, in spite of his thick pre-occupations, a good humour that was exquisite, particularly as it so often had the effect of keeping him on. He could have reached over anybody, and anybody – no matter who – would have let him; but he was so extraordinarily kind that he quite pathetically waited, never waggling things at her out of his turn or saying 'Here!'

with horrid sharpness. He waited for pottering old ladies, for gaping slaveys, for the perpetual Buttonses from Thrupp's; and the thing in all this that she would have liked most unspeakably to put to the test was the possibility of her having for him a personal identity that might in a particular way appeal. There were moments when he actually struck her as on her side, arranging to help, to support, to spare her.

But such was the singular spirit of our young friend, that she could remind herself with a sort of rage that when people had awfully good manners – people of that class, – you couldn't tell. These manners were for everybody, and it might be drearily unavailing for any poor particular body to be overworked and unusual. What he did take for granted was all sorts of facility; and his high pleasantness, his relighting of cigarettes while he waited, his unconscious bestowal of opportunities, of boons, of blessings, were all a part of his magnificent security, the instinct that told him there was nothing such an existence as his could ever lose by. He was, somehow, at once very bright and very grave, very young and immensely complete; and whatever he was at any moment, it was always as much as all the rest the mere bloom of his beatitude. He was sometimes Everard, as he had been at the Hôtel Brighton, and he was sometimes Captain Everard. He was sometimes Philip with his surname and sometimes Philip without it. In some directions he was merely Phil, in others he was merely Captain. There were relations in which he was none of these things, but a quite different person – 'the Count'. There were several friends for whom he was William. There were several for whom, in allusion perhaps to his complexion, he was 'the Pink 'Un'. Once, once only by good luck, he had, coinciding comically, quite miraculously, with another person also near to her, been 'Mudge'. Yes, whatever he was, it was a part of his happiness – whatever he was and probably whatever he wasn't. And his happiness was a part – it became so little by little – of something that, almost from the first of her being at Cocker's, had been deeply with the girl.

5

THIS was neither more nor less than the queer extension of her experience, the double life that, in the cage, she grew at last to lead. As the weeks went on there she lived more and more into the world of whiffs and glimpses, and found her divinations work faster and stretch further. It was a prodigious view as the pressure heightened, a panorama fed with facts and figures, flushed with a torrent of colour and accompanied with wondrous world-music. What it mainly came to at this period was a picture of how London could amuse itself; and that, with the running commentary of a witness so exclusively a witness, turned for the most part to a hardening of the heart. The nose of this observer was brushed by the bouquet, yet she could never really pluck even a daisy. What could still remain fresh in her daily grind was the immense disparity, the difference and contrast, from class to class, of every instant and every motion. There were times when all the wires in the country seemed to start from the little hole-and-corner where she plied for a livelihood, and where, in the shuffle of feet, the flutter of 'forms', the strayings of stamps and the ring of change over the counter, the people she had fallen into the habit of remembering and fitting together with others, and of having her theories and interpretations of, kept up before her their long procession and rotation. What twisted the knife in her vitals was the way the profligate rich scattered about them, in extravagant chatter over their extravagant pleasures and sins, an amount of money that would have held the stricken household of her frightened childhood, her poor pinched mother and tormented father and lost brother and starved sister, together for a lifetime. During her first weeks she had often gasped at the sums people were willing to pay for the stuff they transmitted – the 'much love's, the 'awful' regrets, the compliments and wonderments and vain, vague gestures that cost the price of a new pair of boots. She had

had a way then of glancing at the people's faces, but she had early learned that if you became a telegraphist you soon ceased to be astonished. Her eye for types amounted nevertheless to genius, and there were those she liked and those she hated, her feeling for the latter of which grew to a positive possession, an instinct of observation and detection. There were the brazen women, as she called them, of the higher and the lower fashion, whose squanderings and graspings, whose struggles and secrets and love-affairs and lies, she tracked and stored up against them, till she had at moments, in private, a triumphant, vicious feeling of mastery and power, a sense of having their silly, guilty secrets in her pocket, her small retentive brain, and thereby knowing so much more about them than they suspected or would care to think. There were those she would have liked to betray, to trip up, to bring down with words altered and fatal; and all through a personal hostility provoked by the lightest signs, by their accident of tone and manner, by the particular kind of relation she always happened instantly to feel.

There were impulses of various kinds, alternately soft and severe, to which she was constitutionally accessible and which were determined by the smallest accidents. She was rigid, in general, on the article of making the public itself affix its stamps, and found a special enjoyment in dealing, to that end, with some of the ladies who were too grand to touch them. She had thus a play of refinement and subtlety greater, she flattered herself, than any of which she could be made the subject; and though most people were too stupid to be conscious of this, it brought her endless little consolations and revenges. She recognized quite as much those of her sex whom she would have liked to help, to warn, to rescue, to see more of; and that alternative as well operated exactly through the hazard of personal sympathy, her vision for silver threads and moonbeams and her gift for keeping the clues and finding her way in the tangle. The moonbeams and silver threads presented at moments all the vision of what poor *she* might have made of happiness. Blurred and blank as the whole thing often inevitably, or mercifully, became, she could still, through crevices and crannies, be stupefied, especially by what, in spite of all seasoning, touched the sorest place in her consciousness, the revelation of the golden shower flying about

without a gleam of gold for herself. It remained prodigious to
the end, the money her fine friends were able to spend to get still
more, or even to complain to fine friends of their own that they
were in want. The pleasures they proposed were equalled only
by those they declined, and they made their appointments often
so expensively that she was left wondering at the nature of the
delights to which the mere approaches were so paved with
shillings. She quivered on occasion into the perception of this
and that one whom she would, at all events, have just simply
liked to *be*. Her conceit, her baffled vanity were possibly monstrous; she certainly often threw herself into a defiant conviction
that she would have done the whole thing much better. But her
greatest comfort, on the whole, was her comparative vision of
the men; by whom I mean the unmistakable gentlemen, for she
had no interest in the spurious or the shabby, and no mercy at
all for the poor. She could have found a sixpence, outside, for an
appearance of want; but her fancy, in some directions so alert,
had never a throb of response for any sign of the sordid. The
men she did follow, moreover, she followed mainly in one
relation, the relation as to which the cage convinced her, she
believed, more than anything else could have done, that it was
quite the most diffused.

She found her ladies, in short, almost always in communication with her gentlemen, and her gentlemen with her ladies,
and she read into the immensity of their intercourse stories and
meanings without end. Incontestably she grew to think that the
men cut the best figure; and in this particular, as in many others,
she arrived at a philosophy of her own, all made up of her
private notations and cynicisms. It was a striking part of the
business, for example, that it was much more the women, on the
whole, who were after the men than the men who were after the
women: it was literally visible that the general attitude of the one
sex was that of the object pursued and defensive, apologetic and
attenuating, while the light of her own nature helped her more
or less to conclude as to the attitude of the other. Perhaps she
herself a little even fell into the custom of pursuit in occasionally
deviating only for gentlemen from her high rigour about the
stamps. She had early in the day made up her mind, in fine, that
they had the best manners; and if there were none of them she

noticed when Captain Everard was there, there were plenty she could place and trace and name at other times, plenty who, with their way of being 'nice' to her, and of handling, as if their pockets were private tills, loose, mixed masses of silver and gold, were such pleasant appearances that she could envy them without dislike. *They* never had to give change – they only had to get it. They ranged through every suggestion, every shade of fortune, which evidently included indeed lots of bad luck as well as of good, declining even toward Mr Mudge and his bland, firm thrift, and ascending, in wild signals and rocket-flights, almost to within hail of her highest standard. So, from month to month, she went on with them all, through a thousand ups and downs and a thousand pangs and indifferences. What virtually happened was that in the shuffling herd that passed before her by far the greater part only passed – a proportion but just appreciably stayed. Most of the elements swam straight away, lost themselves in the bottomless common, and by so doing really kept the page clear. On the clearness, therefore, what she did retain stood sharply out; she nipped and caught it, turned it over and interwove it.

6

SHE met Mrs Jordan whenever she could, and learned from her more and more how the great people, under her gentle shake, and after going through everything with the mere shops, were waking up to the gain of putting into the hands of a person of real refinement the question that the shop-people spoke of so vulgarly as that of the floral decorations. The regular dealers in these decorations were all very well; but there was a peculiar magic in the play of taste of a lady who had only to remember, through whatever intervening dusk, all her own little tables, little bowls and little jars and little other arrangements, and the wonderful thing she had made of the garden of the vicarage. This small domain, which her young friend had never seen,

bloomed in Mrs Jordan's discourse like a new Eden, and she
converted the past into a bank of violets by the tone in which
she said, 'Of course you always knew my one passion!' She
obviously met now, at any rate, a big contemporary need,
measured what it was rapidly becoming for people to feel they
could trust her without a tremor. It brought them a peace
that – during the quarter of an hour before dinner in especial –
was worth more to them than mere payment could express.
Mere payment, none the less, was tolerably prompt; she engaged
by the month, taking over the whole thing; and there was an
evening on which, in respect to our heroine, she at last returned
to the charge. 'It's growing and growing, and I see that I must
really divide the work. One wants an associate – of one's own
kind, don't you know? You know the look they want it all to
have? – of having come, not from a florist, but from one of
themselves. Well, I'm sure *you* could give it – because you *are*
one. Then we *should* win. Therefore just come in with me.'

'And leave the P.O.?'

'Let the P.O. simply bring you your letters. It would bring
you lots, you'd see: orders, after a bit, by the dozen.' It was on
this, in due course, that the great advantage again came up: 'One
seems to live again with one's own people.' It had taken some
little time (after their having parted company in the tempest of
their troubles and then, in the glimmering dawn, finally sighted
each other again) for each to admit that the other was, in her
private circle, her only equal; but the admission came, when it
did come, with an honest groan; and since equality *was* named,
each found much personal profit in exaggerating the other's
original grandeur. Mrs Jordan was ten years the older, but her
young friend was struck with the smaller difference this now
made: it had counted otherwise at the time when, much more as
a friend of her mother's, the bereaved lady, without a penny of
provision, and with stop-gaps, like their own, all gone, had,
across the sordid landing on which the opposite doors of the pair
of scared miseries opened and to which they were bewilderedly
bolted, borrowed coals and umbrellas that were repaid in
potatoes and postage-stamps. It had been a questionable help, at
that time, to ladies submerged, floundering, panting, swimming
for their lives, that they *were* ladies; but such an advantage could

come up again in proportion as others vanished, and it had grown very great by the time it was the only ghost of one they possessed. They had literally watched it take to itself a portion of the substance of each that had departed; and it became prodigious now, when they could talk of it together, when they could look back at it across a desert of accepted derogation, and when, above all, they could draw from each other a credulity about it that they could draw from no one else. Nothing was really so marked as that they felt the need to cultivate this legend much more after having found their feet and stayed their stomachs in the ultimate obscure than they had done in the upper air of mere frequent shocks. The thing they could now oftenest say to each other was that they knew what they meant; and the sentiment with which, all round, they knew it was known had been a kind of promise to stick well together again.

Mrs Jordan was at present fairly dazzling on the subject of the way that, in the practice of her beautiful art, she more than peeped in – she penetrated. There was not a house of the great kind – and it was, of course, only a question of those, real homes of luxury – in which she was not, at the rate such people now had things, all over the place. The girl felt before the picture the cold breath of disinheritance as much as she had ever felt it in the cage; she knew, moreover, how much she betrayed this, for the experience of poverty had begun, in her life, too early, and her ignorance of the requirements of homes of luxury had grown, with other active knowledge, a depth of simplification. She had accordingly at first often found that in these colloquies she could only pretend she understood. Educated as she had rapidly been by her chances at Cocker's, there were still strange gaps in her learning – she could never, like Mrs Jordan, have found her way about one of the 'homes'. Little by little, however, she had caught on, above all in the light of what Mrs Jordan's re-demption had materially made of that lady, giving her, though the years and the struggles had naturally not straightened a feature, an almost super-eminent air. There were women in and out of Cocker's who were quite nice and who yet didn't look well; whereas Mrs Jordan looked well and yet, with her extra-ordinarily protrusive teeth, was by no means quite nice. It would seem, mystifyingly, that it might really come from all the greatness she could live with. It was fine to hear her talk so often of dinners of twenty and of her doing, as she said, exactly as she liked with them. She spoke as if, for that matter, she invited the company. 'They simply *give* me the table – all the rest, all the other effects, come afterwards.'

7

'THEN you *do* see them?' the girl again asked.

Mrs Jordan hesitated, and indeed the point had been ambiguous before. 'Do you mean the guests?'

Her young friend, cautious about an undue exposure of innocence, was not quite sure. 'Well – the people who live there.'

'Lady Ventnor? Mrs Bubb? Lord Rye? Dear, yes. Why, they *like* one.'

'But does one personally *know* them?' our young lady went on, since that was the way to speak. 'I mean socially, don't you know? – as you know *me*.'

'They're not so nice as you!' Mrs Jordan charmingly cried. 'But I *shall* see more and more of them.'

Ah, this was the old story. 'But how soon?'

'Why, almost any day. Of course,' Mrs Jordan honestly added, 'they're nearly always out.'

'Then why do they want flowers all over?'

'Oh, that doesn't make any difference.' Mrs Jordan was not philosophic; she was only evidently determined it shouldn't make any. 'They're awfully interested in my ideas, and it's inevitable they should meet me over them.'

Her interlocutress was sturdy enough. 'What do you call your ideas?'

Mrs Jordan's reply was fine. 'If you were to see me some day with a thousand tulips, you'd soon discover.'

'A thousand?' – the girl gaped at such a revelation of the scale of it; she felt, for the instant, fairly planted out. 'Well, but if in fact they never do meet you?' she none the less pessimistically insisted.

'Never? They *often* do – and evidently quite on purpose. We have grand long talks.'

There was something in our young lady that could still stay her from asking for a personal description of these apparitions; that showed too starved a state. But while she considered, she took in afresh the whole of the clergyman's widow. Mrs Jordan couldn't help her teeth, and her sleeves were a distinct rise in the world. A thousand tulips at a shilling clearly took one further than a thousand words at a penny; and the betrothed of Mr Mudge, in whom the sense of the race for life was always acute, found herself wondering, with a twinge of her easy jealousy, if it mightn't after all then, for *her* also, be better – better than where she was – to follow some such scent. Where she was was where Mr Buckton's elbow could freely enter her right side and the counter-clerk's breathing – he had something the matter with his nose – pervade her left ear. It was something to fill an office under Government, and she knew but too well there were places commoner still than Cocker's; but it never required much of a chance to bring back to her the picture of servitude and promiscuity that she must present to the eye of comparative freedom. She was so boxed up with her young men, and anything like a margin so absent, that it needed more art than she should ever possess to pretend in the least to compass, with any one in the nature of an acquaintance – say with Mrs Jordan herself, flying in, as it might happen, to wire sympathetically to Mrs Bubb – an approach to a relation of elegant privacy. She remembered the day when Mrs Jordan *had*, in fact, by the greatest chance, come in with fifty–three words for Lord Rye and a five-pound note to change. This had been the dramatic manner of their reunion – their mutual recognition was so great an event. The girl could at first only see her from the waist up, besides making but little of her long telegram to his lordship. It was a strange whirligig that had converted the clergyman's widow into such a specimen of the class that went beyond the sixpence.

Nothing of the occasion, all the more, had ever become dim; least of all the way that, as her recovered friend looked up from counting, Mrs Jordan had just blown, in explanation, through her teeth and through the bars of the cage. 'I *do* flowers, you know.' Our young woman had always, with her little finger crooked out, a pretty movement for counting; and she had not forgotten the small secret advantage, a sharpness of triumph it might even have been called, that fell upon her at this moment and avenged her for the incoherence of the message, an unintelligible enumeration of numbers, colours, days, hours. The correspondence of people she didn't know was one thing; but the correspondence of people she did had an aspect of its own for her, even when she couldn't understand it. The speech in which Mrs Jordan had defined a position and announced a profession was like a tinkle of bluebells; but, for herself, her one idea about flowers was that people had them at funerals, and her present sole gleam of light was that lords probably had them most. When she watched, a minute later, through the cage, the swing of her visitor's departing petticoats, she saw the sight from the waist down; and when the counter-clerk after a mere male glance, remarked, with an intention unmistakably low, 'Handsome woman!' she had for him the finest of her chills: 'She's the widow of a bishop.' She always felt, with the counter-clerk, that it was impossible sufficiently to put it on; for what she wished to express to him was the maximum of her contempt, and that element in her nature was confusedly stored. 'A bishop' *was* putting it on, but the counter-clerk's approaches were vile. The night, after this, when, in the fulness of time, Mrs Jordan mentioned the grand long talks, the girl at last brought out: 'Should *I* see them? – I mean if I *were* to give up everything for you.'

Mrs Jordan at this became most arch. 'I'd send you to all the bachelors!'

Our young lady could be reminded by such a remark that she usually struck her friend as pretty. 'Do *they* have their flowers?'

'Oceans. And they're the most particular.' Oh, it was a wonderful world. 'You should see Lord Rye's.'

'His flowers?'

'Yes, and his letters. He writes me pages on pages – with the most adorable little drawings and plans. You should see his diagrams!'

8

THE girl had in course of time every opportunity to inspect
these documents, and they a little disappointed her; but in the
meanwhile there had been more talk, and it had led to her
saying, as if her friend's guarantee of a life of elegance were not
quite definite: 'Well, I see every one at *my* place.'

'Every one?'

'Lots of swells. They flock. They live, you know, all round,
and the place is filled with all the smart people, all the fast
people, those whose names are in the papers – mamma has still
the *Morning Post* – and who come up for the season.'

Mrs Jordan took this in with complete intelligence. 'Yes, and
I dare say it's some of your people that *I* do.'

Her companion assented, but discriminated. 'I doubt if you
"do" them as much as I! Their affairs, their appointments and
arrangements, their little games and secrets and vices – those
things all pass before me.'

This was a picture that could impose on a clergyman's widow
a certain strain; it was in intention, moreover, something of a
retort to the thousand tulips. 'Their vices? Have they got vices?'

Our young critic even more remarkably stared; then with a
touch of contempt in her amusement: 'Haven't you found *that*
out?' The homes of luxury, then, hadn't so much to give. 'I find
out everything,' she continued.

Mrs Jordan, at bottom a very meek person, was visibly struck.
'I see. You do "have" them.'

'Oh, I don't care! Much good does it do me!'

Mrs Jordan, after an instant, recovered her superiority.
'No – it doesn't lead to much.' Her own initiations so clearly
did. Still – after all; and she was not jealous: 'There must be a
charm.'

'In seeing them?' At this the girl suddenly let herself go. 'I hate
them; there's that charm!'

Mrs Jordan gaped again. 'The *real* "smarts"?'

'Is that what you call Mrs Bubb? Yes – it comes to me; I've had Mrs Bubb. I don't think she has been in herself, but there are things her maid has brought. Well, my dear!' – and the young person from Cocker's, recalling these things and summing them up, seemed suddenly to have much to say. But she didn't say it; she checked it; she only brought out: 'Her maid, who's horrid – *she* must have her!' Then she went on with indifference: 'They're *too* real! They're selfish brutes.'

Mrs Jordan, turning it over, adopted at last the plan of treating it with a smile. She wished to be liberal. 'Well, of course, they do lay it out.'

'They bore me to death,' her companion pursued with slightly more temperance.

But this was going too far. 'Ah, that's because you've no sympathy!'

The girl gave an ironic laugh, only retorting that she wouldn't have any either if she had to count all day all the words in the dictionary; a contention Mrs Jordan quite granted, the more that she shuddered at the notion of ever failing of the very gift to which she owed the vogue – the rage she might call it – that had caught her up. Without sympathy – or without imagination, for it came back again to that – how should she get, for big dinners, down the middle and toward the far corners at all? It wasn't the combinations, which were easily managed: the strain was over the ineffable simplicities, those that the bachelors above all, and Lord Rye perhaps most of any, threw off – just blew off, like cigarette-puffs – such sketches of. The betrothed of Mr Mudge at all events accepted the explanation, which had the effect, as almost any turn of their talk was now apt to have, of bringing her round to the terrific question of that gentleman. She was tormented with the desire to get out of Mrs Jordan, on this subject, what she was sure was at the back of Mrs Jordan's head; and to get it out of her, queerly enough, if only to vent a certain irritation at it. She knew that what her friend would already have risked if she had not been timid and tortuous was: 'Give him up – yes, give him up: you'll see that with your sure chances you'll be able to do much better.'

Our young woman had a sense that if that view could only be

put before her with a particular sniff for poor Mr Mudge she should hate it as much as she normally ought. She was conscious of not, as yet, hating it quite so much as that. But she saw that Mrs Jordan was conscious of something too, and that there was a sort of assurance she was waiting little by little to gather. The day came when the girl caught a glimpse of what was still wanting to make her friend feel strong; which was nothing less than the prospect of being able to announce the climax of sundry private dreams. The associate of the aristocracy had personal calculations – she pored over them in her lonely lodgings. If she did the flowers for the bachelors, in short, didn't she expect that to have consequences very different from the outlook, at Cocker's, that she had described as leading to nothing? There seemed in very truth something auspicious in the mixture of bachelors and flowers, though, when looked hard in the eye, Mrs Jordan was not quite prepared to say she had expected a positive proposal from Lord Rye to pop out of it. Our young woman arrived at last, none the less, at a definite vision of what was in her mind. This was a vivid foreknowledge that the betrothed of Mr Mudge would, unless conciliated in advance by a successful rescue, almost hate her on the day she should break a particular piece of news. How could that unfortunate otherwise endure to hear of what, under the protection of Lady Ventnor, was after all so possible?

9

MEANWHILE, since irritation sometimes relieved her, the betrothed of Mr Mudge drew straight from that admirer an amount of it that was proportioned to her fidelity. She always walked with him on Sundays, usually in the Regent's Park, and quite often, once or twice a month, he took her, in the Strand or thereabouts, to see a piece that was having a run. The productions he always preferred were the really good ones – Shakespeare, Thompson, or some funny American thing; which,

as it also happened that she hated vulgar plays, gave him ground
for what was almost the fondest of his approaches, the theory
that their tastes were, blissfully, just the same. He was for ever
reminding her of that, rejoicing over it, and being affectionate
and wise about it. There were times when she wondered how in
the world she could bear him, how she could bear any man so
smugly unconscious of the immensity of her difference. It was
just for this difference that, if she was to be liked at all, she
wanted to be liked, and if that was not the source of Mr
Mudge's admiration, she asked herself, what on earth *could* be?
She was not different only at one point, she was different all
round; unless perhaps indeed in being practically human, which
her mind just barely recognized that he also was. She would
have made tremedous concessions in other quarters: there was no
limit, for instance, to those she would have made to Captain
Everard; but what I have named was the most she was prepared
to do for Mr Mudge. It was because *he* was different that, in the
oddest way, she liked as well as deplored him; which was after
all a proof that the disparity, should they frankly recognize it,
wouldn't necessarily be fatal. She felt that, oleaginous – too
oleaginous – as he was, he was somehow comparatively primitive: she had once, during the portion of his time at
that had overlapped her own, seen him collar a drunken soldier,
a big, violent man, who, having come in with a mate to get a
postal-order cashed, had made a grab at the money before his
friend could reach it and had so produced, among the hams and
cheeses and the lodgers from Thrupp's, reprisals instantly
ensuing, a scene of scandal and consternation. Mr Buckton and
the counter-clerk had crouched within the cage, but Mr Mudge
had, with a very quiet but very quick step round the corner,
triumphantly interposed in the scrimmage, parted the com-
batants, and shaken the delinquent in his skin. She had been
proud of him at that moment, and had felt that if their affair had
not already been settled the neatness of his execution would have
left her without resistance.

Their affair had been settled by other things: by the evident
sincerity of his passion and by the sense that his high white apron
resembled a front of many floors. It had gone a great way with
her that he would build a business to his chin, which he carried

quite in the air. This could only be a question of time; he would have all Piccadilly in the pen behind his ear. That was a merit in itself for a girl who had known what she had known. There were hours at which she even found him good-looking, though, frankly, there could be no crown for her effort to imagine, on the part of the tailor or the barber, some such treatment of his appearance as would make him resemble even remotely a gentleman. His very beauty was the beauty of a grocer, and the finest future would offer it none too much room to expand. She had engaged herself, in short, to the perfection of a type, and perfection of anything was much for a person who, out of early troubles, had just escaped with her life. But it contributed hugely at present to carry on the two parallel lines of her contacts in the cage and her contacts out of it. After keeping quiet for some time about this opposition, she suddenly – one Sunday afternoon on a penny chair in the Regent's Park – broke, for him, capriciously, bewilderingly, into an intimation of what it came to. He naturally pressed more and more on the subject of her again placing herself where he could see her hourly, and for her to recognize that she had as yet given him no sane reason for delays she had no need to hear him say that he couldn't make out what she was up to. As if, with her absurd bad reasons, she knew it herself! Sometimes she thought it would be amusing to let him have them full in the face, for she felt she should die of him unless she once in a while stupefied him; and sometimes she thought it would be disgusting and perhaps even fatal. She liked him, however, to think her silly, for that gave her the margin which, at the best, she would always require; and the only difficulty about this was that he hadn't enough imagination to oblige her. It produced, none the less, something of the desired effect – to leave him simply wondering why, over the matter of their reunion, she didn't yield to his arguments. Then at last, simply as if by accident and out of mere boredom on a day that was rather flat, she preposterously produced her own. 'Well, wait a bit. Where I am I still see things.' And she talked to him even worse, if possible, than she had talked to Mrs Jordan.

Little by little, to her own stupefaction, she caught that he was trying to take it as she meant it, and that he was neither astonished nor angry. Oh, the British tradesman – this gave her an idea of his resources! Mr Mudge would be angry only with a person who, like the drunken soldier in the shop, should have an unfavourable effect upon business. He seemed positively to enter, for the time and without the faintest flash of irony or ripple of laughter, into the whimsical grounds of her enjoyment of Cocker's custom, and instantly to be casting up whatever it might, as Mrs Jordan had said, lead to. What he had in mind was not, of course, what Mrs Jordan had had: it was obviously not a source of speculation with him that his sweetheart might pick up a husband. She could see perfectly that this was not, for a moment, even what he supposed she herself dreamed of. What she had done was simply to give his fancy another push into the dim vast of trade. In that direction it was all alert, and she had whisked before it the mild fragrance of a 'connection'. That was the most he could see in any picture of her keeping in with the gentry; and when, getting to the bottom of this, she quickly proceeded to show him the kind of eye she turned on such people and to give him a sketch of what that eye discovered, she reduced him to the particular confusion in which he could still be amusing to her.

10

'THEY'RE the most awful wretches, I assure you – the lot all about there.'

'Then why do you want to stay among them?'

'My dear man, just because they *are*. It makes me hate them so.'

'Hate them? I thought you liked them.'

'Don't be stupid. What I "like" is just to loathe them. You wouldn't believe what passes before my eyes.'

'Then why have you never told me? You didn't mention anything before I left.'

'Oh, I hadn't got into it then. It's the sort of thing you don't believe at first; you have to look round a bit and then you understand. You work into it more and more. Besides,' the girl went on, 'this is the time of the year when the worst lot come up. They're simply packed together in those smart streets. Talk of the numbers of the poor! What *I* can vouch for is the numbers of the rich! There are new ones every day, and they seem to get richer and richer. Oh, they do come up!' she cried, imitating, for her private recreation – she was sure it wouldn't reach Mr Mudge – the low intonation of the counter-clerk.

'And where do they come from?' her companion candidly inquired.

She had to think a moment; then she found something. 'From the "spring meetings". They bet tremendously.'

'Well, they bet enough at Chalk Farm, if that's all.'

'It *isn't* all. It isn't a millionth part!' she replied with some sharpness. 'It's immense fun' – she would tantalize him. Then, as she had heard Mrs Jordan say, and as the ladies at Cocker's even sometimes wired, 'It's quite too dreadful!' She could fully feel how it was Mr Mudge's propriety, which was extreme – he had a horror of coarseness and attended a Wesleyan chapel – that prevented his asking for details. But she gave him some of the more innocuous in spite of himself, especially putting before him how, at Simpkin's and Ladle's, they all made the money fly. That was indeed what he liked to hear: the connection was not direct, but one was somehow more in the right place where the money was flying than where it was simply and meagrely nesting. It enlivened the air, he had to acknowledge, much less at Chalk Farm than in the district in which his beloved so oddly enjoyed her footing. She gave him, she could see, a restless sense that these might be familiarities not to be sacrificed; germs, possibilities, faint foreshowings – heaven knew what – of the initiation it would prove profitable to have arrived at when, in the fulness of time, he should have his own shop in some such paradise. What really touched him – that was discernible – was that she could feed him with so much mere vividness of reminder, keep before him, as by the play of a fan, the very wind of the swift bank-notes and the charm of the existence of a class that Providence had raised up to be the blessing of grocers. He liked to think that the class was there, that it was always there, and that she contributed in her slight but appreciable degree to keep it up to the mark. He couldn't have formulated his theory of the matter, but the exuberance of the aristocracy was the advantage of trade, and everything was knit together in a richness of pattern that it was good to follow with one's finger-tips. It was a comfort to him to be thus assured that there were no symptoms of a drop. What did the sounder, as she called it, nimbly worked, do but keep the ball going?

What it came to, therefore, for Mr Mudge, was that all enjoyments were, in short, interrelated, and that the more people had the more they wanted to have. The more flirtations, as he might roughly express it, the more cheese and pickles. He had even in his own small way been dimly struck with the concatenation between the tender passion and cheap champagne. What he would have liked to say had he been able to work out his thought to the end was: 'I see, I see. Lash them up then, lead them on, keep them going: some of it can't help, some time, coming *our* way.' Yet he was troubled by the suspicion of subtleties on his companion's part that spoiled the straight view. He couldn't understand people's hating what they liked or liking what they hated; above all it hurt him somewhere – for he had his private delicacies – to see anything *but* money made out of his betters. To be curious at the expense of the gentry was vaguely wrong; the only thing that was distinctly right was to be prosperous. Wasn't it just because they were up there aloft that they were lucrative? He concluded, at any rate, by saying to his young friend: 'If it's improper for you to remain at Cocker's, then that falls in exactly with the other reasons that I have put before you for your removal.'

'Improper?' – her smile became a long, wide look at him. 'My dear boy, there's no one like you!'

'I dare say,' he laughed; 'but that doesn't help the question.'

'Well,' she returned, 'I can't give up my friends. I'm making even more than Mrs Jordan.'

Mr Mudge considered. 'How much is *she* making?'

'Oh, you dear donkey!' – and, regardless of all the Regent's Park, she patted his cheek. This was the sort of moment at which she was absolutely tempted to tell him that she liked to be near Park Chambers. There was a fascination in the idea of seeing if, on a mention of Captain Everard, he wouldn't do what she thought he might; wouldn't weigh against the obvious objection the still more obvious advantage. The advantage, of course, could only strike him at the best as rather fantastic; but it was always to the good to keep hold when you *had* hold, and such an attitude would also after all involve a high tribute to her fidelity. Of one thing she absolutely never doubted: Mr Mudge believed in her with a belief – ! She believed in herself too, for that matter: if there was a thing in the world no one could charge her with, it was being the kind of low barmaid person who rinsed tumblers and bandied slang. But she forebore as yet to speak; she had not spoken even to Mrs Jordan; and the hush that on her lips surrounded the Captain's name maintained itself as a kind of symbol of the success that, up to this time, had attended something or other – she couldn't have said what – that she humoured herself with calling, without words, her relation with him.

II

SHE would have admitted indeed that it consisted of little more than the fact that his absences, however frequent and however long, always ended with his turning up again. It was nobody's business in the world but her own if that fact continued to be enough for her. It was of course not enough just in itself; what it had taken on to make it so was the extraordinary possession of the elements of his life that memory and attention had at last given her. There came a day when this possession, on the girl's part, actually seemed to enjoy, between them, while their eyes met, a tacit recognition that was half a joke and half a deep solemnity. He bade her good morning always now; he often quite raised his hat to her. He passed a remark when there was time or room, and once she went so far as to say to him that she had not seen him for 'ages'. 'Ages' was the word she consciously and carefully, though a trifle tremulously, used; 'ages' was exactly what she meant. To this he replied in terms doubtless less anxiously selected, but perhaps on that account not the less remarkable, 'Oh yes, hasn't it been awfully wet?' That was a specimen of their give and take; it fed her fancy that no form of intercourse so transcendent and distilled had ever been established on earth. Everything, so far as they chose to consider it so, might mean almost anything. The want of margin in the cage, when he peeped through the bars, wholly ceased to be appreciable. It was a drawback only in superficial commerce. With Captain Everard she had simply the margin of the universe. It may be imagined, therefore, how their unuttered reference to all she knew about him could, in this immensity, play at its ease. Every time he handed in a telegram it was an addition to her knowledge: what did his constant smile mean to mark if it didn't mean to mark that? He never came into the place without saying to her in this manner: 'Oh yes, you have me by this time so completely at your mercy that it doesn't in the least matter what I give you now. You've become a comfort, I assure you!'

She had only two torments; the greatest of which was that she couldn't, not even once or twice, touch with him on some individual fact. She would have given anything to have been able to allude to one of his friends by name, to one of his engagements by date, to one of his difficulties by the solution. She would have given almost as much for just the right chance – it would have to be tremendously right – to show him in some sharp, sweet way that she had perfectly penetrated the greatest of these last and now lived with it in a kind of heroism of sympathy. He was in love with a woman to whom, and to any view of whom, a lady-telegraphist, and especially one who passed a life among hams and cheeses, was as the sand on the floor; and what her dreams desired was the possibility of its somehow coming to him that her own interest in him could take a pure and noble account of such an infatuation and even of such an impropriety. As yet, however, she could only rub along with the hope that an accident, sooner or later, might give her a lift toward popping out with something that would surprise and perhaps even, some fine day, assist him. What could people mean, moreover – cheaply sarcastic people – by not feeling all that could be got out of the weather? *She* felt it all, and seemed literally to feel it most when she went quite wrong, speaking of the stuffy days as cold, of the cold ones as stuffy, and betraying how little she knew, in her cage, of whether it was foul or fair. It was, for that matter, always stuffy at Cocker's, and she finally settled down to the safe proposition that the outside element was 'changeable'. Anything seemed true that made him so radiantly assent.

This indeed is a small specimen of her cultivation of insidious ways of making things easy for him – ways to which of course she couldn't be at all sure that he did real justice. Real justice was not of this world: she had had too often to come back to that; yet, strangely, happiness was, and her traps had to be set for it in a manner to keep them unperceived by Mr Buckton and the counter-clerk. The most she could hope for apart from the question, which constantly flickered up and died down, of the divine chance of his consciously liking her, would be that, without analysing it, he should arrive at a vague sense that Cocker's was – well, attractive; easier, smoother, sociably brighter, slightly more picturesque, in short more propitious in general to his little affairs, than any other establishment just thereabouts. She was quite aware that they couldn't be, in so huddled a hole, particularly quick; but she found her account in the slowness – she certainly could bear it if *he* could. The great pang was that, just thereabouts, post-offices were so awfully thick. She was always seeing him, in imagination, in other places and with other girls. But she would deny any other girl to follow him as she followed. And though they weren't, for so many reasons, quick at Cocker's, she could hurry for him when, through an intimation light as air, she gathered that he was pressed.

When hurry was, better still, impossible, it was because of the pleasantest thing of all, the particular element of their contact – she would have called it their friendship – that consisted of an almost humorous treatment of the look of some of his words. They would never perhaps have grown half so intimate if he had not, by the blessing of heaven, formed some of his letters with a queerness – ! It was positive that the queerness could scarce have been greater if he had practised it for the very purpose of bringing their heads together over it as far as was possible to heads on different sides of a cage. It had taken her in reality but once or twice to master these tricks, but, at the cost of striking him perhaps as stupid, she could still challenge them when circumstances favoured. The great circumstance that favoured was that she sometimes actually believed he knew she only feigned perplexity. If he knew it, therefore, he tolerated it; if he tolerated it he came back; and if he came back he liked her. This was her seventh heaven; and she didn't ask much of his liking – she only asked of it to reach the point of his not going away because of her own. He had at times to be away for weeks, he had to lead his life; he had to travel – there were places to which he was constantly wiring for 'rooms': all this she granted him, forgave him; in fact, in the long-run, literally blessed and thanked him for. If he had to lead his life, that precisely fostered his leading it so much by telegraph: therefore the benediction was to come in when he could. That was all she asked – that he shouldn't wholly deprive her.

Sometimes she almost felt that he couldn't have done so even had he been minded, on account of the web of revelation that was woven between them. She quite thrilled herself with thinking what, with such a lot of material, a bad girl would do. It would be a scene better than many in her ha'penny novels, this going to him in the dusk of the evening at Park Chambers and letting him at last have it. 'I know too much about a certain person now not to put it to you – excuse my being so lurid – that it's quite worth your while to buy me off. Come, therefore; buy me!' There was a point indeed at which such flights had to drop again – the point of an unreadiness to name, when it came to that, the purchasing medium. It wouldn't, certainly, be anything so gross as money, and the matter accordingly remained rather vague, all the more that *she* was not a bad girl. It was not for any such reason as might have aggravated a mere minx that she often hoped he would again bring Cissy. The difficulty of this, however, was constantly present to her, for the kind of communion to which Cocker's so richly ministered rested on the fact that Cissy and he were so often in different places. She knew by this time all the places – Suchbury, Monkhouse, Whiteroy, Finches, – and even how the parties, on these occasions, were composed; but her subtlety found ways to make her knowledge fairly protect and promote their keeping, as she had heard Mrs Jordan say, in touch. So, when he actually sometimes smiled as if he really felt the awkwardness of giving her again one of the same old addresses, all her being went out in the desire – which her face must have expressed – that he should recognize her forbearance to criticize as one of the finest, tenderest sacrifices a woman had ever made for love.

12

SHE was occasionally worried, all the same, by the impression that these sacrifices, great as they were, were nothing to those that his own passion had imposed; if indeed it was not rather the passion of his confederate, which had caught him up and was whirling him round like a great steam-wheel. He was at any rate in the strong grip of a dizzy, splendid fate; the wild wind of his life blew him straight before it. Didn't she catch in his face, at times even through his smile and his happy habit, the gleam of that pale glare with which a bewildered victim appeals, as he passes, to some pair of pitying eyes? He perhaps didn't even himself know how scared he was; but *she* knew. They were in danger, they were in danger, Captain Everard and Lady Bradeen: it beat every novel in the shop. She thought of Mr Mudge and his safe sentiment; she thought of herself and blushed even more for her tepid response to it. It was a comfort to her at such moments to feel that in another relation – a relation supplying that affinity with her nature that Mr Mudge, deluded creature, would never supply – she should have been no more tepid than her ladyship. Her deepest soundings were on two or three occasions of finding herself almost sure that, if she dared, her ladyship's lover would have gathered relief from 'speaking' to her. She literally fancied once or twice that, projected as he was toward his doom, her own eyes struck him, while the air roared in his ears, as the one pitying pair in the crowd. But how could he speak to her while she sat sandwiched there between the counter-clerk and the sounder?

She had long ago, in her comings and goings, made acquaintance with Park Chambers, and reflected, as she looked up at
their luxurious front, that *they*, of course, would supply the ideal
setting for the ideal speech. There was not a picture in London
that, before the season was over, was more stamped upon her
brain. She went round about to pass it, for it was not on the
short way; she passed on the opposite side of the street and
always looked up, though it had taken her a long time to be sure
of the particular set of windows. She had made that out at last
by an act of audacity that, at the time, had almost stopped her
heart-beats and that, in retrospect, greatly quickened her blushes.
One evening, late, she had lingered and watched – watched for
some moment when the porter who was in uniform and often
on the steps, had gone in with a visitor. Then she had followed
boldly, on the calculation that he would have taken the visitor
up and that the hall would be free. The hall *was* free, and the
electric light played over the gilded and lettered board that
showed the names and numbers of the occupants of the different
floors. What she wanted looked straight at her – Captain
Everard was on the third. It was as if, in the immense intimacy
of this, they were, for the instant and the first time, face to face
outside the cage. Alas! they were face to face but a second or
two: she was whirled out on the wings of a panic fear that he
might just then be entering or issuing. This fear was indeed, in
her shameless deflections, never very far from her, and was
mixed in the oddest way with depressions and disappointments.
It was dreadful, as she trembled by, to run the risk of looking to
him as if she basely hung about; and yet it was dreadful to be
obliged to pass only at such moments as put an encounter out of
the question.

At the horrible hour of her first coming to Cocker's he was
always – it was to be hoped – snug in bed; and at the hour of
her final departure he was of course – she had such things all on
her fingers'-ends – dressing for dinner. We may let it pass that if
she could not bring herself to hover till he was dressed, this was
simply because such a process for such a person could only be
terribly prolonged. When she went in the middle of the day to
her dinner she had too little time to do anything but go straight,

though it must be added that for a real certainty she would joyously have omitted the repast. She had made up her mind as to there being on the whole no decent pretext to justify her flitting casually past at three o'clock in the morning. That was the hour at which, if the ha'penny novels were not all wrong, he probably came home for the night. She was therefore reduced to merely picturing that miraculous meeting toward which a hundred impossibilities would have to conspire. But if nothing was more impossible than the fact, nothing was more intense than the vision. What may not, we can only moralize, take place in the quickened, muffled perception of a girl of a certain kind of soul? All our young friend's native distinction, her refinement of personal grain, of heredity, of pride, took refuge in this small throbbing spot; for when she was most conscious of the abjection of her vanity and the pitifulness of her little flutters and manoeuvres, then the consolation and the redemption were most sure to shine before her in some just discernible sign. He did like her!

13

HE never brought Cissy back, but Cissy came one day without him, as fresh as before from the hands of Marguerite, or only, at the season's end, a trifle less fresh. She was, however, distinctly less serene. She had brought nothing with her, and looked about her with some impatience for the forms and the place to write. The latter convenience, at Cocker's, was obscure and barely adequate, and her clear voice had the light note of disgust which her loves's never showed as she responded with a 'There?' of surprise to the gesture made by the counter-clerk in answer to her sharp inquiry. Our young friend was busy with half a dozen people, but she had despatched them in her most business-like manner by the time her ladyship flung through the bars the light of re-appearance. Then the directness with which the girl managed to receive this missive was the result of the concentration that had caused her to make the stamps fly during the few minutes occupied by the production of it. This concentration, in turn, may be described as the effect of the apprehension of imminent relief. It was nineteen days, counted and checked off, since she had seen the object of her homage; and as, had he been in London, she should, with his habits, have been sure to see him often, she was now about to learn what other spot his presence might just then happen to sanctify. For she thought of them, the other spots, as ecstatically conscious of it, expressively happy in it.

But, gracious, how handsome *was* her ladyship, and what an added price it gave him that the air of intimacy he threw out should have flowed originally from such a source! The girl looked straight through the cage at the eyes and lips that must so often have been so near his own – looked at them with a strange passion that, for an instant, had the result of filling out some of the gaps, supplying the missing answers, in his correspondence. Then, as she made out that the features she thus scanned and associated were totally unaware of it, that they glowed only with the colour of quite other and not at all guessable thoughts, this directly added to their splendour, gave the girl the sharpest impression she had yet received of the uplifted, the unattainable plains of heaven, and yet at the same time caused her to thrill with a sense of the high company she did somehow keep. She was with the absent through her ladyship and with her ladyship through the absent. The only pang – but it didn't matter – was the proof in the admirable face, in the sightless pre-occupation of its possessor, that the latter hadn't a notion of her. Her folly had gone to the point of half believing that the other party to the affair must sometimes mention in Eaton Square the extraordinary little person at the place from which he so often wired. Yet the perception of her visitor's blankness actually helped this extraordinary little person, the next instant, to take refuge in a reflection that could be as proud as it liked. 'How little she knows, how little she knows!' the girl cried to herself; for what did that show after all but that Captain Everard's telegraphic confidant was Captain Everard's charming secret? Our young friend's perusal of her ladyship's telegram was literally prolonged by a momentary daze: what swam between her and the words, making her see them as through rippled, shallow, sunshot water, was the great, the perpetual flood of 'How much *I* know – how much *I* know!' This produced a delay in her catching that, on the face, these words didn't give her what she wanted, though she was prompt enough with her remembrance that her grasp was, half the time, just of what was *not* on the face. 'Miss Dolman, Parade Lodge, Parade Terrace, Dover. Let him instantly know right one, Hôtel de France, Ostend. Make it seven nine four nine six one. Wire me alternative Burfield's.'

The girl slowly counted. Then he was at Ostend. This hooked on with so sharp a click that, not to feel she was as quickly letting it all slip from her, she had absolutely to hold it a minute longer and to do something to that end. Thus it was that she did on this occasion what she never did – threw off an 'Answer paid?' that sounded officious, but that she partly made up for by deliberately affixing the stamps and by waiting till she had done so to give the change. She had, for so much coolness, the strength that she considered she knew all about Miss Dolman.

'Yes – paid.' She saw all sorts of things in this reply, even to a small, suppressed start of surprise at so correct an assumption; even to an attempt, the next minute, at a fresh air of detachment. 'How much, with the answer?' The calculation was not abstruse, but our intense observer required a moment more to make it, and this gave her ladyship time for a second thought. 'Oh, just wait!' The white, begemmed hand bared to write rose in sudden nervousness to the side of the wonderful face which, with eyes of anxiety for the paper on the counter, she brought closer to the bars of the cage. 'I think I must alter a word!' On this she recovered her telegram and looked over it again; but she had a new, obvious trouble, and studied it without deciding and with much of the effect of making our young woman watch her.

This personage, meanwhile, at the sight of her expression, had decided on the spot. If she had always been sure they were in danger, her ladyship's expression was the best possible sign of it. There was a word wrong, but she had lost the right one, and much, clearly, depended on her finding it again. The girl, therefore, sufficiently estimating the affluence of customers and the distraction of Mr Buckton and the counter-clerk, took the jump and gave it. 'Isn't it Cooper's?

It was as if she had bodily leaped – cleared the top of the cage and alighted on her interlocutress. 'Cooper's?' – the stare was heightened by a blush. Yes, she had made Juno blush.

This was all the more reason for going on. 'I mean instead of Burfield's.'

Our young friend fairly pitied her; she had made her in an instant so helpless, and yet not a bit haughty nor outraged. She was only mystified and scared. 'Oh, you know – ?'

'Yes, I know!' Our young friend smiled, meeting the other's eyes, and, having made Juno blush, proceeded to patronize her. '*I'll* do it' – she put out a competent hand. Her ladyship only submitted, confused and bewildered, all presence of mind quite gone; and the next moment the telegram was in the cage again and its author out of the shop. Then quickly, boldly, under all the eyes that might have witnessed her tampering, the extraordinary little person at Cocker's made the proper change. People were really too giddy, and if they *were*, in a certain case, to be caught, it shouldn't be the fault of her own grand memory. Hadn't it been settled weeks before? – for Miss Dolman it was always to be 'Cooper's'.

14

BUT the summer 'holidays' brought a marked difference; they were holidays for almost everyone but the animals in the cage. The August days were flat and dry, and, with so little to feed it, she was conscious of the ebb of her interest in the secrets of the refined. She was in a position to follow the refined to the extent of knowing – they had made so many of their arrangements with her aid – exactly where they were; yet she felt quite as if the panorama had ceased unrolling and the band stopped playing. A stray member of the latter occasionally turned up, but the communications that passed before her bore now largely on rooms at hotels, prices of furnished houses, hours of trains, dates of sailings and arrangements for being 'met': she found them for the most part prosaic and coarse. The only thing was that they brought into her stuffy corner as straight a whiff of Alpine meadows and Scotch moors as she might hope ever to inhale; there were moreover, in especial, fat, hot, dull ladies who had out with her, to exasperation, the terms for seaside lodgings, which struck her as huge, and the matter of the number of beds required, which was not less portentous: this in reference to places of which the names – Eastbourne, Folkstone, Cromer, Scarborough, Whitby – tormented her with something of the sound of the plash of water that haunts the traveller in the desert. She had not been out of London for a dozen years, and the only thing to give a taste to the present dead weeks was the spice of a chronic resentment. The sparse customers, the people she did see, were the people who were 'just off' – off on the decks of fluttered yachts, off to the uttermost point of rocky headlands where the very breeze was then playing for the want of which she said to herself that she sickened.

There was accordingly a sense in which, at such a period, the great differences of the human condition could press upon her more than ever; a circumstance drawing fresh force, in truth, from the very fact of the chance that at last, for a change, did squarely meet her – the chance to be 'off' for a bit, almost as far as anybody. They took their turns in the cage as they took them both in the shop and at Chalk Farm, and she had known these two months that time was to be allowed in September – no less than eleven days – for her personal, private holiday. Much of her recent intercourse with Mr Mudge had consisted of the hopes and fears, expressed mainly by himself, involved in the question of their getting the same dates – a question that, in proportion as the delight seemed assured, spread into a sea of speculation over the choice of where and how. All through July, on the Sunday evenings and at such other odd times as he could seize, he had flooded their talk with wild waves of calculation. It was practically settled that, with her mother, somewhere 'on the south coast' (a phrase of which she liked the sound) they should put in their allowance together; but she already felt the prospect quite weary and worn with the way he went round and round on it. It had become his sole topic, the theme alike of his most

solemn prudences and most placid jests, to which every opening
led for return and revision and in which every little flower of a
foretaste was pulled up as soon as planted. He had announced at
the earliest day – characterizing the whole business, from that
moment, as their 'plans', under which name he handled it as a
syndicate handles a Chinese, or other, Loan – he had promptly
declared that the question must be thoroughly studied, and he
produced, on the whole subject, from day to day, an amount of
information that excited her wonder and even, not a little, as
she frankly let him know, her disdain. When she thought of
the danger in which another pair of lovers rapturously lived,
she inquired of him anew why he could leave nothing to
chance. Then she got for answer that this profundity was just his
pride, and he pitted Ramsgate against Bournemouth and even
Boulogne against Jersey – for he had great ideas – with all the
mastery of detail that was some day, professionally, to carry him
far.

The longer the time since she had seen Captain Everard, the
more she was booked, as she called it, to pass Park Chambers;
and this was the sole amusement that, in the lingering August
days and the long, sad twilights, it was left her to cultivate. She
had long since learned to know it for a feeble one, though its
feebleness was perhaps scarce the reason for her saying to herself
each evening as her time for departure approached: 'No,
no – not tonight.' She never failed of that silent remark, any
more than she failed of feeling, in some deeper place than she
had even yet fully sounded, that one's remarks were as weak as
straws, and that, however one might indulge in them at eight
o'clock, one's fate infallibly declared itself in absolute indifference to them at about eight-fifteen. Remarks were remarks, and
very well for that; but fate was fate, and this young lady's was
to pass Park Chambers every night in the working week. Out of
the immensity of her knowledge of the life of the world there
bloomed on these occasions a specific remembrance that it was
regarded in that region, in August and September, as rather
pleasant just to be caught for something or other in passing
through town. Somebody was always passing and somebody
might catch somebody else. It was in full cognisance of this
subtle law that she adhered to the most ridiculous circuit she

could have made to get home. One warm, dull, featureless
Friday, when an accident had made her start from Cocker's a
little later than usual, she became aware that something of which
the infinite possibilities had for so long peopled her dreams was
at last prodigiously upon her, though the perfection in which the
conditions happened to present it was almost rich enough to be
but the positive creation of a dream. She saw, straight before her,
like a vista painted in a picture, the empty street and the lamps
that burned pale in the dusk not yet established. It was into the
convenience of this quiet twilight that a gentleman on the
door-step of the Chambers gazed with a vagueness that our
young lady's little figure violently trembled, in the approach,
with the measure of its power to dissipate. Everything indeed
grew in a flash terrific and distinct; her old uncertainties fell
away from her, and, since she was so familiar with fate, she felt
as if the very nail that fixed it were driven in by the hard look
with which, for a moment, Captain Everard awaited her.

The vestibule was open behind him and the porter as absent
as on the day she had peeped in; he had just come out – was
in town, in a tweed suit and a pot hat, but between two
journeys – duly bored over his evening and at a loss what to do
with it. Then it was that she was glad she had never met him in
that way before: she reaped with such ecstasy the benefit of his
not being able to think she passed often. She jumped in two
seconds to the determination that he should even suppose it to be
the first time and the queerest chance: this was while she still
wondered if he would identify or notice her. His original
attention had not, she instinctively knew, been for the young
woman at Cocker's; it had only been for any young woman
who might advance with an air of not upholding ugliness. Ah,
but then, and just as she had reached the door, came his second
observation, a long, light reach with which, visibly and quite
amusedly, he recalled and placed her. They were on different
sides, but the street, narrow and still, had only made more of a
stage for the small momentary drama. It was not over, besides,
it was far from over, even on his sending across the way, with
the pleasantest laugh she had ever heard, a little lift of his hat and
an 'Oh, good evening!' It was still less over on their meeting, the
next minute, though rather indirectly and awkwardly, in the

middle of the road – a situation to which three or four steps of
her own had unmistakably contributed, – and then passing not
again to the side on which she had arrived, but back toward the
portal of Park Chambers.

'I didn't know you at first. Are you taking a walk?'

'Oh, I don't take walks at night! I'm going home after my
work.'

'Oh!'

That was practically what they had meanwhile smiled out,
and his exclamation, to which, for a minute, he appeared to have
nothing to add, left them face to face and in just such an attitude
as, for his part, he might have worn had he been wondering if
he could properly ask her to come in. During this interval, in
fact, she really felt his question to be just '*How* properly – ?' It
was simply a question of the degree of properness.

15

SHE never knew afterwards quite what she had done to settle it,
and at the time only knew that they presently moved, with
vagueness, but with continuity, away from the picture of the
lighted vestibule and the quiet stairs and well up the street
together. This also must have been in the absence of a definite
permission, of anything vulgarly articulate, for that matter, on
the part of either; and it was to be, later on, a thing of
remembrance and reflection for her that the limit of what, just
here, for a longish minute, passed between them was his taking
in her thoroughly successful deprecation, though conveyed
without pride or sound or touch, of the idea that she might be,
out of the cage, the very shopgirl at large that she hugged the
theory she was not. Yes, it was strange, she afterwards thought,
that so much could have come and gone and yet not troubled
the air either with impertinence or with resentment, with any of
the horrid notes of that kind of acquaintance. He had taken no
liberty, as she would have called it; and, through not having to

betray the sense of one, she herself had, still more charmingly, taken none. Yet on the spot, nevertheless, she could speculate as to what it meant that, if his relation with Lady Bradeen continued to be what her mind had built it up to, he should feel free to proceed in any private direction. This was one of the questions he was to leave her to deal with – the question whether people of his sort still asked girls up to their rooms when they were so awfully in love with other women. Could people of his sort do that without what people of *her* sort would call being 'false to their love'? She had already a vision of how the true answer was that people of her sort didn't, in such cases, matter – didn't count as infidelity, counted only as something else: she might have been curious, since it came to that, to see exactly what.

Strolling together slowly in their summer twilight and their empty corner of Mayfair, they found themselves emerge at last opposite to one of the smaller gates of the Park; upon which, without any particular word about it – they were talking so of other things – they crossed the street and went in and sat down on a bench. She had gathered by this time one magnificent hope about him – the hope that he would say nothing vulgar. She knew what she meant by that; she meant something quite apart from any matter of his being 'false'. Their bench was not far within; it was near the Park Lane paling and the patchy lamplight and the rumbling cabs and 'buses. A strange emotion had come to her, and she felt indeed excitement within excitement; above all a conscious joy in testing him with chances he didn't take. She had an intense desire he should know the type she really was without her doing anything so low as tell him, and he had surely begun to know it from the moment he didn't seize the opportunities into which a common man would promptly have blundered. These were on the mere surface, and *their* relation was behind and below them. She had questioned so little on the way what they were doing, that as soon as they were seated she took straight hold of it. Her hours, her confinement, the many conditions of service in the post-office, had – with a glance at his own personal resources and alternatives – formed, up to this stage, the subject of their talk. 'Well, here we are, and it may be right enough, but this isn't the least, you know, where I was going.'

'You were going home?'

'Yes, and I was already rather late. I was going to my supper.'

'You haven't had it?'

'No, indeed!'

'Then you haven't eaten – ?'

He looked, of a sudden, so extravagantly concerned that she laughed out. 'All day? Yes, we do feed once. But that was long ago. So I must presently say good-bye.'

'Oh, deary *me*!' he exclaimed, with an intonation so droll and yet a touch so light and a distress so marked – a confession of helplessness for such a case, in short, so unrelieved – that she felt sure, on the spot, she had made the great difference plain. He looked at her with the kindest eyes and still without saying what she had known he wouldn't. She had known he wouldn't say, 'Then sup with *me*!' but the proof of it made her feel as if she had feasted.

'I'm not a bit hungry,' she went on.

'Ah, you *must* be, awfully!' he made answer, but settling himself on the bench as if, after all, that needn't interfere with his spending his evening. 'I've always quite wanted the chance to thank you for the trouble you so often take for me.'

'Yes, I know,' she replied; uttering the words with a sense of the situation far deeper than any pretence of not fitting his allusion. She immediately saw that he was surprised and even a little puzzled at her frank assent; but, for herself, the trouble she had taken could only, in these fleeting minutes – they would probably never come back – be all there like a little hoard of gold in her lap. Certainly he might look at it, handle it, take up the pieces. Yet if he understood anything he must understand all. 'I consider you've already immensely thanked me.' The horror was back upon her of having seemed to hang about for some reward. 'It's awfully odd that you should have been there just the one time – !'

'The one time you've passed my place?'

'Yes; you can fancy I haven't many minutes to waste. There was a place tonight I had to stop at.'

'I see, I see' – he knew already so much about her work. 'It must be an awful grind – for a lady.'

'It is; but I don't think I groan over it any more than my companions – and you've seen *they're* not ladies!' She mildly jested, but with an intention. 'One gets used to things, and there are employments I should have hated much more.' She had the finest conception of the beauty of not, at least, boring him. To whine, to count up her wrongs, was what a barmaid or a shopgirl would do, and it was quite enough to sit there like one of these.

'If you had had another employment,' he remarked after a moment, 'we might never have become acquainted.'

'It's highly probable – and certainly not in the same way.' Then, still with her heap of gold in her lap and something of the pride of it in her manner of holding her head, she continued not to move – she only smiled at him. The evening had thickened now; the scattered lamps were red; the Park, all before them, was full of obscure and ambiguous life; there were other couples on other benches, whom it was impossible not to see, yet at whom it was impossible to look. 'But I've walked so much out of my way with you only just to show you that – that' – with this she paused; it was not, after all, so easy to express – 'that anything you may have thought is perfectly true.'

'Oh, I've thought a tremendous lot!' her companion laughed: 'Do you mind my smoking?'

'Why should I? You always smoke *there*.'

'At your place? Oh yes, but here it's different.'

'No,' she said, as he lighted a cigarette, 'that's just what it isn't. It's quite the same.'

'Well, then, that's because "there" it's so wonderful!'

'Then you're conscious of how wonderful it is?' she returned.

He jerked his handsome head in literal protest at a doubt. 'Why, that's exactly what I mean by my gratitude for all your trouble. It has been just as if you took a particular interest.' She only looked at him in answer to this, in such sudden, immediate embarrassment, as she was quite aware, that, while she remained silent, he showed he was at a loss to interpret her expression. 'You *have* – haven't you? – taken a particular interest?'

'Oh, a particular interest!' she quavered out, feeling the whole thing – her immediate embarrassment – get terribly the better of her, and wishing, with a sudden scare, all the more to keep

her emotion down. She maintained her fixed smile a moment
and turned her eyes over the peopled darkness, unconfused now,
because there was something much more confusing. This, with
a fatal great rush, was simply the fact that they were thus
together. They were near, near, and all that she had imagined of
that had only become more true, more dreadful and overwhelming. She stared straight away in silence till she felt that she
looked like an idiot; then, to say something, to say nothing, she
attempted a sound which ended in a flood of tears.

16

HER tears helped her really to dissimulate, for she had instantly,
in so public a situation, to recover herself. They had come and
gone in half a minute, and she immediately explained them. 'It's
only because I'm tired. It's that – it's that!' Then she added a
trifle incoherently: 'I shall never see you again.'

'Ah, but why not?' The mere tone in which her companion
asked this satisfied her once for all as to the amount of imagination for which she could count on him. It was naturally not
large: it had exhausted itself in having arrived at what he had
already touched upon – the sense of an intention in her poor zeal
at Cocker's. But any deficiency of this kind was no fault in him:
he wasn't obliged to have an inferior cleverness – to have
second-rate resources and virtues. It has been as if he almost
really believed she had simply cried for fatigue, and he had
accordingly put in some kind, confused plea – 'You ought really
to take something: won't you have something or other *somewhere*?' – to which she had made no response but a headshake of
a sharpness that settled it. 'Why shan't we all the more keep
meeting?'

'I mean meeting this way – only this way. At my place
there – *that* I've nothing to do with, and I hope of course you'll
turn up, with your correspondence, when it suits you. Whether
I stay or not, I mean; for I shall probably not stay.'

'You're not going somewhere else?' – he put it with positive anxiety.

'Yes; ever so far away – to the other end of London. There are all sorts of reasons I can't tell you; and it's practically settled. It's better for me, much; and I've only kept on at Cocker's for you.'

'For me?'

Making out in the dusk that he fairly blushed, she now measured how far he had been from knowing too much. Too much, she called it at present; and that was easy, since it proved so abundantly enough for her that he should simply be where he was. 'As we shall never talk this way but to-night – never, never again! – here it all is; I'll say it; I don't care what you think; it doesn't matter; I only want to help you. Besides, you're kind – you're kind. I've been thinking, then, of leaving for ever so long. But you've come so often – at times, – and you've had so much to do, and it has been so pleasant and interesting, that I've remained, I've kept putting off any change. More than once, when I had nearly decided, you've turned up again and I've thought, "Oh no!" That's the simple fact!' She had by this time got her confusion down so completely that she could laugh. 'This is what I meant when I said to you just now that I "knew". I've known perfectly that you knew I took trouble for you; and that knowledge has been for me, and I seemed to see it was for you, as if there were something – I don't know what to call it! – between us. I mean something unusual and good – something not a bit horrid or vulgar.'

She had by this time, she could see, produced a great effect upon him; but she would have spoken the truth to herself if she had at the same moment declared that she didn't in the least care: all the more that the effect must be one of extreme perplexity. What, in it all, was visibly clear for him, none the less, was that he was tremendously glad he had met her. She held him, and he was astonished at the force of it; he was intent, immensely considerate. His elbow was on the back of the seat, and his head, with the pot-hat pushed quite back, in a boyish way, so that she really saw almost for the first time his forehead and hair, rested on the hand into which he had crumpled his gloves. 'Yes,' he assented, 'it's not a bit horrid or vulgar.'

She just hung fire a moment; then she brought out the whole truth. 'I'd do anything for you. I'd do anything for you.' Never in her life had she known anything so high and fine as this, just letting him have it and bravely and magnificently leaving it. Didn't the place, the associations and circumstances, perfectly make it sound what it was not? and wasn't that exactly the beauty?

So she bravely and magnificently left it; and little by little she felt him take it up, take it down, as if they had been on a satin sofa in a boudoir. She had never seen a boudoir, but there had been lots of boudoirs in the telegrams. What she had said, at all events, sank into him, so that after a minute he simply made a movement that had the result of placing his hand on her own – presently indeed that of her feeling herself firmly enough grasped. There was no pressure she need return, there was none she need decline; she had just sat admirably still, satisfied, for the time, with the surprise and bewilderment of the impression she made on him. His agitation was even greater, on the whole, than she had at first allowed for. 'I say, you know, you mustn't think of leaving!' he at last broke out.

'Of leaving Cocker's, you mean?'

'Yes, you must stay on there, whatever happens, and help a fellow.'

She was silent a little, partly because it was so strange and exquisite to feel him watch her as if it really mattered to him and he was almost in suspense. 'Then you *have* quite recognized what I've tried to do?' she asked.

'Why, wasn't that exactly what I dashed over from my door just now to thank you for?'

'Yes; so you said.'

'And don't you believe it?'

She looked down a moment at his hand, which continued to cover her own; whereupon he presently drew it back, rather restlessly folding his arms. Without answering his question she went on: 'Have you ever spoken of me?'

'Spoken of you?'

'Of my being there – of my knowing, and that sort of thing.'

'Oh, never to a human creature!' he eagerly declared.

She had a small drop at this, which was expressed in another

pause; after which she returned to what he had just asked her.
'Oh yes, I quite believe you like it – my always being there and
our taking things up so familiarly and successfully: if not exactly
where we left them,' she laughed, 'almost always, at least, in an
interesting place!' He was about to say something in reply to
this, but her friendly gaiety was quicker. 'You want a great
many things in life, a great many comforts and helps and
luxuries – you want everything as pleasant as possible. Therefore, so far as it's in the power of any particular person to
contribute to all that – ' She had turned her face to him smiling,
just thinking.

'Oh, see here!' But he was highly amused. 'Well, what then?'
he inquired, as if to humour her.

'Why, the particular person must never fail. We must manage
it for you somehow.'

He threw back his head, laughing out; he was really
exhilarated. 'Oh yes, somehow!'

'Well, I think we each do – don't we? – in one little way and
another and according to our limited lights. I'm pleased, at any
rate, for myself, that you are; for I assure you I've done my best.'

'You do better than any one!' He had struck a match for
another cigarette, and the flame lighted an instant his responsive,
finished face, magnifying into a pleasant grimace the kindness
with which he paid her this tribute. 'You're awfully clever, you
know; cleverer, cleverer, cleverer – !' He had appeared on the
point of making some tremendous statement; then suddenly,
puffing his cigarette and shifting almost with violence on his seat,
let it altogether fall.

17

IN spite of this drop, if not just by reason of it, she felt as if Lady
Bradeen, all but named out, had popped straight up; and she
practically betrayed her consciousness by waiting a little before
she rejoined: 'Cleverer than who?'

'Well, if I wasn't afraid you'd think I swagger, I should say – than anybody! If you leave your place there, where shall you go?' he more gravely demanded.

'Oh, too far for you ever to find me!'

'I'd find you anywhere.'

The tone of this was so still more serious that she had but her one acknowledgement. 'I'd do anything for you – I'd do anything for you,' she repeated. She had already, she felt, said it all; so what did anything more, anything less, matter? That was the very reason indeed why she could, with a lighter note, ease him generously of any awkwardness produced by solemnity, either his own or hers. 'Of course it must be nice for you to be able to think there are people all about who feel in such a way.'

In immediate appreciation of this, however, he only smoked without looking at her. 'But you don't want to give up your present work?' he at last inquired. 'I mean you *will* stay in the post-office?'

'Oh yes; I think I've a genius for that.'

'Rather! No one can touch you.' With this he turned more to her again. 'But you can get, with a move, greater advantages?'

'I can get, in the suburbs, cheaper lodgings. I live with my mother. We need some space; and there's a particular place that has other inducements.'

He just hesitated. 'Where is it?'

'Oh, quite out of *your* way. You'd never have time.'

'But I tell you I'd go anywhere. Don't you believe it?'

'Yes. for once or twice. But you'd soon see it wouldn't do for you.'

He smoked and considered; seemed to stretch himself a little and, with his legs out, surrender himself comfortably. 'Well, well, well – I believe everything you say. I take it from you – anything you like – in the most extraordinary way.' It struck her certainly – and almost without bitterness – that the way in which she was already, as if she had been an old friend, arranging for him and preparing the only magnificence she could muster, was quite the most extraordinary. 'Don't, *don't* go!' he presently went on. 'I shall miss you too horribly!'

'So that you just put it to me as a definite request?' – oh, how she tried to divest this of all sound of the hardness of bargaining!

That ought to have been easy enough, for what was she arranging to get? Before he could answer she had continued: 'To be perfectly fair, I should tell you I recognize at Cocker's certain strong attractions. All you people come. I like all the horrors.'

'The horrors?'

'Those you all – you know the set I mean, *your* set – show me with as good a conscience as if I had no more feeling than a letter-box.'

He looked quite excited at the way she put it. 'Oh, they don't know!'

'Don't know I'm not stupid? No, how should they?'

'Yes, how should they?' said the Captain sympathetically. 'But isn't "horrors" rather strong?'

'What you *do* is rather strong!' the girl promptly returned.

'What *I* do?'

'Your extravagance, your selfishness, your immorality, your crimes,' she pursued, without heeding his expression.

'I *say*!' – her companion showed the queerest stare.

'I like them, as I tell you – I revel in them. But we needn't go into that,' she quietly went on; 'for all I get out if it is the harmless pleasure of knowing. I know, I know, I know!' – she breathed it ever so gently.

'Yes; that's what has been between us,' he answered much more simply.

She could enjoy his simplicity in silence, and for a moment she did so. 'If I do stay because you want it – and I'm rather capable of that – there are two or three things I think you ought to remember. One is, you know, that I'm there sometimes for days and weeks together without your ever coming.'

'Oh, I'll come every day!' he exclaimed.

She was on the point, at this, of imitating with her hand his movement of shortly before; but she checked herself, and there was no want of effect in the tranquillizing way in which she said: 'How can you? How can you?' He had, too manifestly, only to look at it there, in the vulgarly animated gloom, to see that he couldn't; and at this point, by the mere action of his silence, everything they had so definitely not named, the whole presence round which they had been circling became a part of their reference, settled solidly between them. It was as if then, for a minute, they sat and saw it all in each other's eyes, saw so much that there was no need of a transition for sounding it at last. 'Your danger, your danger – !' Her voice indeed trembled with it, and she could only, for the moment, again leave it so.

During this moment he leaned back on the bench, meeting her in silence and with a face that grew more strange. It grew so strange that, after a further instant, she got straight up. She stood there as if their talk were now over, and he just sat and watched her. It was as if now – owing to the third person they had brought in – they must be careful; so that the most he could finally say was: 'That's where it is!'

'That's where it is!' the girl as guardedly replied. He sat still, and she added: 'I won't abandon you. Good-bye.'

'Good-bye?' – he appealed, but without moving.

'I don't quite see my way, but I won't abandon you,' she repeated. 'There. Good-bye.'

It brought him with a jerk to his feet, tossing away his cigarette. His poor face was flushed. 'See here – see here!'

'No, I won't; but I must leave you now,' she went on as if not hearing him.

'See here – see here!' He tried, from the bench, to take her hand again.

But that definitely settled it for her: this would, after all, be as bad as his asking her to supper. 'You mustn't come with me – no, no!'

He sank back, quite blank, as if she had pushed him. 'I mayn't see you home?'

'No, no; let me go.' He looked almost as if she had struck him, but she didn't care; and the manner in which she spoke – it was literally as if she were angry – had the force of a command. 'Stay where you are!'

'See here – see here!' he nevertheless pleaded.

'I won't abandon you!' she cried once more – this time quite with passion; on which she got away from him as fast as she could and left him staring after her.

18

MR MUDGE had lately been so occupied with their famous 'plans' that he had neglected, for a while, the question of her transfer; but down at Bournemouth, which had found itself selected as the field of the recreation by process consisting, it seemed, exclusively of innumerable pages of the neatest arithmetic in a very greasy but most orderly little pocket-book, the distracting possible melted away – the fleeting irremediable ruled the scene. The plans, hour by hour, were simply superseded, and it was much of a rest to the girl, as she sat on the pier and overlooked the sea and the company, to see them evaporate in rosy fumes and to feel that from moment to moment there was less left to cipher about. The week proved blissfully fine, and her mother, at their lodgings – partly to her embarrassment and partly to her relief – struck up with the landlady an alliance that left the younger couple a great deal of freedom. This relative took her pleasure of a week at Bournemouth in a stuffy back- kitchen and endless talks; to that degree even that Mr Mudge himself – habitually inclined indeed to a scrutiny of all mysteries and to seeing, as he sometimes admitted, too much in things – made remarks on it as he sat on the cliff with his betrothed, or on the decks of steamers that conveyed them, close-packed items in terrific totals of enjoyment, to the Isle of Wight and the Dorset coast.

He had a lodging in another house, where he had speedily learned the importance of keeping his eyes open, and he made no secret of his suspecting that sinister mutual connivances might spring, under the roof of his companions, from unnatural sociabilities. At the same time he fully recognized that, as a source of anxiety, not to say of expense, his future mother-in-law would have weighted them more in accompanying their steps than in giving her hostess, in the interest of the tendency they considered that they never mentioned, equivalent pledges as

to the tea-caddy and the jam-pot. These were the questions –
these indeed the familiar commodities – that he had now to put
into the scales; and his betrothed had, in consequence, during her
holiday, the odd, and yet pleasant and almost languid, sense of
an anticlimax. She had become conscious of an extraordinary
collapse, a surrender to stillness and to retrospect. She cared
neither to walk nor to sail; it was enough for her to sit on
benches and wonder at the sea and taste the air and not be at
Cocker's and not see the counter-clerk. She still seemed to wait
for something – something in the key of the immense discus-
sions that had mapped out their little week of idleness on the
scale of a world-atlas. Something came at last, but without
perhaps appearing quite adequately to crown the monument.

Preparation and precaution were, however, the natural flowers
of Mr Mudge's mind, and in proportion as these things declined
in one quarter they inevitably bloomed elsewhere. He could
always, at the worst, have on Tuesday the project of their taking
the Swanage boat on Thursday, and on Thursday that of their
ordering minced kidneys on Saturday. He had, moreover, a
constant gift of inexorable inquiry as to where and what they
should have gone and have done if they had not been exactly as
they were. He had in short his resources, and his mistress had
never been so conscious of them; on the other hand they had
never interefered so little with her own. She liked to be as she
was – if it could only have lasted. She could accept even without
bitterness a rigour of economy so great that the little fee paid for
admission to the pier had to be balanced against other delights.
The people at Ladle's and at Thrupp's had *their* ways of amusing
themselves, whereas she had to sit and hear Mr Mudge talk of
what he might do if he didn't take a bath, or of the bath he
might take if he only hadn't taken something else. He was
always with her now, of course, always beside her; she saw him
more than 'hourly', more than ever yet, more even than he had
planned she should do at Chalk Farm. She preferred to sit at the
far end, away from the band and the crowd; as to which she had
frequent differences with her friend, who reminded her often
that they could have only in the thick of it the sense of the
money they were getting back. That had little effect on her, for
she got back her money by seeing many things, the things of the

past year, fall together and connect themselves, undergo the happy relegation that transforms melancholy and misery, passion and effort, into experience and knowledge.

She liked having done with them, as she assured herself she had practically done, and the strange thing was that she neither missed the procession now nor wished to keep her place for it. It had become there, in the sun and the breeze and the sea-smell, a far-away story, a picture of another life. If Mr Mudge himself liked processions, liked them at Bournemouth and on the pier quite as much as at Chalk Farm or anywhere, she learned after a little not to be worried by this perpetual counting of the figures that made them up. There were dreadful women in particular, usually fat and in men's caps and white shoes, whom he could never let alone – not that *she* cared; it was not the great world, the world of Cocker's and Ladle's and Thrupp's, but it offered an endless field to his faculties of memory, philosophy, and frolic. She had never accepted him so much, never arranged so successfully for making him chatter while she carried on secret con- versations. Her talks were with herself; and if they both practised a great thrift, she had quite mastered that of merely spending words enough to keep him imperturbably and continuously going.

He was charmed with the panorama, not knowing – or at any rate not at all showing that he knew – what far other images peopled her mind than the women in the navy caps and the shopboys in the blazers. His observations on these types, his general interpretation of the show, brought home to her the prospect of Chalk Farm. She wondered sometimes that he should have derived so little illumination, during his period, from the society at Cocker's. But one evening, as their holiday cloudlessly waned, he gave her such a proof of his quality as might have made her ashamed of her small reserves. He brought out something that, in all his overflow, he had been able to keep back till other matters were disposed of. It was the announce- ment that he was at last ready to marry – that he saw his way. A rise at Chalk Farm had been offered him; he was to be taken into the business, bringing with him a capital the estimation of which by other parties constituted the handsomest recognition yet made of the head on his shoulders. Therefore their waiting was over — it could be a question of a near date. They would settle this date before going back, and he meanwhile had his eye on a sweet little home. He would take her to see it on their first Sunday.

19

HIS having kept this great news for the last, having had such a card up his sleeve and not floated it out in the current of his chatter and the luxury of their leisure, was one of those incalculable strokes by which he could still affect her; the kind of thing that reminded her of the latent force that had ejected the drunken soldier — an example of the profundity of which his promotion was the proof. She listened a while in silence, on this occasion, to the wafted strains of the music; she took it in as she had not quite done before that her future was now constituted. Mr Mudge was distinctly her fate; yet at this moment she turned her face quite away from him, showing him so long a mere quarter of her cheek that she at last again heard his voice. He couldn't see a pair of tears that were partly the reason of her delay to give him the assurance he required; but he expressed at a venture the hope that she had had her fill of Cocker's.

She was finally able to turn back. 'Oh, quite. There's nothing going on. No one comes but the Americans at Thrupp's, and *they* don't do much. They don't seem to have a secret in the world.'

'Then the extraordinary reason you've been giving me for holding on there has ceased to work?'

She thought a moment. 'Yes, that one. I've seen the thing through — I've got them all in my pocket.'

'So you're ready to come?'

For a little, again, she made no answer. 'No, not yet, all the same. I've still got a reason — a different one.'

He looked her all over as if it might have been something she kept in her mouth or her glove or under her jacket — something she was even sitting upon. 'Well, I'll have it, please.'

'I went out the other night and sat in the Park with a gentleman,' she said at last.

Nothing was ever seen like his confidence in her; and she wondered a little now why it didn't irritate her. It only gave her ease and space, as she felt, for telling him the whole truth that no one knew. It had arrived at present at her really wanting to do that, and yet to do it not in the least for Mr Mudge, but altogether and only for herself. This truth filled out for her there the whole experience she was about to relinquish, suffused and coloured it as a picture that she should keep and that, describe it as she might, no one but herself would ever really see. Moreover she had no desire whatever to make Mr Mudge jealous; there would be no amusement in it, for the amusement she had lately known had spoiled her for lower pleasures. There were even no materials for it. The odd thing was that she never doubted that, properly handled, his passion was poisonable; what had happened was that he had cannily selected a partner with no poison to distil. She read then and there that she should never interest herself in anybody as to whom some other sentiment, some superior view, wouldn't be sure to interfere, for him, with jealousy. 'And what did you get out of that?' he asked with a concern that was not in the least for his honour.

'Nothing but a good chance to promise him I wouldn't forsake him. He's one of my customers.'

'Then it's for him not to forsake *you*.'

'Well, he won't. It's all right. But I must keep on as long as he may want me.'

'Want you to sit with him in the Park?'

'He may want me for that – but I shan't. I rather liked it, but once, under the circumstances, is enough. I can do better for him in another manner.'

'And what manner, pray?'

'Well, elsewhere.'

'Elsewhere? – I *say*!'

This was an ejaculation used also by Captain Everard, but, oh, with what a different sound! 'You needn't "say" – there's nothing to be said. And yet you ought perhaps to know.'

'Certainly I ought. But *what* – up to now?'

'Why, exactly what I told him. That I would do anything for him.'

'What do you mean by "anything"?'

'Everything.'

Mr Mudge's immediate comment on this statement was to draw from his pocket a crumpled paper containing the remains of half a pound of 'sundries'. These sundries had figured conspicuously in his prospective sketch of their tour, but it was only at the end of three days that they had defined themselves unmistakably as chocolate-creams. 'Have another? – *that* one,' he said. She had another, but not the one he indicated, and then he continued: 'What took place afterwards?'

'Afterwards?'

'What did you do when you told him you would do everything?'

'I simply came away.'

'Out of the Park?'

'Yes, leaving him there. I didn't let him follow me.'

'Then what did you let him do?'

'I didn't let him do anything.'

Mr Mudge considered an instant. 'Then what did you go there for?' His tone was even slightly critical.

'I didn't quite know at the time. It was simply to be with him, I suppose – just once. He's in danger, and I wanted him to know I know it. It makes meeting him – at Cocker's, for it's that I want to stay on for – more interesting.'

'It makes it mighty interesting for *me*!' Mr Mudge freely declared. 'Yet he didn't follow you?' he asked. '*I* would!'

'Yes, of course. That was the way you began, you know. You're awfully inferior to him.'

'Well, my dear, you're not inferior to anybody. You've got a cheek! What is he in danger of?'

'Of being found out. He's in love with a lady – and it isn't right – and *I've* found him out.'

'That'll be a look-out for *me*!' Mr Mudge joked. 'You mean she has a husband?'

'Never mind what she has! They're in awful danger, but his is the worst, because he's in danger from her too.'

'Like me from you – the woman *I* love? If he's in the same

funk as me – '

'He's in a worse one. He's not only afraid of the lady – he's afraid of other things.'

Mr Mudge selected another chocolate-cream. 'Well, I'm only afraid of one! But how in the world can you help this party?'

'I don't know – perhaps not at all. But so long as there's a chance – '

'You won't come away?'

'No, you've got to wait for me.'

Mr Mudge enjoyed what was in his mouth. 'And what will he give you?'

'Give me?'

'If you do help him.'

'Nothing. Nothing in all the wide world.'

'Then what will he give *me*?' Mr Mudge inquired. 'I mean for waiting.'

The girl thought a moment; then she got up to walk. 'He never heard of you,' she replied.

'You haven't mentioned me?'

'We never mention anything. What I've told you is just what I've found out.'

Mr Mudge, who had remained on the bench, looked up at her; she often preferred to be quiet when he proposed to walk, but now that he seemed to wish to sit she had a desire to move.

'But you haven't told me what *he* has found out.'

She considered her lover. 'He'd never find *you*, my dear!'

Her lover, still on his seat, appealed to her in something of the attitude in which she had left Captain Everard, but the impression was not the same. 'Then where do I come in?'

'You don't come in at all. That's just the beauty of it!' – and with this she turned to mingle with the multitude collected round the band. Mr Mudge presently overtook her and drew her arm into his own with a quiet force that expressed the serenity of possession; in consonance with which it was only when they parted for the night at her door that he referred again to what she had told him.

'Have you seen him since?'

'Since the night in the Park? No, not once.'

'Oh, what a cad!' said Mr Mudge.

20

IT was not till the end of October that she saw Captain Everard again, and on that occasion – the only one of all the series on which hindrance had been so utter – no communication with him proved possible. She had made out, even from the cage, that it was a charming golden day: a patch of hazy autumn sunlight lay across the sanded floor and also, higher up, quickened into brightness a row of ruddy bottled syrups. Work was slack and the place in general empty; the town, as they said in the cage, had not waked up, and the feeling of the day likened itself to something that in happier conditions she would have thought of romantically as St Martin's summer. The counter-clerk had gone to his dinner; she herself was busy with arrears of postal jobs, in the midst of which she became aware that Captain Everard had apparently been in the shop a minute and that Mr Buckton had already seized him.

He had, as usual, half a dozen telegrams; and when he saw that she saw him and their eyes met, he gave, in bowing to her, an exaggerated laugh in which she read a new consciousness. It was a confession of awkwardness; it seemed to tell her that of course he knew he ought better to have kept his head, ought to have been clever enough to wait, on some pretext, till he should have found her free. Mr Buckton was a long time with him, and her attention was soon demanded by other visitors; so that nothing passed between them but the fulness of their silence. The look she took from him was his greeting, and the other one a simple sign of the eyes sent her before going out. The only token they exchanged, therefore, was his tacit assent to her wish that, since they couldn't attempt a certain frankness, they should attempt nothing at all. This was her intense preference; she could be as still and cold as any one when that was the sole solution.

Yet, more than any contact hitherto achieved, these counted instants struck her as marking a step: they were built so – just in the mere flash – on the recognition of his now definitely knowing what it was she would do for him. The 'anything, anything' she had uttered in the Park went to and fro between them and under the poked-out chins that interposed. It had all at last even put on the air of their not needing now clumsily to manoeuvre to converse: their former little postal make-believes, the intense implications of questions and answers and change, had become in the light of the personal fact, of their having had their moment, a possibility comparatively poor. It was as if they had met for all time – it exerted on their being in presence again an influence so prodigious. When she watched herself, in the memory of that night, walk away from him as if she were making an end, she found something too pitiful in the primness of such a gait. Hadn't she precisely established on the part of each a consciousness that could end only with death?

It must be admitted that, in spite of this brave margin, an irritation, after he had gone, remained with her; a sense that presently became one with a still sharper hatred of Mr Buckton, who, on her friend's withdrawal, had retired with the telegrams to the sounder and left her the other work. She knew indeed she should have a chance to see them, when she would, on file; and she was divided, as the day went on, between the two impressions of all that was lost and all that was re-asserted. What beset her above all, and as she had almost never known it before, was the desire to bound straight out, to overtake the autumn afternoon before it passed away for ever and hurry off to the Park and perhaps be with him there again on a bench. It became, for an hour, a fantastic vision with her that he might just have gone to sit and wait for her. She could almost hear him, through the tick of the sounder, scatter with his stick, in his impatience, the fallen leaves of October. Why should such a vision seize her at this particular moment with such a shake? There was a time – from four to five – when she could have cried with happiness and rage.

Business quickened, it seemed, towards five, as if the town did wake up; she had therefore more to do, and she went through it with little sharp stampings and jerkings: she made the crisp postal-orders fairly snap while she breathed to herself: 'It's the last day – the last day!' The last day of what? She couldn't have told. All she knew now was that if she *were* out of the cage she wouldn't in the least have minded, this time, its not yet being dark. She would have gone straight towards Park Chambers and have hung about there till no matter when. She would have waited, stayed, rung, asked, have gone in, sat on the stairs. What the day was the last of was probably, to her strained inner sense, the group of golden ones, of any occasion for seeing the hazy sunshine slant at the angle into the smelly shop, of any range of chances for his wishing still to repeat to her the two words that, in the Park, she had scarcely let him bring out. 'See here – see here!' – the sound of these two words had been with her perpetually; but it was in her ears today without mercy, with a loudness that grew and grew. What was it they then expressed? What was it he had wanted her to see? She seemed, whatever it was, perfectly to see it now – to see that if she should just chuck the whole thing, should have a great and beautiful courage, he would somehow make everything up to her. When the clock struck five she was on the very point of saying to Mr Buckton that she was deadly ill and rapidly getting worse. This annouce-ment was on her lips, and she had quite composed the pale, hard face she would offer him: 'I can't stop – I must go home. If I feel better, later on, I'll come back. I'm very sorry, but I *must* go.' At that instant Captain Everard once more stood there, producing in her agitated spirit, by his real presence, the strangest, quickest revolution. He stopped her off without knowing it, and by the time he had been a minute in the shop she felt that she was saved.

That was from the first minute what she called it to herself. There were again other persons with whom she was occupied, and again the situation could only be expressed by their silence. It was expressed, in fact, in a larger phrase than ever yet, for her eyes now spoke to him with a kind of supplication. 'Be quiet, be quiet!' they pleaded; and they saw his own reply: 'I'll do whatever you say; I won't even look at you – see, see!' They kept conveying thus, with the friendliest liberality, that they wouldn't look, quite positively wouldn't. What she was to see was that he hovered at the other end of the counter, Mr Buckton's end, surrendered himself again to that frustration. It quickly proved so great indeed that what she was to see further

was how he turned away before he was attended to, and hung
off, waiting, smoking, looking about the shop; how he went
over to Mr Cocker's own counter and appeared to price things,
gave in fact presently two or three orders and put down money,
stood there a long time with his back to her, considerately
abstaining from any glance round to see if she was free. It at last
came to pass in this way that he had remained in the shop longer
than she had ever yet known him to do, and that, nevertheless,
when he did turn about she could see him time himself – she
was freshly taken up – and cross straight to her postal sub-
ordinate, whom some one else had released. He had in his hand
all this while neither letters nor telegrams, and now that he was
close to her – for she was close to the counter-clerk – it brought
her heart into her mouth merely to see him look at her neighbour and open his lips. She was too nervous to bear it. He asked
for a Post-Office Guide, and the young man whipped out a new
one; whereupon he said that he wished not to purchase, but only
to consult one a moment; with which, the copy kept on loan
being produced, he once more wandered off.

What was he doing to her? What did he want of her? Well,
it was just the aggravation of his 'See here!' She felt at this
moment strangely and portentously afraid of him – had in her
ears the hum of a sense that, should it come to that kind of
tension, she must fly on the spot to Chalk Farm. Mixed with her
dread and with her reflection was the idea that, if he wanted her
so much as he seemed to show, it might be after all simply to do
for him the 'anything' she had promised, the 'everything' she
had thought it so fine to bring out to Mr Mudge. He might
want her to help him, might have some particular appeal;
though, of a truth, his manner didn't denote that – denoted, on
the contrary, an embarrassment, an indecision, something of a
desire not so much to be helped as to be treated rather more
nicely that she had treated him the other time. Yes, he
considered quite probably that he had help rather to offer than
to ask for. Still, none the less, when he again saw her free he
continued to keep away from her; when he came back with his
Guide it was Mr Buckton he caught – it was from Mr Buckton
he obtained half-a-crown's-worth of stamps.

After asking for the stamps he asked, quite as a second

thought, for a postal-order for ten shillings. What did he want with so many stamps when he wrote so few letters? How could he enclose a postal-order in a telegram? She expected him, the next thing, to go into the corner and make up one of his telegrams – half a dozen of them – on purpose to prolong his presence. She had so completely stopped looking at him that she could only guess his movements – guess even where his eyes rested. Finally she saw him make a dash that might have been towards the nook where the forms were hung; and at this she suddenly felt that she couldn't keep it up. The counter-clerk had just taken a telegram from a slavey, and, to give herself something to cover her, she snatched it out of his hand. The gesture was so violent that he gave her an odd look, and she also perceived that Mr Buckton noticed it. The latter personage, with a quick stare at her, appeared for an instant to wonder whether his snatching it in *his* turn mightn't be the thing she would least like, and she anticipated this practical criticism by the frankest glare she had ever given him. It sufficed: this time it paralysed him; and she sought with her trophy the refuge of the sounder.

21

IT was repeated the next day; it went on for three days; and at the end of that time she knew what to think. When, at the beginning, she had emerged from her temporary shelter Captain Everard had quitted the shop and he had not come again that evening, as it had struck her he possibly might – might all the more easily that there were numberless persons who came, morning and afternoon, numberless times, so that he wouldn't necessarily have attracted attention. The second day it was different and yet on the whole worse. His access to her had become possible – she felt herself even reaping the fruit of her yesterday's glare at Mr Buckton; but transacting his business with him didn't simplify – it could, in spite of the rigour of circumstance, feed so her new conviction. The rigour was tremendous, and his telegrams – not, now, mere pretexts for getting at her – were apparently genuine; yet the conviction had taken but a night to develop. It could be simply enough expressed; she had had the glimmer of it the day before in her idea that he needed no more help than she had already given; that it was help he himself was prepared to render. He had come up to town but for three or four days; he had been absolutely obliged to be absent after the other time; yet he would, now that he was face to face with her, stay on as much longer as she liked. Little by little it was thus clarified, though from the first flash of his reappearance she had read into it the real essence.

That was what the night before, at eight o'clock, her hour to go, had made her hang back and dawdle. She did last things or pretended to do them; to be in the cage had suddenly become her safety, and she was literally afraid of the alternate self who might be waiting outside. *He* might be waiting; it was he who was her alternate self, and of him she was afraid. The most extraordinary change had taken place in her from the moment of her catching the impression he seemed to have returned on purpose to give her. Just before she had done so, on that bewitched afternoon, she had seen herself approach, without a scruple, the porter at Park Chambers; then, as the effect of the rush of a consciousness quite altered, she had, on at last quitting Cocker's, gone straight home for the first time since her return from Bournemouth. She had passed his door every night for weeks, but nothing would have induced her to pass it now. This change was the tribute of her fear – the result of a change in himself as to which she needed no more explanation than his mere face vividly gave her; strange though it was to find an element of deterrence in the object that she regarded as the most beautiful in the world. He had taken it from her in the Park that night that she wanted him not to propose to her to sup; but he had put away the lesson by this time – he practically proposed supper every time he looked at her. This was what, for that matter, mainly filled the three days. He came in twice on each of these, and it was as if he came in to give her a chance to relent. That was, after all, she said to herself in the intervals, the most that he did. There were ways, she fully recognized, in which he spared her, and other particular ways as to which she meant that her silence should be full, to him, of exquisite pleading. The most particular of all was his not being outside, at the corner, when she quitted the place for the night. This he might so easily have been – so easily if he hadn't been so nice. She continued to recognize in his forbearance the fruit of her dumb supplication, and the only compensation he found for it was the harmless freedom of being able to appear to say: 'Yes, I'm in town only for three or four days, but, you know, I *would* stay on.' He struck her as calling attention each day, each hour, to the rapid ebb of time; he exaggerated to the point of putting it that there were only two days more, that there was at last, dreadfully, only one.

There were other things still that he struck her as doing with a special intention; as to the most marked of which – unless indeed it were the most obscure – she might well have marvelled that it didn't seem to her more horrid. It was either the frenzy of her imagination or the disorder of his baffled passion that gave her once or twice the vision of his putting down redundant money – sovereigns not concerned with the little payments he was perpetually making – so that she might give him some sign of helping him to slip them over to her. What was most extraordinary in his impression was the amount of excuse that, with some incoherence, she found for him. He wanted to pay her because there was nothing to pay her for. He wanted to offer her things that he knew she wouldn't take. He wanted to show her how much he respected her by giving her the supreme chance to show *him* she was respectable. Over the driest transactions, at any rate, their eyes had out these questions. On the third day he put in a telegram that had evidently something of the same point as the stray sovereigns – a message that was, in the first place, concocted, and that, on a second thought, he took back from her before she had stamped it. He had given her time to read it, and had only then bethought himself that he had better not send it. If it was not to Lady Bradeen at Twindle – where she knew her ladyship then to be – this was because an address to Doctor Buzzard at Brickwood was just as good, with the added merit of its not giving away quite so much a person whom he had still, after all, in a manner to consider. It was of course most complicated, only half lighted; but there was, discernibly enough, a scheme of communication in which Lady Bradeen at Twindle and Dr Buzzard at Brickwood were, within limits, one and the same person. The words he had shown her and then taken back consisted, at all events, of the brief but vivid phrase: 'Absolutely impossible.' The point was not that she should transmit it; the point was just that she should see it. What was absolutely impossible was that before he had settled something at Cocker's he should go either to Twindle or to Brickwood.

The logic of this, in turn, for herself, was that she could lend herself to no settlement so long as she so intensely knew. What she knew was that he was, almost under peril of life, clenched in a situation: therefore how could she also know where a poor girl in the P.O. might really stand? It was more and more between them that if he might convey to her that he was free, that everything she had seen so deep into was a closed chapter, her own case might become different for her, she might understand and meet him and listen. But he could convey nothing of the sort, and he only fidgeted and floundered in his want of power. The chapter wasn't in the least closed, not for the other party; and the other party had a pull, somehow and somewhere: this his whole attitude and expression confessed, at the same time that they entreated her not to remember and not to mind. So long as she did remember and did mind he could only circle about and go and come, doing futile things of which he was ashamed. He was ashamed of his two words to Dr Buzzard, and went out of the shop as soon as he had crumpled up the paper again and thrust it into his pocket. It had been an abject little exposure of dreadful, impossible passion. He appeared in fact to be too ashamed to come back. He had left town again, and a first week elapsed, and a second. He had had naturally to return to the real mistress of his fate; she had insisted – she knew how, and he couldn't put in another hour. There was always a day when she called time. It was known to our young friend moreover that he had now been despatching telegrams from other offices. She knew at last so much, that she had quite lost her earlier sense of merely guessing. There were no shades of distinctness – it all bounced out.

22

EIGHTEEN days elapsed, and she had begun to think it probable she should never see him again. He too then understood now: he had made out that she had secrets and reasons and impediments, that even a poor girl at the P.O. might have her complications. With the charm she had cast on him lightened by distance he had suffered a final delicacy to speak to him, had made up his mind that it would be only decent to let her alone. Never so much as during these latter days had she felt the precariousness of their relation – the happy, beautiful, untroubled original one, if it could only have been restored, – in which the public servant and the casual public only were concerned. It hung at the best by the merest silken thread, which was at the mercy of any accident and might snap at any minute. She arrived by the end of the fortnight at the highest sense of actual fitness, never doubting that her decision was now complete. She would give him a few days more to come back to her on a proper impersonal basis – for even to an embarrassing representative of the casual public a public servant with a conscience did owe something, – and then would signify to Mr Mudge that she was ready for the little home. It had been visited, in the further talk she had had with him at Bournemouth, from garret to cellar, and they had especially lingered, with their respectively darkened brows, before the niche into which it was to be broached to her mother that she was to find means to fit.

He had put it to her more definitely than before that his calculations had allowed for that dingy presence, and he had thereby marked the greatest impression he had ever made on her. It was a stroke superior even again to his handling of the drunken soldier. What she considered that, in the fact of it, she hung on at Cocker's for, was something that she could only have described as the common fairness of a last word. Her actual last

word had been, till it should be superseded, that she wouldn't
abandon her other friend, and it stuck to her, through thick and
thin, that she was still at her post and on her honour. This other
friend had shown so much beauty of conduct already that he
would surely, after all, just re-appear long enough to relieve her,
to give her something she could take away. She saw it, caught
it, at times, his parting present; and there were moments when
she felt herself sitting like a beggar with a hand held out to an
almsgiver who only fumbled. She hadn't taken the sovereigns,
but she *would* take the penny. She heard, in imagination, on the
counter, the ring of the copper. 'Don't put yourself out any
longer,' he would say, 'for so bad a case. You've done all there
is to be done. I thank and acquit and release you. Our lives take
us. I don't know much – though I have really been interested –
about yours; but I suppose you've got one. Mine, at any rate,
will take *me* – and where it will. Heigh-ho! Good-bye.' And
then once more, for the sweetest, faintest flower of all: 'Only, I
say – see here!' She had framed the whole picture with a
squareness that included also the image of how again she would
decline to 'see there', decline, as she might say, to see anywhere
or anything. Yet it befell that just in the fury of this escape she
saw more than ever.

He came back one night with a rush, near the moment of
their closing, and showed her a face so different and new, so
upset and anxious, that almost anything seemed to look out of it
but clear recognition. He poked in a telegram very much as if
the simple sense of pressure, the distress of extreme haste, had
blurred the remembrance of where in particular he was. But as
she met his eyes a light came; it broke indeed on the spot into a
positive, conscious glare. That made up for everything for it was
an instant proclamation of the celebrated 'danger'; it seemed to
pour out in a flood. 'Oh yes, here it is – it's upon me at last!
Forget, for God's sake, my having worried or bored you, and
just help me, just *save* me, by getting this off without the loss of
a second!' Something grave had clearly occurred, a crisis declared
itself. She recognized immediately the person to whom the
telegram was addressed – the Miss Dolman, of Parade Lodge, to
whom Lady Bradeen had wired, at Dover, on the last occasion,
and whom she had then, with her recollection of previous

arrangements, fitted into a particular setting. Miss Dolman had figured before and not figured since, but she was now the subject of an imperative appeal. 'Absolutely necessary to see you. Take last train Victoria if you can catch it. If not, earliest morning, and answer me direct either way.'

'Reply paid?' said the girl. Mr Buckton had just departed, and the counter-clerk was at the sounder. There was no other representative of the public, and she had never yet, as it seemed to her, not even in the street or in the Park, been so alone with him.

'Oh yes, reply paid, and as sharp as possible, please.'

She affixed the stamps in a flash. 'She'll catch the train!' she then declared to him breathlessly, as if she could absolutely guarantee it.

'I don't know – I hope so. It's awfully important. So kind of you. Awfully sharp, please.' It was wonderfully innocent now, his oblivion of all but his danger. Anything else that had ever passed between them was utterly out of it. Well, she had wanted him to be impersonal!

There was less of the same need therefore, happily, for herself; yet she only took time, before she flew to the sounder, to gasp at him: 'You're in trouble?'

'Horrid, horrid – there's a row!' But they parted, on it, in the next breath; and as she dashed at the sounder, almost pushing, in her violence, the counter-clerk off the stool, she caught the bang with which, at Cocker's door, in his further precipitation, he closed the apron of the cab into which he had leaped. As he rushed off to some other precaution suggested by his alarm, his appeal to Miss Dolman flashed straight away.

But she had not, on the morrow, been in the place five minutes before he was with her again, still more discomposed and quite, now, as she said to herself, like a frightened child coming to its mother. Her companions were there, and she felt it to be remarkable how, in the presence of his agitation, his mere scared, exposed nature, she suddenly ceased to mind. It came to her as it had never come to her before that with absolute directness and assurance they might carry almost anything off. He had nothing to send – she was sure he had been wiring all over, – and yet his business was evidently huge. There was nothing but that in his eyes – not a glimmer of reference or memory. He was almost haggard with anxiety, and had clearly not slept a wink. Her pity for him would have given her any courage, and she seemed to know at last why she had been such a fool. 'She didn't come?' she panted.

'Oh yes, she came; but there has been some mistake. We want a telegram.'

'A telegram?'

'One that was sent from here ever so long ago. There was something in it that has to be recovered. Something very, *very* important, please – we want it immediately.'

He really spoke to her as if she had been some strange young woman at Knightsbridge or Paddington; but it had no other effect on her than to give her the measure of his tremendous flurry. Then it was that, above all, she felt how much she had missed in the gaps and blanks and absent answers – how much she had had to dispense with: it was black darkness now, save for this little wild red flare. So much as that she saw and possessed. One of the lovers was quaking somewhere out of town, and the other was quaking just where he stood. This was vivid enough, and after an instant she knew it was all she wanted. She wanted no detail, no fact – she wanted no nearer vision of discovery or shame. 'When was your telegram? Do you mean you sent it from here?' She tried to do the young woman at Knightsbridge.

'Oh yes, from here – several weeks ago. Five, six, seven' – he was confused and impatient, – 'don't you remember?'

'Remember?' she could scarcely keep out of her face, at the word, the strangest of smiles.

But the way he didn't catch what it meant was perhaps even stranger still. 'I mean, don't you keep the old ones?'

'For a certain time.'

'But how long?'

She thought; she *must* do the young woman, and she knew exactly what the young woman would say and, still more, wouldn't. 'Can you give me the date?'

'Oh God, no! It was some time or other in August – toward the end. It was to the same address as the one I gave you last night.'

'Oh!' said the girl, knowing at this the deepest thrill she had ever felt. It came to her there, with her eyes on his face, that she held the whole thing in her hand, held it as she held her pencil, which might have broken at that instant in her tightened grip. This made her feel like the very fountain of fate, but the emotion was such a flood that she had to press it back with all her force. That was positively the reason, again, of her flute-like Paddington tone. 'You can't give us anything a little nearer?' Her 'little' and her 'us' came straight from Paddington. These things were no false note for him – his difficulty absorbed them all. The eyes with which he pressed her, and in the depths of which she read terror and rage and literal tears, were just the same he would have shown any other prim person.

'I don't know the date. I only know the thing went from here, and just about the time I speak of. It wasn't delivered, you see. We've got to recover it.'

23

SHE was as struck with the beauty of his plural pronoun as she had judged he might be with that of her own; but she knew now so well what she was about that she could almost play with him and with her new-born joy. 'You say "about the time you speak of ". But I don't think you speak of an exact time – *do* you?'

He looked splendidly helpless. 'That's just what I want to find out. Don't you keep the old ones? – can't you look it up?'

Our young lady – still at Paddington – turned the question over. 'It wasn't delivered?'

'Yes, it *was*; yet, at the same time, don't you know? it wasn't.' He just hung back, but he brought it out. 'I mean it was intercepted, don't you know? and there was something in it.' He paused again and, as if to further his quest and woo and supplicate succes and recovery, even smiled with an effort at the agreeable that was almost ghastly and that turned the knife in her tenderness. What must be the pain of it all, of the open gulf and the throbbing fever, when this was the mere hot breath? 'We want to get what was in it – to know what it was.'

'I see – I see.' She managed just the accent they had at Paddington when they stared like dead fish. 'And you have no clue?'

'Not at all – I've the clue I've just given you.'

'Oh, the last of August?' If she kept it up long enough she would make him really angry.

'Yes, and the address, as I've said.'

'Oh, the same as last night?'

He visibly quivered, as if with a gleam of hope; but it only poured oil on her quietude, and she was still deliberate. She ranged some papers. 'Won't you look?' he went on.

'I remember your coming,' she replied.

He blinked with a new uneasiness; it might have begun to come to him, through her difference, that he was somehow different himself. 'You were much quicker then, you know!'

'So were you – you must do me that justice,' she answered with a smile. 'But let me see. Wasn't it Dover?'

'Yes, Miss Dolman – '

'Parade Lodge, Parade Terrace?'

'Exactly – thank you so awfully much!' He began to hope again. 'Then you *have* it – the other one?'

She hesitated afresh; she quite dangled him. 'It was brought by a lady?'

'Yes; and she put in by mistake something wrong. That's what we've got to get hold of!'

Heavens! what was he going to say? – flooding poor Paddington with wild betrayals! She couldn't too much, for her joy, dangle him, yet she couldn't either, for his dignity, warn or control or check him. What she found herself doing was just to treat herself to the middle way. 'It was intercepted?'

'It fell into the wrong hands. But there's something in it,' he continued to blurt out, 'that *may* be all right. That is, if it's wrong, don't you know? It's all right if it's wrong,' he remarkably explained.

What *was* he, on earth, going to say? Mr Buckton and the counter-clerk were already interested; no one *would* have the decency to come in; and she was divided between her particular terror for him and her general curiosity. Yet she already saw with what brilliancy she could add, to carry the thing off, a little false knowledge to all her real. 'I quite understand,' she said with benevolent, with almost patronizing quickness. 'The lady has forgotten what she did put.'

'Forgotten most wretchedly, and it's an immense inconvenience. It has only just been found that it didn't get there; so that if we could immediately have it − '

'Immediately?'

'Every minute counts. You *have*,' he pleaded, 'surely got them on file.'

'So that you can see it on the spot?'

'Yes, please − this very minute.' The counter rang with his knuckles, with the knob of his stick, with his panic of alarm. 'Do, *do* hunt it up!' he repeated.

'I dare say we could get it for you,' the girl sweetly returned.

'Get it?' − he looked aghast. 'When?'

'Probably by tomorrow.'

'Then it isn't here?' − his face was pitiful.

She caught only the uncovered gleams that peeped out of the blackness, and she wondered what complication, even among the most supposable, the very worst, could be bad enough to account for the degree of his terror. There were twists and turns, there were places where the screw drew blood, that she couldn't guess. She was more and more glad she didn't want to. 'It has been sent on.'

'But how do you know if you don't look?'

She gave him a smile that was meant to be, in the absolute irony of its propriety, quite divine. 'It was August 23rd, and we have nothing later here than August 27th.'

Something leaped into his face. '27th − 23rd? Then you're sure? You know?'

She felt she scarce knew what − as if she might soon be pounced upon for some lurid connection with a scandal. It was the queerest of all sensations, for she had heard, she had read, of these things, and the wealth of her intimacy with them at Cocker's might be supposed to have schooled and seasoned her. This particular one that she had really quite lived with was, after all, an old story; yet what it had been before was dim and distant beside the touch under which she now winced. Scandal? – it had never been but a silly word. Now it was a great palpable surface, and the surface was, somehow, Captain Everard's wonderful face. Deep down in his eyes was a picture, the vision of a great place like a chamber of justice, where, before a watching crowd, a poor girl, exposed but heroic, swore with a quavering voice to a document, proved an *alibi*, supplied a link. In this picture she bravely took her place. 'It was the 23rd.'

'Then can't you get it this morning – or some time today?'

She considered, still holding him with her look, which she then turned on her two companions, who were by this time unreservedly enlisted. She didn't care – not a scrap, and she glanced about for a piece of paper. With this she had to recognize the rigour of official thrift – a morsel of blackened blotter was the only loose paper to be seen. 'Have you got a card?' she said to her visitor. He was quite away from Paddington now, and the next instant, with a pocket-book in his hand, he had whipped a card out. She gave no glance at the name on it – only turned it to the other side. She continued to hold him, she felt at present, as she had never held him; and her command of her colleagues was, for the moment, not less marked. She wrote something on the back of the card and pushed it across to him.

He fairly glanced at it. 'Seven, nine, four – '

'Nine, six, one' – she obligingly completed the number. 'Is it right?' she smiled.

He took the whole thing in with a flushed intensity; then there broke out in him a visibility of relief that was simply a tremendous exposure. He shone at them all like a tall lighthouse, embracing even, for sympathy, the blinking young men. 'By all the powers – it's wrong!' And without another look, without a word of thanks, without time for anything or anybody, he turned on them the broad back of his great stature, straightened his triumphant shoulders, and strode out of the place.

She was left confronted with her habitual critics. 'If it's wrong it's all right!' she extravagantly quoted to them.

The counter-clerk was really awe-stricken. 'But how did you know, dear?'

'I remembered, love!'

Mr Buckton, on the contrary, was rude. 'And what game is that, miss?'

No happiness she had ever known came within miles of it, and some minutes elapsed before she could recall herself sufficiently to reply that it was none of his business.

24

IF life at Cocker's, with the dreadful drop of August, had lost something of its savour, she had not been slow to infer that a heavier blight had fallen on the graceful industry of Mrs Jordan. With Lord Rye and Lady Ventnor and Mrs Bubb all out of town, with the blinds down on all the homes of luxury, this ingenious woman might well have found her wonderful taste left quite on her hands. She bore up, however, in a way that began by exciting much of her young friend's esteem; they perhaps even more frequently met as the wine of life flowed less free from other sources, and each, in the lack of better diversion, carried on with more mystification for the other an intercourse that consisted not a little of peeping out and drawing back. Each waited for the other to commit herself, each profusely curtained for the other the limits of low horizons. Mrs Jordan was indeed probably the more reckless skirmisher; nothing could exceed her frequent incoherence unless it was indeed her occasional bursts of confidence. Her account of her private affairs rose and fell like a flame in the wind – sometimes the bravest bonfire and sometimes a handful of ashes. This our young woman took to be an effect of the position, at one moment and another, of the famous door of the great world. She had been struck in one of her ha'penny volumes with the translation of a French proverb according to which a door had to be either open or shut; and it seemed a part of the precariousness of Mrs Jordan's life that hers mostly managed to be neither. There had been occasions when it appeared to gape wide – fairly to woo her across its threshold; there had been others, of an order distinctly disconcerting, when it was all but banged in her face. On the whole, however, she had evidently not lost heart; these still belonged to the class of things in spite of which she looked well. She intimated that the profits of her trade had swollen so as to float her through any state of the tide, and she had, beside this, a hundred profundities and explanations.

She rose superior, above all, on the happy fact that there were always gentlemen in town and that gentlemen were her greatest admirers; gentlemen from the City in especial – as to whom she was full of information about the passion and pride excited in such breasts by the objects of her charming commerce. The City men *did*, in short, go in for flowers. There was a certain type of awfully smart stockbroker – Lord Rye called them Jews and 'bounders', but she didn't care – whose extravagance, she more than once threw out, had really, if one had any conscience, to be forcibly restrained. It was not perhaps a pure love of beauty: it was a matter of vanity and a sign of business; they wished to crush their rivals, and that was one of their weapons. Mrs Jordan's shrewdness was extreme; she knew, in any case, her customer – she dealt, as she said, with all sorts; and it was, at the worst, a race for her – a race even in the dull months – from one set of chambers to another. And then, after all, there were also still the ladies; the ladies of stockbroking circles were perpetually up and down. They were not quite perhaps Mrs Bubb or Lady Ventnor; but you couldn't tell the difference unless you quarrelled with them, and then you knew it only by their making-up sooner. These ladies formed the branch of her subject on which she most swayed in the breeze; to that degree that her confidant had ended with an inference or two tending to banish regret for opportunities not embraced. There were indeed tea-gowns that Mrs Jordan described – but tea-gowns were not the whole of respectability, and it was odd that a clergyman's widow should sometimes speak as if she almost thought so. She came back, it was true, unfailingly, to Lord Rye, never, evidently, quite losing sight of him even on the longest excursions. That he was kindness itself had become in fact the very moral it all pointed – pointed in strange flashes of the poor woman's nearsighted eyes. She launched at her young friend many portentous looks, solemn heralds of some extraordinary communication. The communication itself, from week to week, hung fire; but it was to the facts over which it hovered that she owed her power of going on. 'They *are*, in one way *and* another,' she often emphasized, 'a tower of strength'; and as the allusion was to the aristocracy, the girl could quite wonder why, if they were so in 'one' way, they should require to be so in two. She thoroughly knew, however, how many ways Mrs Jordan counted in. It all meant simply that her fate was pressing her close. If that fate was to be sealed at the matrimonial altar it was perhaps not remarkable that she shouldn't came all at once to the scratch of overwhelming a mere telegraphist. It would necessarily present to such a person a prospect of regretful sacrifice. Lord Rye – if it *was* Lord Rye – wouldn't be 'kind' to a nonentity of that sort, even though people quite as good had been.

One Sunday afternoon in November they went, by arrangement, to church together; after which – on the inspiration of the moment; the arrangement had not included it – they proceeded to Mrs Jordan's lodging in the region of Maida Vale. She had raved to her friend about her service of predilection; she was excessively 'high', and had more than once wished to introduce the girl to the same comfort and privilege. There was a thick brown fog, and Maida Vale tasted of acrid smoke; but they had been sitting among chants and incense and wonderful music, during which, though the effect of such things on her mind was great, our young lady had indulged in a series of reflections but indirectly related to them. One of these was the result of Mrs Jordan's having said to her on the way, and with a certain fine significance, that Lord Rye had been some time in town. She had spoken as if it were a circumstance to which little required to be added – as if the bearing of such an item on her life might easily be grasped. Perhaps it was the wonder of whether Lord Rye wished to marry her that made her guest, with thoughts straying to that quarter, quite determine that some other nuptials also should take place at St Julian's. Mr Mudge was still an attendant at his Wesleyan chapel, but this was the least of her worries – it had never even vexed her enough for her to so much as name it to Mrs Jordan. Mr Mudge's form of worship was one of several things – they made up in superiority and beauty for what they wanted in number – that she had long ago settled he should take from her, and she had now moreover for the first time definitely established her own. Its principal feature was that it was to be the same as that of Mrs Jordan and Lord Rye; which was indeed very much what she said to her hostess as they sat together later on. The brown fog was in this hostess's little parlour, where it acted as a postponement of the question of there being, besides, anything else than the teacups and a pewter pot, and a very black little fire, and a paraffin lamp without a shade. There was at any rate no sign of a flower; it was not for herself Mrs Jordan gathered sweets. The girl waited till they had had a cup of tea – waited for the announcement that she fairly believed her friend had, this time, possessed herself of her formally at last to make; but nothing came, after the interval, save a little poke at the fire, which was like the clearing of a throat for a speech.

25

'I THINK you must have heard me speak of Mr Drake?' Mrs Jordan had never looked so queer, nor her smile so suggestive of a large benevolent bite.

'Mr Drake? Oh yes; isn't he a friend of Lord Rye?'

'A great and trusted friend. Almost – I may say – a loved friend.'

Mrs Jordan's 'almost' had such an oddity that her companion was moved, rather flippantly perhaps, to take it up. 'Don't people as good as love their friends when they "trust" them?'

It pulled up a little the eulogist of Mr Drake. 'Well, my dear, I love *you* – '

'But you don't trust me?' the girl unmercifully asked.

Again Mrs Jordan paused – still she looked queer. 'Yes,' she replied with a certain austerity; 'that's exactly what I'm about to give you rather a remarkable proof of.' The sense of its being remarkable was already so strong that, while she bridled a little, this held her auditor in a momentary muteness of submission. 'Mr Drake has rendered his lordship, for several years, services that his lordship has highly appreciated and that make it all the more – a – unexpected that they should, perhaps a little suddenly, separate.'

'Separate?' Our young lady was mystified, but she tried to be interested; and she already saw that she had put the saddle on the wrong horse. She had heard something of Mr Drake, who was a member of his lordship's circle – the member with whom, apparently, Mrs Jordan's avocations had most happened to throw her. She was only a little puzzled at the 'separation'. 'Well, at any rate,' she smiled, 'if they separate as friends – !'

'Oh, his lordship takes the greatest interest in Mr Drake's future. He'll do anything for him; he has in fact just done a great deal. There *must*, you know, be changes – !'

'No one knows it better than I,' the girl said. She wished to draw her interlocutress out. 'There will be changes enough for me.'

'You're leaving Cocker's?'

The ornament of that establishment waited a moment to answer, and then it was indirect. 'Tell me what *you're* doing.'

'Well, what will you think of it?'

'Why, that you've found the opening you were always so sure of.'

Mrs Jordan, on this, appeared to muse with embarrassed intensity. 'I was always sure, yes – and yet I often wasn't!'

'Well, I hope you're sure now. Sure, I mean, of Mr Drake.'

'Yes, my dear, I think I may say I *am*. I kept him going till I was.'

'Then he's yours?'

'My very own.'

'How nice! And awfully rich?' our young woman went on.

Mrs Jordan showed promptly enough that she loved for higher things. 'Awfully handsome – six foot two. And he *has* put by.'

'Quite like Mr Mudge, then!' that gentleman's friend rather desperately exclaimed.

'Oh, not *quite*!' Mr Drake's was ambiguous about it, but the name of Mr Mudge had evidently given her some sort of stimulus. 'He'll have more opportunity now, at any rate. He's going to Lady Bradeen.'

'To Lady Bradeen?' This was bewilderment. ' "Going – "?'

The girl had seen, from the way Mrs Jordan looked at her, that the effect of the name had been to make her let something out. 'Do you know her?'

She hesitated; then she found her feet. 'Well, you'll remember I've often told you that if you have grand clients, I have them too.'

'Yes,' said Mrs Jordan; 'but the great difference is that you hate yours, whereas I really love mine. *Do* you know Lady Bradeen?' she pursued.

'Down to the ground! She's always in and out.'

Mrs Jordan's foolish eyes confessed, in fixing themselves on this sketch, to a degree of wonder and even of envy. But she bore up and, with a certain gaiety, 'Do you hate *her*?' she demanded.

Her visitor's reply was prompt. 'Dear no! – not nearly so much as some of them. She's too outrageously beautiful.'

Mrs Jordan continued to gaze. 'Outrageously?'

'Well, yes; deliciously.' What was really delicious was Mrs Jordan's vagueness. 'You don't know her – you've not seen her?' her guest lightly continued.

'No, but I've heard a great deal about her.'

'So have I!' our young lady exclaimed.

Mrs Jordan looked an instant as if she suspected her good faith or at least her seriousness. 'You know some friend – ?'

'Of Lady Bradeen's? Oh yes – I know one.'

'Only one?'

The girl laughed out. 'Only one – but he's so intimate.'

Mrs Jordan just hesitated. 'He's a gentleman?'

'Yes, he's not a lady.'

Her interlocutress appeared to muse. 'She's immensely surrounded.'

'She *will* be – with Mr Drake!'

Mrs Jordan's gaze became strangely fixed. 'Is she *very* good-looking?'

'The handsomest person I know.'

Mrs Jordan continued to contemplate. 'Well, *I* know some

beauties.' Then, with her odd jerkiness, 'Do you think she looks *good*?' she inquired.

'Because that's not always the case with the good-looking?' – the other took it up. 'No, indeed, it isn't: that's one thing Cocker's has taught me. Still, there are some people who have everything. Lady Bradeen, at any rate, has enough: eyes and a nose and a mouth, a complexion, a figure – '

'A figure?' Mrs Jordan almost broke in.

'A figure, a head of hair!' The girl made a little conscious motion that seemed to let the hair all down, and her companion watched the wonderful show. 'But Mr Drake *is* another – ?'

'Another?' – Mrs Jordan's thoughts had to come back from a distance.

'Of her ladyship's admirers. He's "going", you say, to her?'

At this Mrs Jordan really faltered. 'She has engaged him.'

'Engaged him?' – our young woman was quite at sea.

'In the same capacity as Lord Rye.'

'And was Lord Rye engaged?'

26

MRS JORDAN looked away from her now – looked, she thought, rather injured and, as if trifled with, even a little angry. The mention of Lady Bradeen had frustrated for a while the convergence of our heroine's thoughts; but with this impression of her old friend's combined impatience and diffidence they began again to whirl round her, and continued it till one of them appeared to dart at her, out of the dance, as if with a sharp peck. It came to her with a lively shock, with a positive sting, that Mr Drake was – could it be possible? With the idea she found herself afresh on the edge of laughter, of a sudden and strange perversity of mirth. Mr Drake loomed, in a swift image, before her; such a figure as she had seen in open doorways of houses in Cocker's quarter – majestic, middle-aged, erect, flanked on either side by a footman and taking the name of a visitor. Mr

Drake then verily *was* a person who opened the door! Before she had time, however, to recover from the effect of her evocation, she was offered a vision which quite engulphed it. It was communicated to her somehow that the face with which she had seen it rise prompted Mrs Jordan to dash, at a venture, at something that might attenuate criticism. 'Lady Bradeen is re-arranging – she's going to be married.'

'Married?' The girl echoed it ever so softly, but there it was at last.

'Didn't you know it?'

She summoned all her sturdiness. 'No, she hasn't told me.'

'And her friends – haven't they?'

'I haven't seen any of them lately. I'm not so fortunate as *you*.'

Mrs Jordan gathered herself. 'Then you haven't even heard of Lord Bradeen's death?'

Her comrade, unable for a moment to speak, gave a slow headshake. 'You know it from Mr Drake?' It was better surely not to learn things at all than to learn them by the butler.

'She tells him everything.'

'And he tells *you* – I see.' Our young lady got up; recovering her muff and her gloves, she smiled. 'Well, I haven't, unfortunately, any Mr Drake. I congratulate you with all my heart. Even without your sort of assistance, however, there's a trifle here and there that I do pick up. I gather that if she's to marry any one, it must quite necessarily be my friend.'

Mrs Jordan was now also on her feet. 'Is Captain Everard your friend?'

The girl considered, drawing on a glove. 'I saw, at one time, an immense deal of him.'

Mrs Jordan looked hard at the glove, but she had not, after all, waited for that to be sorry it was not cleaner. 'What time was that?'

'It must have been the time you were seeing so much of Mr Drake.' She had now fairly taken it in: the distinguished person Mrs Jordan was to marry would answer bells and put on coals and superintend, at least, the cleaning of boots for the other distinguished person whom *she* might – well, whom she might have had, if she had wished, so much more to say to. 'Good-bye,' she added; 'good-bye.'

Mrs Jordan, however, again taking her muff from her, turned it over, brushed it off, and thoughtfully peeped into it. 'Tell me this before you go. You spoke just now of your own changes. Do you mean that Mr Mudge – ?'

'Mr Mudge has had great patience with me – he has brought me at last to the point. We're to be married next month and have a nice little home. But he's only a grocer, you know' – the girl met her friend's intent eyes – 'so that I'm afraid that, with the set you've got into, you won't see your way to keep up our friendship.'

Mrs Jordan for a moment made no answer to this; she only held the muff up to her face, after which she gave it back. 'You don't like it. I see, I see.'

To her guest's astonishment there were tears now in her eyes. 'I don't like what?' the girl asked.

'Why, my engagement. Only, with your great cleverness,' the poor lady quavered out, 'you put it in your own way. I mean that you'll cool off. You already *have* – !' And on this, the next instant, her tears began to flow. She succumbed to them and collapsed; she sank down again, burying her face and trying to smother her sobs.

Her young friend stood there, still in some rigour, but taken much by surprise even if not yet fully moved to pity. 'I don't put anything in any "way", and I'm very glad you're suited. Only, you know, you did put to *me* so splendidly what, even for me, if I had listened to you, it might lead to.'

Mrs Jordan kept up a mild, thin, weak wail; then, drying her eyes, as feebly considered this reminder. 'It has led to my not starving!' she faintly gasped.

Our young lady, at this, dropped into the place beside her, and now, in a rush, the small, silly misery was clear. She took her hand as a sign of pitying it, then, after another instant, confirmed this expression with a consoling kiss. They sat there together; they looked out, hand in hand, into the damp, dusky, shabby little room and into the future, of no such very different suggestion, at last accepted by each. There was no definite utterance, on either side, of Mr Drake's position in the great world, but the temporary collapse of his prospective bride threw all further necessary light; and what our heroine saw and felt for in the whole business was the vivid reflection of her own dreams and delusions and her own return to reality. Reality, for the poor things they both were, could only be ugliness and obscurity, could never be the escape, the rise. She pressed her friend – she had tact enough for that – with no other personal question, brought on no need of further revelations, only just continued to hold and comfort her and to acknowledge by stiff little forbearances the common element in their fate. She felt indeed magnanimous in such matters; for if it was very well, for condolence or re-assurance, to suppress just then invidious shrinkings, she yet by no means saw herself sitting down, as she might say, to the same table with Mr Drake. There would luckily, to all appearances, be little question of tables; and the circumstance that, on their peculiar lines, her friend's interests would still attach themselves to Mayfair flung over Chalk Farm the first radiance it had shown. Where was one's pride and one's passion when the real way to judge of one's luck was by making not the wrong, but the right, comparison? Before she had again gathered herself to go she felt very small and cautious and thankful. 'We shall have our own house,' she said, 'and you must come very soon and let me show it you.'

'*We* shall have our own too,' Mrs Jordan replied; 'for don't you know, he makes it a condition that he sleeps out?'

'A condition?' – the girl felt out of it.

'For any new position. It was on that he parted with Lord Rye. His lordship can't meet it; so Mr Drake has given him up.'

'And all for you?' – our young woman put it as cheerfully as possible.

'For me and Lady Bradeen. Her ladyship's too glad to get him at any price. Lord Rye, out of interest in us, has in fact quite *made* her take him. So, as I tell you, he will have his own establishment.'

Mrs Jordan, in the elation of it, had begun to revive; but there was nevertheless between them rather a conscious pause – a pause in which neither visitor nor hostess brought out a hope or an invitation. It expressed in the last resort that, in spite of submission and sympathy, they could now, after all, only look at each other across the social gulf. They remained together, as if it would be indeed their last chance, still sitting, though

awkwardly, quite close, and feeling also – and this most unmistakably – that there was one thing more to go into. By the
time it came to the surface, moreover, our young friend had
recognized the whole of the main truth, from which she even
drew again a slight irritation. It was not the main truth perhaps
that most signified; but after her momentary effort, her
embarrassment and her tears, Mrs Jordan had begun to sound
afresh – and even without speaking – the note of a social
connection. She hadn't really let go of it that she was marrying
into society. Well, it was a harmless compensation, and it was all
that the prospective bride of Mr Mudge had to leave with her.

27

THIS young lady at last rose again, but she lingered before
going. 'And has Captain Everard nothing to say to it?'

'To what, dear?'

'Why, to such questions – the domestic arrangements, things
in the house.'

'How *can* he, with any authority, when nothing in the house
is his?'

'Not his?' The girl wondered, perfectly conscious of the
appearance she thus conferred on Mrs Jordan of knowing, in
comparison with herself, so tremendously much about it. Well,
there were things she wanted so to get at that she was willing at
last, though it hurt her, to pay for them with humiliation.

'Why are they not his?'

'Don't you know, dear, that he has nothing?'

'Nothing?' It was hard to see him in such a light, but Mrs
Jordan's power to answer for it had a superiority that began, on
the spot, to grow. 'Isn't he rich?'

Mrs Jordan looked immensely, looked both generally and
particularly, informed. 'It depends on what you call – ! Not, at
any rate, in the least as *she* is. What does he bring? Think what
she has. And then, my love, his debts.'

'His debts?' His young friend was fairly betrayed into helpless innocence. She could struggle a little, but she had to let herself go; and if she had spoken frankly she would have said: 'Do tell me, for I don't know so much about him as *that!*' As she didn't speak frankly she only said: 'His debts are nothing – when she so adores him.'

Mrs Jordan began to fix her again, and now she saw that she could only take it all. That was what it had come to: his having sat with her there, on the bench and under the trees, in the summer darkness, and put his hand on her, making her know what he would have said if permitted; his having returned to her afterwards, repeatedly, with supplicating eyes and a fever in his blood; and her having, on her side, hard and pedantic, helped by some miracle and with her impossible condition, only answered him, yet supplicating back, through the bars of the cage, – all simply that she might hear of him, now for ever lost, only through Mrs Jordan, who touched him through Mr Drake, who reached him through Lady Bradeen. 'She adores him – but of course that wasn't all there was about it.'

The girl met her eyes a minute, then quite surrendered. 'What was there else about it?'

'Why, don't you know?' – Mrs Jordan was almost compassionate.

Her interlocutress had, in the cage, sounded depths, but there was a suggestion here somehow of an abyss quite measureless. 'Of course I know that she would never let him alone.'

'How *could* she – fancy! – when he had so compromised her?'

The most artless cry they had ever uttered broke, at this, from the younger pair of lips. '*Had* he so – ?'

'Why, don't you know the scandal?'

Our heroine thought, recollected; there was something, whatever it was, that she knew, after all, much more of than Mrs Jordan. She saw him again as she had seen him come that morning to recover the telegram – she saw him as she had seen him leave the shop. She perched herself a moment on this. 'Oh, there was nothing public.'

'Not exactly public – no. But there was an awful scare and an awful row. It was all on the very point of coming out. Something was lost – something was found.'

'Ah yes,' the girl replied, smiling as if with the revival of a blurred memory; 'something was found.'

'It all got about – and there was a point at which Lord Bradeen had to act.'

'Had to – yes. But didn't.'

Mrs Jordan was obliged to admit it. 'No, he didn't. And then, luckily for them, he died.'

'I didn't know about his death,' her companion said.

'It was nine weeks ago, and most sudden. It has given them a prompt chance.'

'To get married' – this was a wonder – 'within nine weeks?'

'Oh, not immediately, but – in all the circumstances – very quietly and, I assure you, very soon. Every preparation's made. Above all, she holds him.'

'Oh yes, she holds him!' our young friend threw off. She had this before her again a minute; then she continued: 'You mean through his having made her talked about?'

'Yes, but not only that. She has still another pull.'

'Another?'

Mrs Jordan hesitated. 'Why, he was *in* something.'

Her comrade wondered. 'In what?'

'I don't know. Something bad. As I tell you, something was found.'

The girl stared. 'Well?'

'It would have been very bad for him. But she helped him some way – she recovered it, got hold of it. It's even said she stole it!'

Our young woman considered afresh. 'Why, it was what was found that precisely saved him.'

Mrs Jordan, however, was positive. 'I beg your pardon. I happen to know.'

Her disciple faltered but an instant. 'Do you mean through Mr Drake. Do they tell *him* these things?'

'A good servant,' said Mrs Jordan, now thoroughly superior and proportionately sententious, 'doesn't need to be told! Her ladyship saved – as a woman so often saves! – the man she loves.'

This time our heroine took longer to recover herself, but she found a voice at last. 'Ah well – of course I don't know! The great thing was that he got off. They seem then, in a manner,' she added, 'to have done a great deal for each other.'

'Well, it's she that has done most. She has him tight.'

'I see, I see. Good-bye.' The women had already embraced and this was not repeated; but Mrs Jordan went down with her guest to the door of the house. Here again the younger lingered, reverting, though three or four other remarks had on the way passed between them, to Captain Everard and Lady Bradeen. 'Did you mean just now that if she hadn't saved him, as you call it, she wouldn't hold him so tight?'

'Well, I daresay.' Mrs Jordan, on the door-step, smiled with a reflection that had come to her; she took one of her big bites of the brown gloom. 'Men always dislike one when they have done one an injury.'

'But what injury had he done her?'

'The one I've mentioned. He *must* marry her, you know.'

'And didn't he want to?'

'Not before.'

'Not before she recovered the telegram?'

Mrs Jordan was pulled up a little. 'Was it a telegram?'

The girl hesitated. 'I thought you said so. I mean whatever it was.'

'Yes, whatever it was, I don't think she saw *that*.'

'So she just nailed him?'

'She just nailed him.' The departing friend was now at the bottom of the little flight of steps; the other was at the top, with a certain thickness of fog. 'And when am I to think of you in your little home? – next month?' asked the voice from the top.

'At the very latest. And when am I to think of you in yours?'

'Oh, even sooner. I feel, after so much talk with you about it, as if I were already there!' Then 'Good-bye' came out of the fog.

'Good-*bye*!' went into it. Our young lady went into it also, in the opposed quarter, and presently, after a few sightless turns, came out on the Paddington canal. Distinguishing vaguely what the low parapet enclosed, she stopped close to it and stood a while, very intently, but perhaps still sightlessly, looking down on it. A policeman, while she remained, strolled past her; then, going his way a little further and half lost in the atmosphere, paused and watched her. But she was quite unaware – she was full of her thoughts. They were too numerous to find a place just here, but two of the number may at least be mentioned. One of these was that, decidedly, her little home must be not for next month, but for next week; the other, which came indèed as she resumed her walk and went her way, was that it was strange such a matter should be at last settled for her by Mr Drake.

TWO ESSAYS AND A REVIEW

JAMES'S ESSAY, *The Suburbs of London*, appeared in a New York monthly, the *Galaxy*, in December 1877 and was the (somewhat misleadingly-titled) fruit of many excursions during his first full year in London. His unsigned review of Augustus Hare's *Walks in London* was published by the prestigious New York weekly, *The Nation*, on June 20th, 1878. The major set-piece essay, *London*, was sent by James in January 1887 to the editor of the American *Century* magazine, Robert Underwood Johnson: 'I can only say of it that it proved damnably difficult to put so much into a little . . . The article itself is by no means so pictorial as I had at first intended – but perhaps it makes it up in other ways.'[1] The wheels of publication ground slowly, and almost a year later James wrote to the American illustrator Joseph Pennell about the question of illustrations for the article:

I have really nothing to suggest save that you follow your own fancy. If you too are fond of London let that fondness be your guide and you will fall in sufficiently with my text. The article from being so general is difficult to illustrate – and the thing, I should say, ought to be freely and fancifully done; *not* with neat, definite, photographic 'views'. Into that, however, you are not in danger of falling. Street vistas, characteristic corners (that of Hyde Park, say), something in the City, or on the way to it (say that church at the end of the Strand, where the road forks), etc. I should put in a plea for some view of (or in) the Green Park – with the dim and ugly pinnacles of Buckingham Palace. I lived close to it for nine years and was always crossing it. But do your own London, and it will be sufficiently mine.[2]

London eventually appeared in the *Century* in December 1888, with illustrations by Pennell, and was reprinted in revised form in *Essays in London and Elsewhere* (1893). Subsequently, that revised version was the first essay in his *English Hours* (1905).

1. *Letters, Volume III* (1980), pp 160–1.
2. Ibid, p 218.

THE SUBURBS OF LONDON

THE term 'suburban' has always seemed to me to have a peculiarly English meaning. It suggests images that are not apt to present themselves in America. American cities have suburbs, but they have to a very limited extent what may be called suburban scenery. The essence of suburban scenery in the western world is to be straggling, shabby, inexpensive; to consist of rail fences and loose planks, vacant, dusty lots in which carpet-beating goes forward, Irish cabins, lumber yards, and rudely bedaubed advertisements of quack medicines. The peculiar function of the neighbourhood of most foreign towns, on the other hand, is to be verdant and residential, thickly inhabited, and replete with devices for making habitation agreeable. Some of the prettiest things in England and France are to be found in the immediate vicinity of the capitals of those countries. There is nothing more charming in Europe than the great terrace at Saint Germain; there are few things so picturesque as Richmond bridge and the view thence along either bank of the Thames. There are certainly ugly things enough in the neighbourhood of London, and there is much agreeable detail to be found within an hour's drive of several American towns; but the suburban quality, the mingling of density and rurality, the ivy-covered brick walls, the riverside holiday-making, the old royal seats at an easy drive, the little open-windowed inns, where the charm of rural seclusion seems to merge itself in that of proximity to the city market – these things must be caught in neighbourhoods that have been longer a-growing.

Murray (of the Hand-Books) has lately put forward a work which I have found very full of entertaining reading: a couple of well-sized volumes treating of every place of the smallest individuality within a circuit of twenty miles round London. The number of such places is surprising; so large an amount of English history has gone on almost within sight of the tower or

the Abbey. From time to time, as the days grow long, the
contemplative stranger finds a charm in the idea of letting
himself loose in this interesting circle. Even to a tolerably
inveterate walker London itself will not appear in the long run a
very delightful field for pedestrian exercise. London is too
monotonous and, in plain English, too ugly to supply that
wayside entertainment which the observant pedestrian demands.
The shabby quarters are too dusky, too depressing, English low
life is too unrelieved by out-of-door picturesqueness, to be
treated as a daily spectacle. There are too many gin-shops, and
too many miserable women at their doors; too many, far too
many dirty-faced children sprawling between one's legs; the
young ladies of the neighbourhood are too much addicted to
violent forms of coquetry. On the other hand, the Squares and
Crescents, the Roads and Gardens, are too rigidly, too blankly
genteel. They are enlivened by groups of charming children,
coming out to walk with their governesses or nursemaids, and
by the figures of superior flunkies, lingering, in the consciousness
of elegant leisure, on the doorstep. But, although these groups –
the children and the flunkies – are the most beautiful specimens
in the world of their respective classes, they hardly avail to
impart a lively interest to miles of smoke-darkened stucco, sub-
divided into porticoes and windows. The most entertaining
walk, therefore, is a suburban walk, which will introduce you to
fewer butlers and footmen, but to children as numerous and as
rosy, and to something more unexpected in the way of
architecture.

There is a charming place of refuge from the London streets
of which I fain would speak, although it hardly belongs to my
modest programme. There was a time when Kensington was a
suburb, but the suburban phase of its history has pretty well
passed away. Nothing can well be conceived less suburban than
the vast expanses of residential house frontage of which this
region now chiefly consists; and yet to go thither is the shortest
way of getting out of London. Step into Kensington Gardens,
and a ten minutes' walk will carry you practically fifty miles
from the murky Babylon on the other side of the railing. It may
really be said that Kensington Gardens contain some of the finest
rural scenery in England. If they were not a huge city square,

they would be an admirable nobleman's park. To sit down for an hour at the base of one of the great elms and see them studding the grass around you in vistas, which, as you do not perceive their limits, may be as long-drawn as you choose to suppose them, is one of the most accessible as well as one of the most agreeable methods of spending a June afternoon.

Whenever, toward six o'clock, I have mustered the spirit to go to Hyde Park, I have ended, after a duly dazzled gaze at the wonderful throng that assembles there, by slinking away into the comparative wilderness of the neighbouring enclosure. I use the expression 'slinking', because I have usually taken this course with a bad conscience. In Hyde Park you see fine people; in Kensington Gardens you see only fine trees; and the observant stranger feels that it is upon eminent specimens of the human rather than of the vegetable race that he should bestow his attention. Every one in London, as the phrase is, goes to Hyde Park of a fine afternoon; and the spectacle, therefore, may be presumed to have no small impressiveness.

It is certainly a very brilliant mob, and the copper coin which you pay for the use of your little chair is a small equivalent for the greatness of the privilege. Before you is the Drive, with its serried ranks of carriages; behind you is the Row, with its misty, red-earthed vista, and its pacing and bounding equestrians; between the two is the broad walk in which your fellow starers are gathered together lolling back in the tightly-packed chairs or shuffling along with wistful looks at them. The first time the observant stranger betakes himself to the park, he certainly is struck with the splendor of the show. There seems to be so much of everything; there are so many carriages, so many horses, so many servants, so many policemen, so many people in the carriages, on horseback, in the chairs, on foot. The observant stranger is again reminded of those constant factors in every more distinctively 'social' spectacle in England – the boundless wealth and the boundless leisure. Leisure is suggested even more forcibly if he goes to the park of a fine summer morning. In the afternoon people may be supposed to have brought the day's labours to a close, to have done their usual stint of work and earned the right to *flâner*. But American eyes do not easily accustom themselves to the sight of a great multitude in a busy metropolis, beginning the day's entertainment, a couple of hours after breakfast, by going to sit in a public garden and watch several hundred ladies and gentlemen gallop past them on horseback. To the great commercial *bourgeoisie*, which constitutes 'American society', this free disposal of the precious morning hours is an unattainable luxury. The men are attending to business; they are immersed in offices, counting-houses, and 'stores'. The ladies are ordering the dinner, setting the machinery of the household in motion for the day, finding occupation among their children. To people brought up in these traditions there is, therefore, something very – what shall I call it? – very picturesque, in these elegant matutinal groups, for whom the work of life is done to order, and who lose so little time of a morning in beginning the play.

They seem to have time enough, in all conscience; why should they be in such a hurry to begin? Here you catch that 'leisured class' the absence of which is so often pointed out to you as the distinguishing feature of our awkward civilization, and the existence of which in England is, to many good Americans, a source of envy, admiration, and despair – here you catch it in the very act, as it were; and you may stroll about and envy and admire it as much as you find warrant for. It is very good looking, very well dressed; it sits very quietly, looking without eagerness at passing things, and talking about them without striking animation. Women, all over the world, have less to do than men; and these unmortgaged hours are, on the ladies' parts, comparatively natural. What an American particularly notices is the number of disengaged men; well dressed, gentlemanly, agreeable fellows, who have nothing more urgent to do, at twelve o'clock in the morning, than to stroll about under green trees, with a stick and a pair of gloves in their hands, or to sit with their legs crossed and murmur soft nothings to a lady in a Gainsborough hat. And in all this I am speaking only of the spectators; I am not including the show itself – the fine folks in the carriages and the happy folks on horseback.

If the spectators testify to English leisure, the carriages testify more particularly to English incomes. To keep a carriage and pair in London costs, I believe, about five hundred pounds a year; the number of people driving about at this expense defies any powers of calculation at the command of the contemplative stranger. The carriages flock into the park in thousands; they roll along in dense, far-stretching masses; they stand locked together in a wilderness of wheels and cockades. In the morning, however, they are few in number, and you may bestow your attention upon the Row, which is at any time, indeed, a much prettier sight. It is the prettiest sight possible, and it shows you the finest side of English idleness. There is every kind of horse save the ugly one, and if it is not quite equally true that there is every kind of rider save the bad one, at least the bad ones are few and far between. The good Homer sometimes nods, and the good Englishman has sometimes a slippery saddle. I have heard American ladies say that they were 'disappointed' in Rotten Row; but for myself, I was never disappointed. I don't exactly know what my countrywomen expected; but they have in everything, I know, a high standard. A young English girl, in a habit without a wrinkle, mounted upon a beautiful English horse, with health in her cheek and modesty in her eye, pulling up, flushed and out of breath, at the end of a long gallop, is a picture in which I can pretend to pick no flaws. 'Ah, pulling up,' my disappointed countrywomen will say; 'when they have pulled up they are doubtless very well; it is their rapid motion that is not what we have been taught to believe it.' And she will go on to say that these disappointments are an old story, and that there is nothing like coming to Europe and seeing for one's self.

However few my own disappointments, I have, as I said just now, usually brought my sessions in Hyde Park to a premature close, and wandered away to the shady precinct of the old red palace which stares across the pond, and which has, I believe, a respectable collection of historical associations. It was, I believe, in Kensington Palace that the present Queen passed a large part of her youth; it was there that the news of her accession was brought to her. It is a modest, homely, but delightful old residence, and so much more agreeable of aspect than the villanous pile which overlooks St James's Park, that the privilege of living there might reconcile one to being on the steps of the throne rather than on the throne itself (Buckingham Palace being habitable, I believe, only by the sovereign, and Kensington being allotted to the sovereign's near relations). London – apropos of this matter – is, compared with continental capitals, singularly destitute of royal residences. Buckingham Palace is lamentably ugly; St James's Palace is less shabby only because it is less pretentious; Marlborough House is hidden away in a court-yard, and presents no face whatever to the world. Marlborough House is, indeed, completely effaced, as the French say, by the neighbouring clubs in Pall Mall. You have to go but a short distance out of London, however, to see two of the most beautiful of all royal seats. One of the first of your excursions in the lengthening days is, as a matter of course, to Windsor. Windsor Castle, as you see it from the train, while you are yet at some distance from the station, massing its long cluster of towers and battlements against the sky, is quite as impressive as the one considerable residence of English sovereigns should be.

If these sovereigns have fewer dwelling places than most other members of the royal fraternity, they may at least claim that their single castle is the most magnificent of castles. Nothing can well be more royal than the tremendous mass of Windsor, looking down from its height over the valley of the Thames, and the vast expanse of its park and forest. As you turn into the town, out of the station, you find yourself confronted with the foundations of the castle, along whose rugged base, and the steep on which it is perched, the little High Street wanders in pygmy fashion. It has been my misfortune that at the time of each of my visits to Windsor the interior of the palace was not being shown; this is the case whenever the Queen is living there. But I must add that I use the term 'misfortune' here in a great measure for form's sake. The rooms at Windsor are, I believe, numerous and interesting; they contain, among other treasures, some very fine pictures. But when I reflect that I should have had to go through them in the company of a large assemblage of fellow starers, 'personally conducted', like Mr Cook's tourists, by a droning custodian, and shuffling in dull, gregarious fashion over the miles of polished floor and through the vistas of gilded chambers in which they are requested not to 'touch' – when the memory of this ordeal, frequently repeated in earlier years, comes back to me, I cannot help feeling a diminution of regret.

The 'observant stranger' ought perhaps to be ashamed to confess to such levity, but a couple of years of indoor sight-seeing will have done a great deal toward making him ask himself whether the most beautiful rooms in the world are worth visiting in one of these bands of centripetal stragglers. The thing is disagreeable; one is not bound to say how or why. It is disagreeable to wander about any house – be it even Windsor Castle – without entering into relation with the master; and at Windsor and some other great houses the casual visitor is not only referred to the servants, but actually denied entrance unless the proprietor be absent. It is, however, one's fellow starers, one's fellow shufflers, that make the shoe pinch. It appears to be a fundamental rule of human nature, lying lower than the plummet of analysis will drop, that one shall, for the time, despise such people. On the continent, perhaps, you can keep better terms with them; they are usually, like yourself, foreigners in the country, and this gives them a cosmopolitan, independent air which tempers their subjection to the housekeeper or the beadle. But in England, wherever you go, there are usually fifty English people there before you; and the class which, in England, indulges in the inspection of native monuments, appears to be for the most part the class for which the housekeeper and the beadle have irresistible terrors.

Even when the apartments at Windsor are closed, the great terrace behind the castle is open, and this lordly platform is one of the finest things in the world. I talk of its being 'behind' the castle, but I have no warrant for attempting to distinguish between back and front in an edifice of such irregular magnificence. The terrace, at any rate, looks over a beautiful country, and straight down at the playing fields of Eton, which are bordered by the sinuous Thames. It is not beneath the dignity of this line of observation to relate that the last time I was at Windsor I strolled along the terrace – it has a magnificent length – toward a point at which a portion of it is marked off by an iron railing for the use of the inhabitants of the castle. Here a gentleman was standing, with his back against the parapet, looking up intently at the wall. At the narrow window of a tower was placed the face of a housemaid, which was removed a moment after I had perceived it. The gentleman carried, slung over his shoulder, an opera glass, of which he appeared not to have made use. Turning to me very solemnly – 'I think it was the Queen,' he said.

'Do you mean that person at the window?' I inquired.

'Yes; she looked at me a long time, and I looked at her.'

'I thought it was a housemaid,' I rejoined.

He shook his head. 'She looked very much like the Queen. She looked just like her photographs.'

'Possibly,' I said. 'But she had on a housemaid's cap.'

Once more he shook his head and lifted his eyes to the empty window. 'She looked at me a long time,' he murmured, 'and I looked at her. I am sure it was the Queen.' And I left him in the happy faith that he had sustained the awful gaze of royalty out of a back staircase window.

I left him in order to walk back under the castle arches and through the triple courts, through the town and across the bridge to Eton; and then come up into the town again, hire a vehicle at the stand beneath the granite walls, and take a long drive in the park. Eton College is on the other side of the Thames; you approach it by a long, dull, provincial street, consisting apparently chiefly of print shops, filled with portraits of the pretty women of the period. I approached it with a certain sentimental agitation, for I had always had a theory that the great English schools are delightful places to have been to. A few weeks before this I had paid a short visit to Winchester, and in the grounds of the venerable college which adjoins that ancient town I had seen hundred rosy lads playing cricket (I am counting the lookers-on), with as business-like a jollity as if the ball were rebounding from the maternal bosom of Britannia herself. The courts of the old college, empty and silent in the eventide; the mellow light on the battered walls; the great green meadows, where the little clear-voiced boys made gigantic shadows; the neighbourhood of the old cathedral city, with its admirable church, where early kings are buried – all this seemed to make a charming background for boyish lives, and to offer a provision of tender, picturesque memories to the grown man who has passed through it. Eton, of a clear June evening, must be quite as good, or indeed a great deal better.

The day I speak of was a half-holiday, and the college itself was pretty well deserted. It consists of a couple of not particularly ornamental quadrangles, a good deal the worse for wear, a fine old chapel, and a queer bronze statue of Henry II, the founder of the school. All this stands near the river, among goodly trees, and hard by are the masters' houses, in which the boys are lodged. A good many of the boys were strolling about, in their little man's hats and broad collars; this was apparently a holiday costume. Some of them were buying tarts from a wheedling Jew, who had rested his basket on the parapet of the school-house green; some were looking at the types of female beauty in the print-sellers' windows; one was very carefully carrying a jug full of some foaming liquid home from the pastry cook's. Beyond the houses, toward the river, some of them were playing at their eternal cricket. The river, just here, is very pretty; the great elms, in the meadows beside it, are magnificent; there is a bosky-looking little island in the middle, and silvery reaches up and down; and from the further side the castle looks down with a kind of maternal majesty. This is the extent of my knowledge of Eton. I had a letter of introduction to an excellent little boy – it was from his mamma; but I had not the heart to spoil his half-holiday by making him play *cicerone* to my dismal seniority.

So, as I said, I drove away through Windsor Park; through the Long Walk, which stretches from the castle gates for the space of three miles, bordered with trees as old, very nearly, as the English monarchy, and quite as solid, to a great grassy mound on which a rather ridiculous statue of George III is perched. The statue stares across the interval at the castle, and the great avenue – thanks to its very perfection – looks like a much smaller affair than it is. But nothing in Windsor Park is small. I drove for some fifteen miles, and everywhere the great trees were scattered over the slopes and lawns; everywhere there was a glimpse of browsing deer; everywhere, at the end of cross-roads, the same wooded horizon. It is the perfection of park scenery, the noblest of all parks. I drove to Virginia Water, and left my carriage to come and meet me at some unknown point, to which my driver directed my steps. The walk proved charming; it led me over the grass and under the trees – and such trees, always – for a couple of miles, beside an agreeable lake. It was all delightfully sylvan, and almost solitary; and yet it retained the comfortable park character. There was no losing of one's way nor scratching away underbrush; and there was at the end a little inn, as pretty as a tavern in a comic opera, at which it was not impossible to lunch. I drove back through other avenues and over other slopes, with an occasional view of the long-outlined castle above the tree tops. There had been a great deal of it, and yet I had seen nothing of the forest.

Hampton Court Palace is always open, and you are free to wander through the apartments as you list. They form indeed a museum of second and third-rate works of art – a kind of pictorial hospital. Most of the pictures are doubtful specimens of the great masters whose names are affixed to their frames; there are a few very good ones, however, of a more modest attribution. The long row of great drawings in tempera by Andrea Mantegna, representing the triumph of Julius Caesar, are alone worth a moderate pilgrimage; and the collection of meretricious countesses of the Restoration, by Lely, is very brilliant in its own peculiar way. The great charm of Hampton Court is not, however, in the pictures; it would not be even if these were a great deal better. It is the old red palace itself that is chiefly delightful; its great round-windowed, stone-embossed courts; its long, warm-coloured front and sides; its brown old chambers with their dusky canvases, their fireplaces, and their tapestry; its beautiful formal garden, with its close-clipt lawns, its shaded walks, its curious yews, and its Dutch-looking canal.

Of all the suburban lions Hampton Court is the most cockneyfied; London holiday-makers flock down there in hundreds, and spread themselves over the place, which is especially dedicated to that form of popular entertainment known as 'school feasts'. These simple festivals are celebrated within the enclosure of Bushey Park, just beyond the palace gardens. There would be something inhuman in saying that they spoil the place for the solitary, selfish stroller; inasmuch as they are a source of entertainment to crowds of underfed little Londoners, who make a juvenile uproar under the great horse-chestnuts. I hasten, therefore, to say that on the three or four occasions when I have spent the afternoon at Hampton Court, the presence of the London contingent has never been fatal to my enjoyment. The place has such an honest, friendly charm, that it seems good-naturedly to refuse to be vulgarized; and your fellow cockneys become, as it were, a part of the homely animation of the landscape, like the greedy swans in the canal or the very tame deer in the park. The school children, moreover, with their dusky pinafores and clumsy gambols, their tea tables and omnibuses, all, for reasons best known to themselves, herd together near the park gates. Ten minutes' walk will carry you out of sight or sound of them; and you may stroll down the great vistas of horse-chestnut without the fear of encountering any object more displeasing than a young man on an occasional bench, encircling the waist of his sweetheart, or a young person sketching difficult foliage at the base of one of the trees.

Bushey Park consists of a single long avenue of trees in a double row; that is, there are four lines of trees. At about a quarter of its length this avenue is crossed by another, which puts out two arms – two high green corridors – of almost equal magnitude. All this foliage is magnificent; and we know what the horse-chestnut is capable of. One afternoon it was very warm – warm enough (far too rare a blessing in England) to fling one's self on the grass at the base of one of the giant trunks. I made a point of doing so, and spent a couple of hours in this attitude, in the faintly stirred shade, watching the soft, still evening close in. You must do something of this kind, to feel the charm of an old English park. It has more to say to you, a great deal more, than it can ever say as you pass by in the most neatly appointed 'fly', or even as you stroll along in company the most exempt from a vulgar sense of unexpectedness. During an idle lounge in the mellowing, fading light, the beautiful quality of the place steals irresistibly over your spirit, the air seems charged with serene antiquity and accumulated peace, and the rustle of the leaves strikes you as the continuous sound made in their passage by the hours and years which have given all this its quiet chance to grow. To the contemplative stranger who permits himself not only to talk sentimental nonsense, but to think it, it seems as if, somehow, all England had been gathered up into such a place – as if nothing less than her glorious past, her wealth, her power, her honour, her uninvaded centuries, had been needed to produce it.

Another charm of Hampton Court is its being directly up the river, which flows beside the long, ivy-muffled brick wall of the gardens. Nothing can be prettier than the walk on the further side of this wall, whose charming old mottled red extent you have on one hand, as you have the grassy bank of the Thames on the other. After a while the wall stops and a tall iron paling begins. Its interstices are choked with shrubbery, but they permit you to look into the great, peaceful, private expanse of the Home Park. Its timbered acres stretch away with a very grand air, and it seems to be simply a park for a park's sake. The reduced gentlewomen who occupy apartments in the palace, at the Queen's pleasure, are free to take their exercise there; and for picturesqueness's sake I ought certainly to have seen a couple of them, in eventide gossip, dragging a scanty train over the soft grass. I must add that you see more of the Home Park from within the gardens. The limit of these is marked by a sort of semicircular canal, of the quaintest aspect, ornamented with shaven banks, and with huge water-lilies and swans. Directly opposite the centre of the palace this artificial pool puts forth a long, straight arm, which stretches away into the Home Park to a great distance, and makes one of those geometrical vistas that old-fashioned monarchs used to like to look at from their palace windows. This one is bordered with tall, stiff trees, and is a model of its kind. Round about it the park expands immensely, and you may look at it all across the canal, over a little fence.

As for the river, in talking about London suburbs we should have come to that first of all. The Thames is the great feature of suburban London; and these neighbourhoods are, for the most part, worth describing only as they bear some relation to it. Londoners appreciate their river in the highest degree; and they manifest their regard in a thoroughly practical fashion. They use the Thames: it might almost be said they abuse it. They use it, I mean, for pleasure; for above Chelsea Bridge there are happily few traces of polluting traffic. When once indeed, going up the stream, you fairly emerge from the region of the London bridges, the Thames turns rural with surprising quickness. At every bend and reach it throws off something of its metropolitan degradation; with each successive mile it takes on another prettiness. By the time you reach Richmond, which is only nine miles from London, this suburban prettiness touches its maximum. Higher in its course the Thames is extremely pretty; but nothing can well be so charming as what you see of it from Richmond Bridge and just above. The bridge itself is a very happy piece of picturesqueness. Sketches and photographs have, I believe, made it more or less classical. The banks are lined compactly with villas embowered in walled gardens, which lie on the slope of Richmond Hill, whose crest, as seen from below, is formed by the long, bosky mass of Richmond Park.

To speak of Richmond Park is to speak of one of the loveliest spots in England. It has not the vast extent of Windsor, but in other respects it is quite as fine. It is poor work talking of English parks, for one is reduced to ringing the changes on a few lamentably vague epithets of praise. One talks of giant oaks and grassy downs, of browsing deer and glades of bracken; and yet nine-tenths of what one would say remains unsaid. I will therefore content myself with observing that, to take a walk in Richmond Park and afterward repair to the Star and Garter inn to satisfy the appetite you have honestly stimulated, is as complete an entertainment as you are likely to find. It is rounded off by your appreciation of the famous view of the Thames from the windows of the inn – the view which Turner has painted and poets have versified, and which certainly is as charming as possible, though to an American eye it just grazes, a trifle painfully, the peril of over-tameness. But the river makes a graceful, conscious bend, and wanders away into that thick detail of distance characteristic of the English landscape.

Richmond is in every way the most beautiful of the environs of London. I had a sense of it during a couple of visits that I lately paid to a delightful old house on the outskirts of the town. This was such an old house as we should go barefoot to see in America, though in this happy land of domiciles with ante-cedents it enjoys no particular distinction. It stands close to the river; it dates from the reign of Queen Anne; it has a red brick front and elaborate cornices and copings; it is guarded by a high brick wall and tall iron gates. Within, it is rich in wainscoted parlours, with rococo mouldings and carvings, to which you ascend by a great square staircase that is panelled and embellished in proportion. Opposite, on the other side of the river, are the villas and lawns of Twickenham. Close at hand, among con-verging, overshadowing elms, is a strange, haunted-looking mansion, with weedy gardens and foreign medallions set in its face. Beyond this are the great botanical gardens of Kew; behind is Sudbrook Park and the greater extent of Richmond Park. Staying there, one need not be at loss for a walk.

And then you have the river. When I said just now that Londoners and suburbans use their river, I meant in the first place that they dwell upon its edges as closely as possible, and in the second place that they set themselves afloat upon it in tremendous force. From early spring to the last of the autumn, the river is given up to boating. Wherever you approach it the symptoms of this pastime are in the foreground; there are always a dozen young men with bare legs and jerseys pulling themselves up and down in cigar-shaped boats. There are boats, indeed, of every form and dimension: sharp-cutting wherries, in which the occupant seems to be sitting on the back of a knife-blade; uncomfortable canoes, in which he paddles with an awkward movement, as if he were bailing out a sinking craft; capacious barges, containing a party in which a lady usually reclines in the stern and plays coxswain. Of a summer afternoon these innumerable water parties make a very pretty bustle. I took a boat at Richmond on such a afternoon, and rowed up to Teddington, whence I walked along the towing path to Hampton Court. Between Richmond and Teddington the riverside is an unbroken succession of small country houses, each perched upon a lawn as smooth as a billiard table and dipping its border into the water. The prettiness, smoothness, trimness, cottage-of-gentility look of all this is quite inexpressible.

I said just now that the view from Richmond was 'over-tame', and I hardly know how to qualify the impression it produces when looked at in detail. It seems like a country that is over-ripe; that cannot afford any more mellowing. The innumerable boats, the little green carpet-patches on the banks, the perfectly appointed cottages, the people sitting on the painted-looking lawns, with whom you can almost converse from across the stream – these things suggest a kind of imminent repletion, a climax of maturity. And yet I don't suppose that another season's sunshine will begin to bruise the mellow earth, or that the boats will crowd the water out of its channel. The villas and cottages will go on being let as eligible residences, and young men in white flannel will feather their oars for all generations to come. It has lately become greatly the fashion to row down from Oxford, devoting a week to the voyage, and sleeping at the riverside inns. I can imagine nothing more charming, if – to measure the matter rather grossly – you carry a week's dinner in the boat.

If I had not almost exhausted my space I should here devote a parenthesis to the singular meagreness of the British larder as exemplified at the village inn whose scented porch and latticed windows the poets and story-tellers have taught us in America to venerate. During a series of suburban afternoons it often happens that one applies for the evening meal at a tavern of prepossessing aspect, but usually with no greater profit than the right to register one's experience in that list of strange anomalies in which the tradition of English 'comfort' is so prolific. One day I came down the river to Teddington, which I reached at half-past seven in the evening. As I had the prospect of not arriving in London till nearly ten o'clock, I went in quest of a house of entertainment. I found one on the river bank, standing in a garden, the perfection apparently of a rural hostelry, and adorned with the sign of the 'Angler'. I enter the establishment and am met on the threshold, with every manifestation of hospitality, by a prosperous-looking host and hostess who have emerged from a snug and shining bar. I ask if I can be provided with dinner, and I receive an affirmative answer. It seems, however, to lack a certain savoury downrightness, and I further inquire of what the dinner will be composed. I am informed that it will be composed of *cold 'am*, and I can prevail upon my entertainers to add nothing else to the *menu*. This is apparently considered by an English innkeeper a very handsome offer; the *ultima ratio* of the frigid joint is thrust at you with a stolid complacency which in the anguish of a disappointed stomach you pardonably qualify as barbaric. But the phase of disappointment passes away, and you permit yourself to decide, once for all, that the English innkeeper lacks the culinary sense. Public opinion asks too little of him.

One evening I came back late from the country; it was a quarter past nine when I arrived in London. My dinner had been too long deferred, and I determined to obtain it without further delay. The station at which I had alighted was adorned, like most of the London stations, with a huge railway hotel. I entered this establishment, and, being directed to the coffee room, ascended a monumental staircase and passed along a corridor remarkable for its sober-coloured massiveness and elegance. Everything here was a pledge of comfort, abundance, succulence. The coffee room was as vast and impressive as a cathedral; and the high priest and his acolyte – the waiter and a little page – approached me with a solemnity which seemed to promise a formal initiation into its most savoury mysteries. The usual request for dinner was followed by the usual offer of cold meat, to which, being faint from inanition, I reluctantly assented. This attractive repast was set before me, flanked on either side by a chunk of bread and a mustard pot. It made a pitiful figure beneath the gilded vault of the coffee room, and I succumbed to a pardonable desire to give it an harmonious accessory. A simple expedient to this end seemed to be to ask for some potatoes. Hereupon followed this dialogue:

'We have no potatoes, sir.'

'You have no potatoes?'

'No, sir. We have no potatoes, sir.'

'Isn't that very extraordinary?'

'Yes, sir. We have no potatoes, sir.'

'You never have potatoes, perhaps. The absence of potatoes is perhaps a speciality of this hotel?'

'Yes, sir. We have no potatoes after nine o'clock, sir.'

The waiter was a very 'fine man'; he was in evening dress. Near him stood the little page, with a hundred polished buttons on his jacket. I looked from one to the other, and then I looked up at the gilded dome and the stately pilasters of the room. This operation concluded, I addressed myself to what I have called the frigid – and I may now add the rigid – joint. But I am sorry to conclude in this plaintive key. If I had not exhausted my space, I should speak of the satisfaction of going down to Greenwich, at the duskier end of the Thames, and eating at the Ship Hotel the best of all possible dinners.

WALKS IN LONDON

MR HARE, in attempting to do for London what he had done for Rome, has produced a book that will be found very useful, and that, without having the charm of colouring of the 'Walks in Rome', will yet appear entertaining and readable even to persons not consulting it on the spot as a guide-book. We must add, however, that the exercise of a little finer sort of art might have made this lively compilation something better than a mere modified itinerary. Mr Hare's descriptive powers are rather meagre, and he gives his readers fewer pictures by the way than might have been expected from a writer at once minutely familiar with London and addicted to observing the pictorial aspect of things. The author writes, indeed, as if he were but partially familiar with the great city by the Thames – as if, in fact, he had not been much of a walker there. His book has a rather perfunctory and done-to-order air – a quality much less apparent in the volumes of Messrs Peter Cunningham and John Timbs, whom one feels to be genuine Londoners as well as antiquaries. But if Mr Hare has 'got up' his London, he has got it up very well, and to those American tourists who, on the long spring days, emerge from the by-ways of Piccadilly with an oppressive sense of long distances, accumulated cab-fares, and historic associations, he may be recommended as an edifying companion. About a place that has been so enormously lived in as London there was plenty to be said; the only thing was to gather it together. Mr Hare has been able to make a great many quotations, for though London has not figured so largely in literature as Rome, yet most English writers, at least, have paid their respects to it in some shape or other. Mr Hare divides his walks into districts, beginning with Charing Cross and moving thence Cityward. It is in the eastward direction, of course, that associations and memories are thickest – along the line that stretches from Charing Cross to the Tower – and Mr Hare's first volume, which covers this large expanse, is accordingly the more interesting, though the second contains two very copious and detailed chapters upon Westminster Abbey.

We have not the space here to tread in our author's footsteps, and we are afraid, we confess, that even the very appreciative American sightseer, proposing to himself to grapple with the great commercial Babylon, will sometimes find his energy failing him. The modern tumult and uproar of the City, the daily press and jostle, are sadly hostile to contemplation. The spirit of historical enquiry is merged in the baser instinct of self-preservation. The love of research must be mighty within you to enable you to hold your ground for the purpose of staring at the front of a house in which a British Classic was born, when a death-dealing hansom-cab is bearing straight down upon you. It is only on Sunday, as Mr Hare says, that you can really look at the City, and give yourself an idea of what it contains. Then, indeed, in the blank, empty streets, among the closed shops, with only the tall policemen stationed at intervals for landmarks, you may discover how much curious and interesting detail lurks amid the general duskiness and ugliness. It must be added, however, that no one will have a right to accuse you of bad taste if you succumb to the depressing influence of Sunday-morning street scenery. A Sunday's worth of London City vistas is not an entertainment to be lightly recommended. Among other discoveries, on such an occasion, you come to a sense of the very large number of the City churches, and of the fact that some of these structures have a good deal of architectural merit. Most of the time, with the great human tides surging in front of them, and their steeples lost in the week-day smoke and fog, you are hardly aware of their presence. During the Great Fire (in 1666) there was an immense destruction of places of worship, and in the course of the next thirty or forty years there went forward a wholesale building and rebuilding of churches. Sir Christopher Wren alone built more than a hundred. The best that can be said of most of these buildings is that they are of varying degrees of badness. Here and there, however, is a success, as in the case of the beautiful steeple of St Mary-le-Bow – the famous tower of Bow-bells – which is such an odd mixture of the *baroque* and the conventional, and yet is so light and graceful. Within, some of the older churches – those that escaped the Fire – are rich in curious monuments. It is worth the long pilgrimage from the West End any day to visit such a museum of quaint sepulchral records as St Helen's, Bishopsgate, or to examine so grand a relic of Norman architecture as St Bartholo- mew the Great. We should rank this latter edifice, which forms a part of the mass of buildings of St Bartholomew's Hospital (itself, in its well-ordered antiquity, well worth a visit), as second only in impressiveness to the Abbey and to St Paul's. Empty and desolate, yet magnificently solid, it suggests to the visitor, once he stands within it, that he is a hundred miles away from the vulgar industrial bustle of the modern Smithfield on the other side of the door.

Mr Hare reconstructs in a measure 'the great palaces of the Strand' – the noble residences of immense proportions that once edged the water-side of the great westward thoroughfare. As regards the destruction of the last-removed of them (North-umberland House, at Charing Cross), he indulges in something like an imprecation. The present aspect of Charing Cross is certainly most discreditable; but we hardly agree with Mr Hare that Northumberland House was a great architectural honour to London. It must have seemed to foreign visitors a sad proof of architectural poverty that this low, plain, meagrely-Jacobean structure should have been counted as a gem. The stiff-tailed little lion on top was always amusing; but the building itself did hardly more than contribute its part to the incongruous ineffectiveness of 'the finest site in Europe,' as Trafalgar Square has been properly enough called. The thought that in the Strand there were once other palaces as large as Somerset House, and that at Whitehall there was a great royal residence, only increases the shame of what modern London has contrived to make of her naturally magnificent river-front. Temple Bar has gone the way of Northumberland House; but it must be confessed that Temple Bar was practically rather a nuisance. It was incontestable that, so far as you could ever stop to look at it – a difficult achieve-ment, in the force of the current beneath it – it was a rather 'thin' and unbeautiful piece of antiquity; and at present, in compensation for its disappearance, rises beside its site the mighty pile of the new Inns of Court, which bids fair to be, in mass and general effect, one of the most splendid and imposing modern buildings in Europe. No real lover of London – and London may be sturdily loved – can fail to take satisfaction in the thought that his swarthy metropolitan Dulcinea is at last waking up to some sense of the desirableness of beautifying herself.

That some such process is greatly needed we are vividly reminded as we turn those pages of Mr Hare's book which treat of the West End. The author is very fond of the adjective 'frightful,' and in speaking of these regions – regions in which a Baker Street and a Harley Street have become possible – he has frequent opportunity to use it. There is, however, every reason to believe that in regard to architectural dreariness London has touched bottom and done its worst. Harley Street and Baker Street cannot, in their own peculiar way, be surpassed, and it is not likely they will be imitated. London is the most interesting city in the world, and is wonderfully well adapted for becoming the handsomest. The climate, the atmosphere, the manner in which a population of four millions reacts upon the natural local conditions, all contribute to the picturesqueness of the place. Nowhere is there such a play of light and shade, such a confusion of haze and cloud and smoke, such a mystery and variety of perspective. If all this is striking in an ugly London, what would it be in a stately and beautiful one? It will be seen that we speak appreciatively; our appreciation has been quickened by Mr Hare's full and agreeable volumes.

LONDON

I

THERE IS a certain evening that I count as virtually a first
impression – the end of a wet, black Sunday, twenty years ago,
about the first of March. There had been an earlier vision, but it
had turned to grey, like faded ink, and the occasion I speak of
was a fresh beginning. No doubt I had mystic prescience of how
fond of the murky modern Babylon I was one day to become;
certain it is that as I look back I find every small circumstance of
those hours of approach and arrival still as vivid as if the
solemnity of an opening era had breathed upon it. The sense of
approach was already almost intolerably strong at Liverpool,
where, as I remember, the perception of the English character of
everything was as acute as a surprise, though it could only be a
surprise without a shock. It was expectation exquisitely gratified,
superabundantly confirmed. There was a kind of wonder,
indeed, that England should be as English as, for my entertainment, she took the trouble to be; but the wonder would have
been greater, and all the pleasure absent, if the sensation had not
been violent. It seems to sit there again like a visiting presence,
as it sat opposite to me at breakfast at a small table in a window
of the old coffee-room of the Adelphi Hotel – the unextended
(as it then was), the unimproved, the unblushingly local Adelphi.
Liverpool is not a romantic city, but that smoky Saturday
returns to me as a supreme success, measured by its association
with the kind of emotion in the hope of which, for the most
part, we betake ourselves to far countries.

It assumed this character at an early hour – or rather, indeed,
twenty-four hours before – with the sight, as one looked across
the wintry ocean, of the strange, dark, lonely freshness of the
coast of Ireland. Better still, before we could come up to the
city, were the black steamers knocking about in the yellow

Mersey, under a sky so low that they seemed to touch it with their funnels, and in the thickest, windiest light. Spring was already in the air, in the town; there was no rain, but there was still less sun – one wondered what had become, on this side of the world, of the big white splotch in the heavens; and the grey mildness, shading away into black at every pretext, appeared in itself a promise. This was how it hung about me, between the window and the fire, in the coffee-room of the hotel – late in the morning for breakfast, as we had been long disembarking. The other passengers had dispersed, knowingly catching trains for London (we had only been a handful); I had the place to myself, and I felt as if I had an exclusive property in the impression. I prolonged it, I sacrificed to it, and it is perfectly recoverable now, with the very taste of the national muffin, the creak of the waiter's shoes as he came and went (could anything be so English as his intensely professional back? it revealed a country of tradition), and the rustle of the newspaper I was too excited to read.

I continued to sacrifice for the rest of the day; it didn't seem to me a sentient thing, as yet, to inquire into the means of getting away. My curiosity must indeed have languished, for I found myself on the morrow in the slowest of Sunday trains, pottering up to London with an interruptedness which might have been tedious without the conversation of an old gentleman who shared the carriage with me, and to whom my alien as well as comparatively youthful character had betrayed itself. He instructed me as to the sights of London, and impressed upon me that nothing was more worthy of my attention than the great cathedral of St Paul. 'Have you seen St Peter's in Rome? St Peter's is more highly embellished, you know; but you may depend upon it that St Paul's is the better building of the two.' The impression I began with speaking of was, strictly, that of the drive from Euston, after dark, to Morley's Hotel in Trafalgar Square. It was not lovely – it was in fact rather horrible; but as I move again through dusky, tortuous miles, in the greasy four-wheeler to which my luggage had compelled me to commit myself, I recognise the first step in an initiation of which the subsequent stages were to abound in pleasant things. It is a kind of humiliation in a great city not to know where you are going, and Morley's Hotel was then, to my imagination, only a vague ruddy spot in the general immensity. The immensity was the great fact, and that was a charm; the miles of housetops and viaducts, the complication of junction and signals through which the train made its way to the station had already given me the scale. The weather had turned to wet, and we went deeper and deeper into the Sunday night. The sheep in the fields, on the way from Liverpool, had shown in their demeanour a certain consciousness of the day; but this momentous cab-drive was an introduction to the rigidities of custom. The low black houses were as inanimate as so many rows of coal-scuttles, save where at frequent corners, from a gin-shop, there was a flare of light more brutal still than the darkness. The custom of gin – that was equally rigid, and in this first impression the public-houses counted for much.

Morley's Hotel proved indeed to be a ruddy spot; brilliant, in my recollection, is the coffee-room fire, the hospitable mahogany, the sense that in the stupendous city this, at any rate for the hour, was a shelter and a point of view. My remembrance of the rest of the evening – I was probably very tired – is mainly a remembrance of a vast four-poster. My little bedroom-candle, set in its deep basin, caused this monument to project a huge shadow and to make me think, I scarce knew why, of 'The Ingoldsby Legends'. If at a tolerably early hour the next day I found myself approaching St Paul's, it was not wholly in obedience to the old gentleman in the railway-carriage: I had an errand in the City, and the City was doubtless prodigious. But what I mainly recall is the romantic consciousness of passing under the Temple Bar, and the way two lines of 'Henry Esmond' repeated themselves in my mind as I drew near the masterpiece of Sir Christopher Wren. 'The stout, red-faced woman' whom Esmond had seen tearing after the staghounds over the slopes at Windsor was not a bit like the effigy 'which turns its stony back upon St Paul's and faces the coaches struggling up Ludgate Hill'. As I looked at Queen Anne over the apron of my hansom – she struck me as very small and dirty, and the vehicle ascended the mild incline without an effort – it was a thrilling thought that the statue had been familiar to the hero of the incomparable novel. All history appeared to live again, and the continuity of things to vibrate through my mind.

To this hour, as I pass along the Strand, I take again the walk I took there that afternoon. I love the place to-day, and that was the commencement of my passion. It appeared to me to present phenomena, and to contain objects of every kind, of an inexhaustible interest; in particular it struck me as desirable and even indispensable that I should purchase most of the articles in most of the shops. My eyes rest with a certain tenderness on the places where I resisted and on those where I succumbed. The fragrance of Mr Rimmel's establishment is again in my nostrils; I see the slim young lady (I hear her pronunciation) who waited upon me there. Sacred to me to-day is the particular aroma of the hair-wash that I bought of her. I pause before the granite portico of Exeter Hall (it was unexpectedly narrow and wedge-like), and it evokes a cloud of associations which are none the less impressive because they are vague; coming from I don't know where – from *Punch*, from Thackeray, from volumes of the *Illustrated London News* turned over in childhood; seeming connected with Mrs Beecher Stowe and 'Uncle Tom's Cabin'. Memorable is a rush I made into a glover's at Charing Cross – the one you pass, going eastward, just before you turn into the station; that, however, now that I think of it, must have been in the morning, as soon as I issued from the hotel. Keen within me was a sense of the importance of deflowering, of despoiling the shop.

A day or two later, in the afternoon, I found myself staring at my fire, in a lodging of which I had taken possession on foreseeing that I should spend some weeks in London. I had just come in, and, having attended to the distribution of my luggage, sat down to consider my habitation. It was on the ground floor, and the fading daylight reached it in a sadly damaged condition. It struck me as stuffy and unsocial, with its mouldy smell and its decoration of lithographs and wax-flowers – an impersonal black hole in the huge general blackness. The uproar of Piccadilly hummed away at the end of the street, and the rattle of a heartless hansom passed close to my ears. A sudden horror of the whole place came over me, like a tiger-pounce of homesickness which had been watching its moment. London was hideous, vicious, cruel, and above all overwhelming; whether or no she was 'careful of the type', she was as indifferent as Nature herself to the single life. In the course of an hour I should have to go out to my dinner, which was not supplied on the premises, and that effort assumed the form of a desperate and dangerous quest. It appeared to me that I would rather remain dinnerless, would rather even starve, than sally forth into the infernal town, where the natural fate of an obscure stranger would be to be trampled to death in Piccadilly and have his carcass thrown into the Thames. I did not starve, however, and I eventually attached myself by a hundred human links to the dreadful, delightful city. That momentary vision of its smeared face and stony heart has remained memorable to me, but I am happy to say that I can easily summon up others.

2

IT IS, no doubt, not the taste of every one, but for the real London-lover the mere immensity of the place is a large part of its savour. A small London would be an abomination, as it fortunately is an impossibility, for the idea and the name are beyond everything an expression of extent and number. Practically, of course, one lives in a quarter, in a plot; but in imagination and by a constant mental act of reference the accommodated haunter enjoys the whole – and it is only of him that I deem it worth while to speak. He fancies himself, as they say, being a particle in so unequalled an aggregation; and its immeasurable circumference, even though unvisited and lost in smoke, gives him the sense of a social, an intellectual margin. There is a luxury in the knowledge that he may come and go without being noticed, even when his comings and goings have no nefarious end. I don't mean by this that the tongue of London is not a very active member; the tongue of London would indeed be worthy of a chapter by itself. But the eyes which at least in some measure feed its activity are fortunately for the common advantage solicited at any moment by a thousand different objects. If the place is big, everything it contains is certainly not so; but this may at least be said, that if small questions play a part there, they play it without illusions about its importance. There are too many questions, small or great; and each day, as it arrives, leads its children, like a kind of mendicant mother, by the hand. Therefore perhaps the most general characteristic is the absence of insistence. Habits and inclinations flourish and fall, but intensity is never one of them. The spirit of the great city is not analytic, and, as they come up, subjects rarely receive at its hands a treatment drearily earnest or tastelessly thorough. There are not many − of those of which London disposes with the assurance begotten of its large experience − that wouldn't lend themselves to a tenderer manipulation elsewhere. It takes a very great affair, a turn of the Irish screw or a divorce case lasting many days, to be fully threshed out. The mind of Mayfair, when it aspires to show what it really can do, lives in the hope of a new divorce case, and an indulgent providence − London is positively in certain ways the spoiled child of the world − abundantly recognises this particular aptitude and humours the whim.

The compensation is that material does arise; that there is a great variety, if not morbid subtlety; and that the whole of the procession of events and topics passes across your stage. For the moment I am speaking of the inspiration there may be in the sense of far frontiers; the London-lover loses himself in this swelling consciousness, delights in the idea that the town which encloses him is after all only a paved country, a state by itself. This is his condition of mind quite as much if he be an adoptive as if he be a matter-of-course son. I am by no means sure even that he need be of Anglo-Saxon race and have inherited the birthright of English speech; though, on the other hand, I make no doubt that these advantages minister greatly to closeness of allegiance. The great city spreads her dusky mantle over innumerable races and creeds, and I believe there is scarcely a known form of worship that has not some temple there (have I not attended at the Church of Humanity, in Lamb's Conduit, in company with an American lady, a vague old gentleman, and several seamstresses?) or any communion of men that has not some club or guild. London is indeed an epitome of the round world, and just as it is a commonplace to say that there is nothing one can't 'get' there, so it is equally true that there is nothing one may not study at first hand.

One doesn't test these truths every day, but they form part of the air one breathes (and welcome, says the London-hater — for there be such perverse reasoners — to the pestilent compound). They colour the thick, dim distances which in my opinion are the most romantic town-vistas in the world; they mingle with the troubled light to which the straight, ungarnished aperture in one's dull, undistinctive housefront affords a passage and which makes an interior of friendly corners, mysterious tones and unbetrayed ingenuities, as well as with the low, magnificent medium of the sky, where the smoke and fog and the weather in general, the strangely undefined hour of the day and season of the year, the emanations of industries and the reflection of furnaces, the red gleams and blurs that may or may not be of sunset — as you never see any *source* of radiance you can't in the least tell — all hang together in a confusion, a complication, a shifting but irremovable canopy. They form the undertone of the deep, perpetual voice of the place. One remembers them when one's loyalty is on the defensive; when it is a question of introducing as many striking features as possible into the list of fine reasons one has sometimes to draw up, that eloquent catalogue with which one confronts the hostile indictment — the array of *other* reasons which may easily be as long as one's arm. According to these other reasons it plausibly and conclusively stands that, as a place to be happy in, London will never do. I don't say it is necessary to meet so absurd an allegation except for one's personal complacency. If indifference, in so gorged an organism, is still livelier than curiosity, you may avail yourself of your own share in it simply to feel that since such and such a person doesn't care for real richness, so much the worse for such and such a person. But once in a while the best believer recognises the impulse to set his religion in order, to sweep the temple of his thoughts and trim the sacred lamp. It is at such hours as this that he reflects with elation that the British capital is the particular spot in the world which communicates the greatest sense of life.

3

THE READER will perceive that I do not shrink even from the
extreme concession of speaking of our capital as British, and this
in a shameless connection with the question of loyalty on the
part of an adoptive son. For I hasten to explain that if half the
source of one's interest in it comes from feeling that it is the
property and even the home of the human race – Hawthorne,
that best of Americans, says so somewhere, and places it in this
sense side by side with Rome – one's appreciation of it is really
a large sympathy, a comprehensive love of humanity. For the
sake of such a charity as this one may stretch one's allegiance;
and the most alien of the cockneyfied, though he may bristle
with every protest at the intimation that England has set its
stamp upon him, is free to admit with conscious pride that he
had submitted to Londonisation. It is a real stroke of luck for a
particular country that the capital of the human race happens to
be British. Surely every other people would have it theirs if they
could. Whether the English deserve to hold it any longer might
be an interesting field of inquiry; but as they have not yet let it
slip, the writer of these lines professes without scruple that the
arrangement is to his personal taste. For, after all, if the sense of
life is greatest there, it is a sense of the life of people of our
consecrated English speech. It is the headquarters of that
strangely elastic tongue; and I make this remark with a full sense
of the terrible way in which the idiom is misused by the
populace in general, than whom it has been given to few races
to impart to conversation less of the charm of tone. For a man
of letters who endeavours to cultivate, however modestly,
the medium of Shakespeare and Milton, of Hawthorne and
Emerson, who cherishes the notion of what it has achieved and
what it may even yet achieve, London must ever have a great
illustrative and suggestive value, and indeed a kind of sanctity. It
is the single place in which most readers, most possible lovers,

are gathered together; it is the most inclusive public and the largest social incarnation of the language, of the tradition. Such a personage may well let it go for this and leave the German and the Greek to speak for themselves, to express the grounds of *their* predilection, presumably very different.

When a social product is so vast and various it may be approached on a thousand different sides, and liked and disliked for a thousand different reasons. The reasons of Piccadilly are not those of Camden Town, nor are the curiosities and discouragements of Kilburn the same as those of Westminster and Lambeth. The reasons of Piccadilly – I mean the friendly ones – are those of which, as a general thing, the rooted visitor remains most conscious; but it must be confessed that even these, for the most part, do not lie upon the surface. The absence of style, or rather of the intention of style, is certainly the most general characteristic of the face of London. To cross to Paris under this impression is to find one's self surrounded with far other standards. There everything reminds you that the idea of beautiful and stately arrangement has never been out of fashion, that the art of composition has always been at work or at play. Avenues and squares, gardens and quays, have been distributed for effect, and to-day the splendid city reaps the accumulation of all this ingenuity. The result is not in every quarter interesting, and there is a tiresome monotony of the 'fine' and the symmetrical above all, of the deathly passion for making things 'to match'. On the other hand the whole air of the place is architectural. On the banks of the Thames it is a tremendous chapter of accidents—the London-lover has to confess to the existence of miles upon miles of the dreariest, stodgiest commonness. Thousands of acres are covered by low black houses of the cheapest construction, without ornament, without grace, without character or even identity. In fact there are many, even in the best quarters, in all the region of Mayfair and Belgravia, of so paltry and inconvenient, especially of so dimunitive a type (those that are let in lodgings – such poor lodgings as they make – may serve as an example), that you wonder what peculiarly limited domestic need they were constructed to meet. The great misfortune of London to the eye (it is true that this remark applies much less to the City) is the want of elevation.

There is no architectural impression without a certain degree of height, and the London street-vista has none of that sort of pride.

All the same, if there be not the intention, there is at least the accident, of style, which, if one looks at it in a friendly way, appears to proceed from three sources. One of these is simply the general greatness, and the manner in which that makes a difference for the better in any particular spot; so that, though you may often perceive yourself to be in a shabby corner, it never occurs to you that this is the end of it. Another is the atmosphere, with its magnificent mystifications, which flatters and superfuses, makes everything brown, rich, dim, vague, magnifies distances and minimises details, confirms the inference of vastness by suggesting that, as the great city makes every-thing, it makes its own system of weather and its own optical laws. The last is the congregation of the parks, which constitute an ornament not elsewhere to be matched and give the place a superiority that none of its uglinesses overcome. They spread themselves with such a luxury of space in the centre of the town that they form a part of the impression of any walk, of almost any view, and, with an audacity altogether their own, make a pastoral landscape under the smoky sky. There is no mood of the rich London climate that is not becoming to them – I have seen them look delightfully romantic, like parks in novels, in the wettest winter – and there is scarcely a mood of the appreciative resident to which they have not something to say. The high things of London, which here and there peep over them, only make the spaces vaster by reminding you that you are, after all, not in Kent or Yorkshire; and these things, whatever they be – rows of 'eligible' dwellings, towers of churches, domes of institutions – take such an effective grey-blue tint that a clever water-colourist would seem to have put them in for pictorial reasons.

The view from the bridge over the Serpentine has an extraordinary nobleness, and it has often seemed to me that the Londoner twitted with his low standard may point to it with every confidence. In all the town-scenery of Europe there can be few things so fine; the only reproach it is open to is that it begs the question by seeming – in spite of its being the pride of five millions of people – not to belong to a town at all. The towers of Notre Dame, as they rise in Paris from the island that divides the Seine, present themselves no more impressively than those of Westminster as you see them looking doubly far beyond the shining stretch of Hyde Park water. Equally delectable is the large river-like manner in which the Serpentine opens away between its wooded shores. Just after you have crossed the bridge (whose very banisters, old and ornamental, of yellowish-brown stone, I am particularly fond of), you enjoy on your left, through the gate of Kensington Gardens as you go towards Bayswater, an altogether enchanting vista – a footpath over the grass, which loses itself beneath the scattered oaks and elms exactly as if the place were a 'chase'. There could be nothing less like London in general than this particular morsel, and yet it takes London, of all cities, to give you such an impression of the country.

4

IT TAKES London to put you in the way of a purely rustic walk from Notting Hill to Whitehall. You may traverse this immense distance – a most comprehensive diagonal – altogether on soft, fine turf, amid the song of birds, the bleat of lambs, the ripple of ponds, the rustle of admirable trees. Frequently have I wished that, for the sake of such a daily luxury and of exercise made romantic, I were a government-clerk living, in snug domestic conditions, in a Pembridge villa – let me suppose – and having my matutinal desk in Westminster. I should turn into Kensington Gardens at their north-west limit, and I should have my choice of a hundred pleasant paths to the gates of Hyde Park. In Hyde Park I should follow the water-side, or the Row, or any other fancy of the occasion; liking best perhaps, after all, the Row in its morning mood, with the mist hanging over the dark red course, and the scattered early riders taking an identity as the soundless gallop brings them nearer. I am free to admit that in the Season, at the conventional hours, the Row becomes a weariness (save perhaps just for a glimpse once a year, to remind one's self how much it is like Du Maurier); the preoccupied citizen eschews it and leaves it for the most part to the gaping barbarian. I speak of it now from the point of view of the pedestrian; but for the rider as well it is at its best when he passes either too early or too late. Then, if he be not bent on comparing it to its disadvantage with the bluer and boskier alleys of the Bois de Boulogne, it will not be spoiled by the fact that, with its surface that looks like tan, its barriers like those of the ring on which the clown stands to hold up the hoop to the young lady, its empty benches and chairs, its occasional orange-peel, its mounted policemen patrolling at intervals like expectant supernumeraries, it offers points of real contact with a circus whose lamps are out. The sky that bends over it is frequently not a bad imitation of the dingy tent of such an establishment. The ghosts of past cavalcades seem to haunt the foggy arena, and somehow they are better company than the mashers and elongated beauties of current seasons. It is not without interest to remember that most of the salient figures of English society during the present century – and English society means, or rather has hitherto meant, in a large degree English history – have bobbed in the saddle between Apsley House and Queen's Gate. You may call the roll if you care to, and the air will be thick with dumb voices and dead names, like that of some Roman amphitheatre.

It is doubtless a signal proof of being a London-lover *quand même* that one should undertake an apology for so bungled an attempt at a great public place as Hyde Park Corner. It is certain that the improvements and embellishments recently enacted there have only served to call further attention to the poverty of the elements, and to the fact that this poverty is terribly illustrative of general conditions. The place is the beating heart of the great West End, yet its main features are a shabby, stuccoed hospital, the low park-gates in their neat but un-imposing frame, the drawing-room windows of Apsley House, and of the commonplace frontages on the little terrace beside it; to which must be added, of course, the only item in the whole prospect that is in the least monumental – the arch spanning the private road beside the gardens of Buckingham Palace. This structure is now bereaved of the rueful effigy which used to surmount it – the Iron Duke in the guise of a tin soldier – and has not been enriched by the transaction as much as might have been expected. There is a fine view of Piccadilly and Knightsbridge, and of the noble mansions, as the house-agents call them, of Grosvenor Place, together with a sense of generous space beyond the vulgar little railing of the Green Park; but, except for the impression that there would be room for something better, there is nothing in all this that speaks to the imagination: almost as much as the grimy desert of Trafalgar Square the prospect conveys the idea of an opportunity wasted.

None the less has it on a fine day in spring an expressiveness of which I shall not pretend to explain the source further than by saying that the flood of life and luxury is immeasurably great there. The edifices are mean, but the social stream itself is monumental, and to an observer not purely stolid there is more excitement and suggestion than I can give a reason for in the long, distributed waves of traffic, with the steady policemen marking their rhythm, which roll together and apart for so many hours. Then the great dim city becomes bright and kind, the pall of smoke turns into a veil of haze carelessly worn, the air is coloured and almost scented by the presence of the biggest society in the world, and most of the things that meet the eye – or perhaps I should say more of them, for the most in London is, no doubt, ever the realm of the dingy – present themselves as 'well-appointed'. Everything shines more or less, from the window-panes to the dog-collars. So it all looks, with its myriad variations and qualifications, to one who surveys it over the apron of a hansom, while that vehicle of vantage, better than any box at the opera, spurts and slackens with the current.

It is not in a hansom, however, that we have figured our punctual young man, whom we must not desert as he fares to the south-east, and who has only to cross Hyde Park Corner to find his way all grassy again. I have a weakness for the convenient, familiar, treeless, or almost treeless, expanse of the Green Park, and the friendly part it plays as a kind of encouragement to Piccadilly. I am so fond of Piccadilly that I am grateful to any one or anything that does it a service, and nothing is more worthy of appreciation than the southward look it is permitted to enjoy just after it passes Devonshire House – a sweep of horizon which it would be difficult to match among other haunts of men, and thanks to which, of a summer's day, you may spy, beyond the browsed pastures of the foreground and middle distance, beyond the cold chimneys of Buckingham Palace and the towers of Westminster and the swarming riverside and all the southern parishes, the hard modern twinkle of the roof of the Crystal Palace.

If the Green Park is familiar, there is still less of the exclusive in its pendant, as one may call it – for it literally hangs from the other, down the hill – the remnant of the former garden of the queer,shabby old palace whose black, inelegant face stares up St James's Street. This popular resort has a great deal of character, but I am free to confess that much of its character comes from its nearness to the Westminster slums. It is a park of intimacy, and perhaps the most democratic corner of London, in spite of its being in the royal and military quarter and close to all kinds of stateliness. There are few hours of the day when a thousand smutty children are not sprawling over it, and the unemployed lie thick on the grass and cover the benches with a brotherhood of greasy corduroys. If the London parks are the drawing-rooms and clubs of the poor – that is, of those poor (I admit it cuts down the number) who live near enough to them to reach them – these particular grass-plots and alleys may be said to constitute the very *salon* of the slums.

I know not why, being such a region of greatness – great towers, great names, great memories; at the foot of the Abbey, th Parliament, the fine fragment of Whitehall, with the quarters of the sovereign right and left – but the edge of Westminster evokes as many associations of misery as of empire. The neighbourhood has been much purified of late, but it still contains a collection of specimens – though it is far from unique in this – of the low, black element. The air always seems to me heavy and thick, and here more than elsewhere one hears old England – the panting, smoke-stained Titan of Matthew Arnold's fine poem – draw her deep breath with effort. In fact one is nearer to her heroic lungs, if those organs are figured by the great pinnacled and fretted talking-house on the edge of the river. But this same dense and conscious air plays such everlasting tricks to the eye that the Foreign Office, as you see it from the bridge, often looks romantic, and the sheet of water it overhangs poetic – suggests an Indian palace bathing its feet in the Ganges. If our pedestrian achieves such a comparison as this he has nothing left but to go on to his work – which he will find close at hand. He will have come the whole way from the far-north-west on the green – which is what was to be demonstrated.

5

I FEEL as if I were taking a tone almost of boastfulness, and no doubt the best way to consider the matter is simply to say – without going into the treachery of reasons – that, for one's self, one likes this part or the other. Yet this course would not be unattended with danger, inasmuch as at the end of a few such professions we might find ourselves committed to a tolerance of much that is deplorable. London is so clumsy and so brutal, and has gathered together so many of the darkest sides of life, that it is almost ridiculous to talk of her as a lover talks of his mistress, and almost frivolous to appear to ignore her disfigurements and cruelties. She is like a mighty ogress who devours human flesh; but to me it is a mitigating circumstance – though it may not seem so to every one – that the ogress herself is human. It is not in wantonness that she fills her maw, but to keep herself alive and do her tremendous work. She has no time for fine discriminations, but after all she is as good–natured as she is huge, and the more you stand up to her, as the phrase is, the better she takes the joke of it. It is mainly when you fall on your face before her that she gobbles you up. She heeds little what she takes, so long as she has her stint, and the smallest push to the right or the left will divert her wavering bulk from one form of prey to another. It is not to be denied that the heart tends to grow hard in her company; but she is a capital antidote to the morbid, and to live with her successfully is an education of the temper, a consecration of one's private philosophy. She gives one a surface for which in a rough world one can never be too thankful. She may take away reputations, but she forms character. She teaches her victims not to 'mind', and the great danger for them is perhaps that they shall learn the lesson too well.

It is sometimes a wonder to ascertain what they do mind, the best-seasoned of her children. Many of them assist, without winking, at the most unfathomable dramas, and the common speech of others denotes a familiarity with the horrible. It is her theory that she both produces and appreciates the exquisite; but if you catch her in flagrant repudiation of both responsibilities and confront her with the shortcoming, she gives you a look, with a shrug of her colossal shoulders, which establishes a private relation with you for evermore. She seems to say: 'Do you really take me so seriously as that, you dear, devoted, voluntary dupe, and don't you know what an immeasurable humbug I am?' You reply that you shall know it henceforth; but your tone is good-natured, with a touch of the cynicism that she herself has taught you; for you are aware that if she makes herself out better than she is, she also makes herself out much worse. She is immensely democratic, and that, no doubt, is part of the manner in which she is salutary to the individual; she teaches him his 'place' by an incomparable discipline, but deprives him of complaint by letting him see that she has exactly the same lash for every other back. When he has swallowed the lesson he may enjoy the rude but unfailing justice by which, under her eye, reputations and positions elsewhere esteemed great are reduced to the relative. There are so many reputations, so many positions, that supereminence breaks down, and it is difficult to be so rare that London can't match you. It is a part of her good-nature and one of her clumsy coquetries to pretend sometimes that she hasn't your equivalent, as when she takes it into her head to hunt the lion or form a ring round a celebrity. But this artifice is so very transparent that the lion must be very candid or the celebrity very obscure to be taken by it. The business is altogether subjective, as the philosophers say, and the great city is primarily looking after herself. Celebrities are convenient – they are one of the things that people are asked to 'meet' – and lion-cutlets, put upon ice, will nourish a family through periods of dearth.

This is what I mean by calling London democratic. You may be in it, of course, without being of it; but from the moment you *are* of it – and on this point your own sense will soon enough enlighten you – you belong to a body in which a general equality prevails. However exalted, however able, however rich, however renowned you may be, there are too many people at least as much so for your own idiosyncrasies to count. I think it is only by being beautiful that you may really prevail very much; for the loveliness of woman it has long been noticeable that London will go most out of her way. It is when she hunts that particular lion that she becomes most dangerous; then there are really moments when you would believe, for all the world, that she is thinking of what she can give, not of what she can get. Lovely ladies, before this, have paid for believing it, and will continue to pay in days to come. On the whole the people who are least deceived are perhaps those who have permitted themselves to believe, in their own interest, that poverty is not a disgrace. It is certainly not considered so in London, and indeed you can scarcely say where – in virtue of diffusion – it would more naturally be exempt. The possession of money is, of course, immensely an advantage, but that is a very different thing from a disqualification in the lack of it.

Good-natured in so many things in spite of her cynical tongue, and easy-going in spite of her tremendous pace, there is nothing in which the large indulgence of the town is more shown than in the liberal way she looks at obligations of hospitality and the margin she allows in these and cognate matters. She wants above all to be amused; she keeps her books loosely, doesn't stand on small questions of a chop for a chop, and if there be any chance of people's proving a diversion, doesn't know or remember or care whether they have 'called'. She forgets even if she herself have called. In matters of ceremony she takes and gives a long rope, wasting no time in phrases and circumvallations. It is no doubt incontestable that one result of her inability to stand upon trifles and consider details is that she has been obliged in some ways to lower rather portentously the standard of her manners. She cultivates the abrupt – for even when she asks you to dine a month ahead the invitation goes off like the crack of a pistol – and approaches her ends not exactly *par quatre chemins*. She doesn't pretend to attach importance to the lesson conveyed in Matthew Arnold's poem of 'The Sick King in Bokhara', that,

> Though we snatch what we desire,
> We may not snatch it eagerly.

London snatches it more than eagerly if that be the only way she can get it. Good manners are a succession of details, and I don't mean to say that she doesn't attend to them when she has time. She has it, however, but seldom – *que voulez-vous?* Perhaps the matter of note-writing is as good an example as another of what certain of the elder traditions inevitably have become in her hands. She lives by notes – they are her very heartbeats; but those that bear her signatures are as disjointed as the ravings of delirium, and have nothing but a postage-stamp in common with the epistolary art.

6

IF SHE doesen't go into particulars it may seem a very presumptuous act to have attempted to do so on her behalf, and the reader will doubtless think I have been punished by having egregiously failed in my enumeration. Indeed nothing could well be more difficult than to add up the items – the column would be altogether too long. One may have dreamed of turning the glow – if glow it be – of one's lantern on each successive facet of the jewel; but, after all, it may be success enough if a confusion of brightness be the result. One has not the alternative of speaking of London as a whole, for the simple reason that there is no such thing as the whole of it. It is immeasurable – embracing arms never meet. Rather it is a collection of many wholes, and of which of them is it most important to speak?

Inevitably there must be a choice, and I know of none more scientific than simply to leave out what we may have to apologise for. The uglinesses, the 'rookeries', the brutalities, the night-aspect of many of the streets, the gin-shops and the hour when they are cleared out before closing – there are many elements of this kind which have to be counted out before a genial summary can be made.

And yet I should not go so far as to say that it is a condition of such geniality to close one's eye upon the immense misery; on the contrary, I think it is partly because we are irremediably conscious of that dark gulf that the most general appeal of the great city remains exactly what it is, the largest chapter of human accidents. I have no idea of what the future evolution of the strangely mingled monster may be; whether the poor will improve away the rich, or the rich will expropriate the poor, or they will all continue to dwell together on their present imperfect terms of intercourse. Certain it is, at any rate, that the impression of suffering is a part of the general vibration; it is one of the things that mingle with all the others to make the sound that is supremely dear to the consistent London-lover – the rumble of the tremendous human mill. This is the note which, in all its modulations, haunts and fascinates and inspires him. And whether or no he may succeed in keeping the misery out of the picture, he will freely confess that the latter is not spoiled for him by some of its duskiest shades. We are far from liking London well enough till we like its defects: the dense darkness of much of its winter, the soot on the chimney-pots and everywhere else, the early lamplight, the brown blur of the houses, the splashing of hansoms in Oxford Street or the Strand on December afternoons.

There is still something that recalls to me the enchantment of children – the anticipation of Christmas, the delight of a holiday walk – in the way the shop-fronts shine into the fog. It makes each of them seem a little world of light and warmth, and I can still waste time in looking at them with dirty Bloomsbury on one side and dirtier Soho on the other. There are winter effects, not intrinsically sweet, it would appear, which somehow, in absence, touch the chords of memory and even the fount of tears; as for instance the front of the British Museum on a black afternoon, or the portico, when the weather is vile, of one of the big square clubs in Pall Mall. I can give no adequate account of the subtle poetry of such reminiscences; it depends upon associations of which we have often lost the thread. The wide colonnade of the Museum, its symmetrical wings, the high iron fence in its granite setting, the sense of the misty halls within, where all the treasures lie – these things loom patiently through atmospheric layers which instead of making them dreary impart to them something of a cheer of red lights in a storm. I think the romance of a winter afternoon in London arises partly from the fact that, when it is not altogether smothered, the general lamplight takes this hue of hospitality. Such is the colour of the interior glow of the clubs in Pall Mall, which I positively like best when the fog loiters upon their monumental staircases.

In saying just now that these retreats may easily be, for the exile, part of the phantasmagoria of homesickness, I by no means alluded simply to their solemn outsides. If they are still more solemn within, that does not make them any less dear, in retrospect at least, to a visitor much bent upon liking his London to the end. What is the solemnity but a tribute to your nerves, and the stillness but a refined proof of the intensity of life? To produce such results as these the balance of many tastes must be struck, and that is only possible in a very high civilisation. If I seem to intimate that this last abstract term must be the cheer of him who has lonely possession of a foggy library, without even the excitement of watching for some one to put down the magazine he wants, I am willing to let the supposition pass, for the appreciation of a London club at one of the empty seasons is nothing but the strong expression of a preference for the great city – by no means so unsociable as it may superficially appear – at periods of relative abandonment. The London year is studded with holidays, blessed little islands of comparative leisure – intervals of absence for good society. Then the wonderful English faculty for 'going out of town for a little change' comes into illimitable play, and families transport their nurseries and their bath-tubs to those rural scenes which form the real substratum of the national life. Such moments as these are the paradise of the genuine London-lover, for he then finds himself face to face with the object of his passion: he can give himself up to an intercourse which at other times is obstructed by his rivals. Then every one he knows is out of town, and the exhilarating sense of the presence of every one he doesn't know becomes by so much the deeper.

This is why I pronounce his satisfaction not an unsociable, but a positively affectionate emotion. It is the mood in which he most measures the immense humanity of the place, and in which its limits recede furthest into a dimness peopled with possible illustrations. For his acquaintance, however numerous it may be, is finite; whereas the other, the unvisited London, is infinite. It is one of his pleasures to think of the experiments and excursions he may make in it, even when these adventures don't particularly come off. The friendly fog seems to protect and enrich them – to add both to the mystery and security, so that it is most in the winter months that the imagination weaves such delights. They reach their climax perhaps during the strictly social desolation of Christmas week, when the country-houses are crowded at the expense of the capital. Then it is that I am most haunted with the London of Dickens, feel most as if it were still recoverable, still exhaling its queerness in patches perceptible to the appreciative. Then the big fires blaze in the lone twilight of the clubs, and the new books on the tables say 'Now at last you have time to read me', and the afternoon tea and toast, and the torpid old gentleman who wakes up from a doze to order potash-water, appear to make the assurance good. It is not a small matter either, to a man of letters, that this is the best time for writing, and that during the lamplit days the white page he tries to blacken becomes, on his table, in the circle of the lamp, with the screen of the climate folding him in, more vivid and absorbent. Those to whom it is forbidden to sit up to work in the small hours may, between November and March, enjoy a semblance of this luxury in the morning. The weather makes a kind of sedentary midnight and muffles the possible interruptions. It is bad for the eyesight, but excellent for the image.

7

OF COURSE it is too much to say that all the satisfaction of life in London comes from literally living there, for it is not a paradox that a great deal of it consists in getting away. It is almost easier to leave it than not to, and much of its richness and interest proceeds from its ramifications, the fact that all England is in a suburban relation to it. Such an affair it is in comparison to get away from Paris or to get into it. London melts by wide, ugly zones into the green country, and becomes pretty insidiously, inadvertently – without stopping to change. It is the spoiling, perhaps, of the country but it is the making of the insatiable town, and if one is a helpless and shameless cockney that is all one is obliged to look at. Anything is excusable which enlarges one's civic consciousness. It ministers immensely to that of the London-lover that, thanks to the tremendous system of coming and going, to the active, hospitable habits of the people, to the elaboration of the railway-service, the frequency and rapidity of trains, and last, though not least, to the fact that much of the loveliest scenery in England lies within a radius of fifty miles – thanks to all this he has the rural picturesque at his door and may cultivate unlimited vagueness as to the line of division between centre and circumference. It is perfectly open to him to consider the remainder of the United Kingdom, or the British empire in general, or even, if he be an American, the total of the English-speaking territories of the globe, as the mere margin, the fitted girdle.

Is it for this reason – because I like to think how great we all are together in the light of heaven and the face of the rest of the world, with the bond of our glorious tongue, in which we labour to write articles and books for each other's candid perusal, how great we all are and how great is the great city which we may unite fraternally to regard as the capital of our race – is it for this that I have a singular kindness for the London railway-stations, that I like them aesthetically, that they interest and fascinate me, and that I view them with complacency even when I wish neither to depart nor to arrive? They remind me of all our reciprocities and activities, our energies and curiosities, and our being all distinguished together from other people by our great common stamp of perpetual motion, our passion for seas and deserts and the other side of the globe, the secret of the impression of strength – I don't say of social roundness and finish – that we produce in any collection of Anglo-Saxon types. If in the beloved foggy season I delight in the spectacle of Paddington, Euston or Waterloo – I confess I prefer the grave northern stations – I am prepared to defend myself against the charge of puerility; for what I seek and what I find in these vulgar scenes is at bottom simply so much evidence of our larger way of looking at life. The exhibition of variety of type is in general one of the bribes by which London induces you to condone her abominations, and the railway-platform is a kind of compendium of that variety. I think that nowhere so much as in London do people wear – to the eye of observation – definite signs of the sort of people they may be. If you like above all things to know the sort, you hail this fact with joy; you recognise that if the English are immensely distinct from other people they are also socially – and that brings with it, in England, a train of moral and intellectual consequences – extremely distinct from each other. You may see them all together, with the rich colouring of their differences, in the fine flare of one of Mr W. H. Smith's bookstalls – a feature not to be omitted in any enumeration of the charms of Paddington and Euston. It is a focus of warmth and light in the vast smoky cavern; it gives the idea that literature is a thing of splendour, of a dazzling essence, of infinite gas-lit red and gold. A glamour hangs over the glittering booth, and a tantalising air of clever new things. How brilliant must the books all be, how veracious and courteous the fresh, pure journals! Of a Saturday afternoon, as you wait in your corner of the compartment for the starting of the train, the window makes a frame for the glowing picture. I say of a Saturday afternoon because that is the most characteristic time – it speaks most of the constant circulation and in particular of the quick jump, by express, just before dinner, for the Sunday, into the hall of the country-house and the forms of closer friendliness, the prolonged talks, the familiarising walks which London excludes.

There is the emptiness of summer as well, when you may have the town to yourself, and I would discourse of it – counting the summer from the first of August – were it not that I fear to seem ungracious in insisting so much on the negative phases. In truth they become positive in another manner, and I have an endearing recollection of certain happy accidents attached to the only period when London life may be said to admit of accident. It is the most luxurious existence in the world, but of that especial luxury – the unexpected, the extemporised – it has in general too little. In a very tight crowd you can't scratch your leg, and in London the social pressure is so great that it is difficult to deflect from the perpendicular or to move otherwise than with the mass. There is too little of the loose change of time; every half-hour has its preappointed use, written down month by month in a little book. As I intimated, however, the pages of this volume exhibit from August to November an attractive blankness; they represent the season during which you may taste of that highest kind of inspiration, the inspiration of the moment.

This is doubtless what a gentleman had in mind who once said to me, in regard to the vast resources of London and its having something for every taste: 'Oh, yes; when you are bored, or want a little change, you can take the boat down to Blackwall.' I have never had occasion yet to resort to this particular remedy. Perhaps it's a proof that I have never been bored. Why Blackwall? I indeed asked myself at the time; nor have I yet ascertained what distractions the mysterious name represents. My interlocutor probably used it generically, as a free, comprehensive allusion to the charms of the river at large. Here the London-lover goes with him all the way, and indeed the Thames is altogether such a wonderful affair that he feels he has distributed his picture very clumsily not to have put it in the very forefront. Take it up or take it down, it is equally an adjunct of London life, an expression of London manners.

From Westminster to the sea its uses are commercial, but none the less pictorial for that; while in the other direction – taking it properly a little further up – they are personal, social, athletic, idyllic. In its recreative character it is absolutely unique. I know of no other classic stream that is so splashed about for the mere fun of it. There is something almost droll and at the same time almost touching in the way that on the smallest pretext of holiday or fine weather the mighty population takes to the boats. They bump each other in the narrow, charming channel; between Oxford and Richmond they make an uninterrupted procession. Nothing is more suggestive of the personal energy of the people and their eagerness to take, in the way of exercise and adventure, whatever they can get. I hasten to add that what they get on the Thames is exquisite, in spite of the smallness of the scale and the contrast between the numbers and the space. In a word, if the river is the busiest suburb of London it is also by far the prettiest. That term applies to it less, of course, from the bridges down, but it is only because in this part of its career it deserves a larger praise. To be consistent, I like it best when it is all dyed and disfigured with the town, and you look from bridge to bridge – they seem wonderfully big and dim – over the brown, greasy current, the barges and the penny-steamers, the black, sordid, heterogeneous shores. This prospect, of which so many of the elements are ignoble, etches itself to the eye of the lover of 'bits' with a power that is worthy perhaps of a better cause.

The way that with her magnificent opportunity London has neglected to achieve a river-front is, of course, the best possible proof that she has rarely, in the past, been in the architectural mood which at present shows somewhat inexpensive signs of settling upon her. Here and there a fine fragment apologises for the failure which it doesn't remedy. Somerset House stands up higher, perhaps, than anything else on its granite pedestal, and the palace of Westminster reclines – it can hardly be said to stand – on the big parliamentary bench of its terrace. The Embankment, which is admirable if not particularly interesting, does what it can, and the mannered houses of Chelsea stare across at Battersea Park like eighteenth-century ladies surveying a horrid wilderness. On the other hand, the Charing Cross railway-station, placed where it is, is a national crime; Millbank prison is a worse act of violence than any it was erected to punish, and the water-side generally a shameless renunciation of effect. We acknowledge, however, that its very cynicism is expensive; so that if one were to choose again – short of there being a London Louvre – between the usual English irresponsibility in such matters and some particular flight of conscience, one would perhaps do as well to let the case stand. We know what it is, the stretch from Chelsea to Wapping, but we know not what it might be. It doesn't prevent my being always more or less thrilled, of a summer afternoon, by the journey on a penny-steamer to Greenwich.

8

BUT WHY do I talk of Greenwich and remind myself of one of the unexecuted vignettes with which it had been my plan that these desultory and, I fear, somewhat incoherent remarks should be studded? They will present to the reader no vignettes but those which the artist who has kindly consented to associate himself with my vagaries may be so good as to bestow upon them. Why should I speak of Hampstead, as the question of summer afternoons just threatened to lead me to do after I should have exhausted the subject of Greenwich, which I may not even touch? Why should I be so arbitrary when I have cheated myself out of the space privately intended for a series of vivid and ingenious sketches of the particular physiognomy of the respective quarters of the town? I had dreamed of doing them all, with their idiosyncrasies and the signs by which you shall know them. It is my pleasure to have learned these signs – a deeply interesting branch of observation – but I must renounce the display of my lore.

I have not the conscience to talk about Hampstead, and what a pleasant thing it is to ascend the long hill which overhangs, as it were, St John's Wood and begins at the Swiss Cottage – you must mount from there, it must be confessed, as you can – and pick up a friend at a house of friendship on the top, and stroll with him on the rusty Heath, and skirt the garden-walls of the old square Georgian houses which survive from the time when, near as it is to-day to London, the place was a kind of provincial centre, with Joanna Baillie for its muse, and take the way by the Three Spaniards – I would never miss that – and look down at the smoky city or across at the Scotch firs and the red sunset. It would never do to make a tangent in that direction when I have left Kensington unsung and Bloomsbury unattempted and have said never a word about the mighty eastward region – the queer corners, the dark secrets, the rich survivals and mementoes of the City. I particularly regret having sacrificed Kensington, the once-delightful, the Thackerayan, with its literary vestiges, its quiet, pompous red palace, its square of Queen Anne, its house of Lady Castlewood, its Greyhound tavern, where Henry Esmond lodged.

But I can reconcile myself to this when I reflect that I have also sacrificed the Season, which doubtless, from an elegant point of view, ought to have been the central *morceau* in the panorama. I have noted that the London-lover loves everything in the place, but I have not cut myself off from saying that his sympathy has degrees, or from remarking that the sentiment of the author of these pages has never gone all the way with the dense movement of the British carnival. That is really the word for the period from Easter to midsummer; it is a fine, decorous, expensive, Protestant carnival, in which the masks are not of velvet or silk, but of wonderful deceptive flesh and blood, the material of the most beautiful complexions in the world. Holding that the great interest of London is the sense the place gives us of multitudinous life, it is doubtless an inconsequence not to care most for the phase of greatest intensity. But there is life and life, and the rush and crush of these weeks of fashion is after all but a tolerably mechanical expression of human forces. Nobody would deny that it is a more universal, brilliant, spectacular one than can be seen anywhere else; and it is not a defect that these forces often take the form of women extremely beautiful. I risk the declaration that the London season brings together year by year an unequalled collection of handsome persons. I say nothing of the ugly ones; beauty has at the best been allotted to a small minority, and it is never, at the most, anywhere, but a question of the number by which that minority is least insignificant.

There are moments when one can almost forgive the follies of June for the sake of the smile which the sceptical old city puts on for the time and which, as I noted in an earlier passage of this disquisition, fairly breaks into laughter where she is tickled by the vortex of Hyde Park Corner. Most perhaps does she seem to smile at the end of the summer days, when the light lingers and lingers, though the shadows lengthen and the mists redden and the belated riders, with dinners to dress for, hurry away from the trampled arena of the Park. The population at that hour surges mainly westward and sees the dust of the day's long racket turned into a dull golden haze. There is something that has doubtless often, at this particular moment, touched the fancy even of the bored and the *blasés* in such an emanation of hospitality, of waiting dinners, of the festal idea, of the whole spectacle of the West End preparing herself for an evening six parties deep. The scale on which she entertains is stupendous, and her invitations and 'reminders' are as thick as the leaves of the forest.

For half an hour, from eight to nine, every pair of wheels presents the portrait of a diner-out. To consider only the rattling hansoms, the white neckties and 'dressed' heads which greet you from over the apron in a quick, interminable succession, conveys the overwhelming impression of a complicated world. Who are they all, and where are they all going, and whence have they come, and what smoking kitchens and gaping portals and marshalled flunkeys are prepared to receive them, from the southernmost limits of a loosely interpreted, an almost trans-pontine Belgravia, to the hyperborean confines of St John's Wood? There are broughams standing at every door, and carpets laid down for the footfall of the issuing if not the entering reveller. The pavements are empty now, in the fading light, in the big sallow squares and the stuccoed streets of gentility, save for the groups of small children holding others that are smaller – Ameliar-Ann intrusted with Sarah Jane – who collect, wherever the strip of carpet lies, to see the fine ladies pass from the carriage or the house. The West End is dotted with these pathetic little gazing groups; it is the party of the poor – *their* Season and way of dining out, and a happy illustration of 'the sympathy that prevails between classes'. The watchers, I should add, are by no means all children, but the lean mature also, and I am sure these wayside joys are one of the reasons of an inconvenience much deplored – the tendency of the country poor to flock to London. They who dine only occasionally or never at all have plenty of time to contemplate those with whom the custom has more amplitude. However, it was not my intention to conclude these remarks in a melancholy strain, and goodness knows that the diners are a prodigious company. It is as moralistic as I shall venture to be if I drop a very soft sigh on the paper as I confirm that truth. Are they all illuminated spirits and is their conversation the ripest in the world? This is not to be expected, nor should I ever suppose it to be desired that an agreeable society should fail to offer frequent opportunity for intellectual rest. Such a shortcoming is not one of the sins of the London world in general, nor would it be just to complain of that world, on any side, on grounds of deficiency. It is not what London fails to do that strikes the observer, but the general fact that she does everything in excess. Excess is her highest reproach, and it is her incurable misfortune that there is really too much of her. She overwhelms you by quantity and number – she ends by making human life, by making civilisation, appear cheap to you. Wherever you go, to parties, exhibitions, concerts, 'private views', meetings, solitudes, there are already more people than enough on the field. How it makes you understand the high walls with which so much of English life is surrounded, and the priceless blessing of a park in the country, where there is nothing animated but rabbits and pheasants and, for the worst, the importunate nightingales! And as the monster grows and grows for ever, she departs more and more – it must be acknowledged – from the ideal of a convenient society, a society in which intimacy is possible, in which the associated meet often and sound and select and measure and inspire each other, and relations and combinations have time to form themselves. The substitute for this, in London, is the momentary concussion of a million of atoms. It is the difference between seeing a great deal of a few and seeing a little of every one. 'When did you come – are you "going on"?' and it is over; there is no time even for the answer. This may seem a perfidious arraignment, and I should not make it were I not prepared, or rather were I not eager, to add two qualifications. One of these is that, cumbrously vast as the place may be, I would not have had it smaller by a hair's-breadth, or have missed one of the fine and fruitful impatiences with which it inspires you and which are at bottom a heartier tribute, I think, than any great city receives. The other is that out of its richness and its inexhaustible good humour it belies the next hour any generalisation you may have been so simple as to make about it.

REMINISCENCES

FOLLOWING the death of his brother William in 1910, Henry James began to write his autobiography. In the course of two complete volumes and one unfinished, he more or less reached 1870. The style of these books has justly been described as '*late* late James', but for all their density they contain many remarkable passages, including several about his formative visits to London. The first recalls the Mayfair, long gone, of 1855:

The vivid yields again to the vague – I scarce know why so utterly – till consciousness, waking up in London, renews itself, late one evening and very richly, at the Gloucester Hotel (or Coffee-House, as I think it was then still called), which occupied that corner of Piccadilly and Berkeley Street where more modern establishments have since succeeded it, but where a fatigued and famished American family found on that occasion a fine old British virtue in cold roast beef and bread and cheese and ale; their expert acclamation of which echoes even now in my memory. It keeps company there with other matters equally British and, as we say now, early Victorian; the thick gloom of the inn rooms, the faintness of the glimmering tapers, the blest inexhaustibility of the fine joint, surpassed only by that of the grave waiter's reserve – plain, immutably plain fare all, but prompting in our elders an emphasis of relief and relish, the 'There's nothing like it after all!' tone, which re-excited expectation, which in fact seemed this time to re-announce a basis for faith and joy.

That basis presently shrank to the scale of a small house hard by the hotel, at the entrance of Berkeley Square – expeditiously lighted on, it would thus appear, which again has been expensively superseded, but to the ancient little facts of which I fondly revert, since I owe them what I feel to have been, in the far past, the prime faint revelation, the small broken expression, of the London I was afterwards to know. The place wears on the spot, to this day, no very different face; the house that has risen on the site of ours is still immediately neighboured at the left by the bookseller, the circulating-librarian and news-agent, who modestly flourished in our time under the same name; the great establishment of Mr Gunter, just further along, is as soberly and solidly seated;[1] the mews behind the whole row, from the foot of Hay Hill at the right, wanders away to Bruton Street with the irregular grace that spoke to my young fancy; Hay Hill itself is somehow less sharply precipitous, besides being no longer paved, as I seem to recall its having been, with big boulders, and I was on the point of saying that its antique charm in some degree abides. Nothing, however, could be further from the truth; its antique charm quite succumbed, years ago, to that erection of lumpish 'mansions' which followed the demolition of the old-world town-residence, as the house-agents say, standing, on the south side, between court and I suppose garden, where Dover Street gives way to Grafton; a house of many histories, of vague importances and cold reserves and deep suggestions, I used to think after scaling the steep quite on purpose to wonder about it. A whole chapter of life was condensed, for our young sensibility, I make out, into the couple of months – they can scarce have been more – spent by us in these quarters, which must have proved too narrow and too towny.[2]

Late in 1855 the James family moved into a furnished house in St John's Wood, from where the children were taken by their tutor on enormously long walks. They were walks of intense fascination to the young Henry:

I seem to see to-day that the London of the 'fifties was even to the weak perception of childhood a much less generalised, a much more eccentrically and variously characterised place, than the present great accommodated and accommodating city; it had fewer resources but it had many more features, scarce one of which failed to help the whole to bristle with what a little gaping American could take for an intensity of difference from *his* supposed order . . .[3]

The London people had an exuberance of type; we found it in particular a world of costume, often of very odd costume – the most intimate notes of which were the postmen in their frock-coats of military red and their black beaver hats; the milkwomen, in hats that often emulated these, in little shawls and strange short, full frocks, revealing enormous boots, with their pails swung from their shoulders on wooden yokes; the inveterate footmen hooked behind the coaches of the rich, frequently in pairs and carrying staves, together with the mounted and belted grooms without the attendance of whom riders, of whichever sex – and riders then were much more numerous – almost never went forth. The range of character, on the other hand, reached rather dreadfully down; there were embodied and exemplified 'horrors' in the streets beside which any present exhibition is pale, and I well remember the almost terrified sense of their salience produced in me a couple of years later, on the occasion of a flying return from the Continent with my father, by a long, an interminable drive westward from the London Bridge railway-station. It was a soft June evening, with a lingering light and swarming crowds, as they then seemed to me, of figures reminding me of George Cruikshank's Artful Dodger and his Bill Sikes and his Nancy, only with the bigger brutality of life, which pressed upon the cab, the early-Victorian fourwheeler, as we jogged over the Bridge, and cropped up in more and more gas-lit patches for all our course, culminating, somewhere far to the west, in the vivid picture, framed by the cab-window, of a woman reeling backward as a man felled her to the ground with a blow in the face. The London view at large had in fact more than a Cruikshank, there still survived in it quite a Hogarth, side – which I had of course then no name for, but which I was so sharply to recognise on coming back years later that it fixed for me the veracity of the great pictorial chronicler. Hogarth's mark is even yet not wholly overlaid; though time has *per contra* dealt with that stale servility of address which most expressed to our young minds the rich burden of a Past, the consequence of too much history. I liked for my own part a lot of history, but felt in face of certain queer old obsequi-osities and appeals, whinings and sidlings and hand-rubbings and curtsey-droppings, the general play of apology and humility, behind which the great dim social complexity seemed to mass itself, that one didn't quite want so inordinate a quantity. Of that particular light and shade, however, the big broom of change has swept the scene bare; more history still has been after all what it wanted.[4]

When James returned to London as a young man in 1869, his landlord in Half Moon Street suggested the Albany in Arlington Street as the best place for him to dine. There James habitually repaired:

It was a small eating-house of the very old English tradition, as I then supposed at least, just opposite the much greater establishment of the same name, which latter it had borrowed, and I remember wondering whether the tenants of the classic chambers, the beadle-guarded cluster of which was impressive even to the deprecated approach, found their conception of the 'restaurant' – we still pronounced it in the French manner – met by the small compartments, narrow as horse-stalls, formed by the high straight backs of hard wooden benches and accommodating respectively two pairs of feeders, who were thus so closely face to face as fairly to threaten with knife and fork each others' more forward features.

The scene was sordid, the arrangements primitive, the detail of the procedure, as it struck me, wellnigh of the rudest; yet I remember rejoicing in it all – as one indeed might perfectly rejoice in the juiciness of joints and the abundance of accessory pudding; for I said to myself under every shock and at the hint of every savour that this was what it was for an exhibition to reek with local colour, and one could dispense with a napkin, with a crusty roll, with room for one's elbows or one's feet, with an immunity from intermittence of the 'plain boiled', much better than one could dispense with that. There were restaurants galore even at that time in New York and in Boston, but I had never before had to do with an eating-house and had not yet seen the little old English world of Dickens, let alone of the ever-haunting Hogarth, of Smollett and of Boswell, drenched with such a flood of light. As one sat there one *understood*; one drew out the severe séance not to stay the assault of precious conspiring truths, not to break the current of inrushing telltale suggestion. Every face was a documentary scrap, half a dozen broken words to piece with half a dozen others, and so on and on; every sound was strong, whether rich and fine or only queer and coarse; everything in this order drew a positive sweetness from never being – whatever else it was – gracelessly flat. The very rudeness was ripe, the very commonness was conscious – that is not related to mere other forms of the same, but to matters as different as possible, into which it shaded off and off or up and up; the image in fine was organic, rounded and complete, as definite as a Dutch picture of low life hung on a museum wall. 'Low' I say in respect to the life; but that was the point for me, that whereas the smartness and newness beyond the sea supposedly disavowed the low, they did so but thinly and vainly, falling markedly short of the high; which the little boxed and boiled Albany attained to some effect of, after a fashion of its own, just by having its so thoroughly appreciable note-value in a scheme of manners. It was imbedded, so to speak, in the scheme, and in borrowed lights, it borrowed even glooms, from so much neighbouring distinction.[5]

Another recommendation that James received, from a fellow-passenger on his Atlantic crossing in 1869, was to try Craven Street off the Strand for bachelor lodgings:

I didn't in the event, as has been seen, go to Craven Street for rooms, but I did go, on the very first occasion, for atmosphere, neither more nor less – the young man of the ship, building so much better than he knew, had guaranteed me such a rightness of that; and it belongs to this reminiscence, for the triviality of which I should apologize did I find myself at my present pitch capable of apologizing for anything, that I had on the very spot there one of those hallucinations as to the precious effect dreadful to lose and yet impossible to render which interfused the aesthetic dream in presence of its subject with the mortal drop of despair (as I should insist at least didn't the despair itself seem to have acted here as the preservative). The precious effect in the case of Craven Street was that it absolutely reeked, to my fond fancy, with associations born of the particular ancient piety embodied in one's private altar to Dickens; and that this upstart little truth alone would revel in explanations that I should for the time have feverishly to forego. The exquisite matter was not the identification with the scene of special shades or names; it was just that the whole Dickens procession marched up and down, the whole Dickens world looked out of its queer, quite sinister windows – for it was the socially sinister Dickens, I am afraid, rather than the socially encouraging or confoundingly comic who still at that moment was most apt to meet me with his reasons. Such a reason was just that look of the inscrutable riverward street, packed to blackness with accumulations of suffered experience, these, indescribably, disavowed and confessed at one and the same time, and with the fact of its blocked old Thames-side termination, a mere fact of more oppressive enclosure now, telling all sorts of vague loose stories about it.[6]

From the perspective of almost half a century later, James had no doubt that the visit to London in 1869 was one of the key events of his life. In his autobiography he tried, in some of his most challenging and at times impenetrable prose, to express his deepest feelings about mid-Victorian London and that city's subsequent development:

I began to shudder before a confidence, not to say an impudence, of diminution in the aspects by which the British capital differed so from those of all the foreign together as to present throughout the straight contradiction to them. That straight contradiction, testifying invaluably at every turn, had been from far back the thing, romantically speaking, to clutch and keep the clue and the logic of; thanks to it the whole picture, every element, objects and figures, background and actors, nature and art, hung consummately together, appealing in their own light and under their own law – interesting ever in every case by instituting comparisons, sticking on the contrary to their true instinct and suggesting only contrast. They were the *opposite*, the assured, the absolute, the unashamed, in respect to whatever might be of a generally similar intention elsewhere: this was their dignity, their beauty and their strength – to look back on which is to wonder if one didn't quite consciously tremble, before the exhibition, for any menaced or mitigated symptom in it. I honestly think one did, even in the first flushes of recognition, more or less so tremble; I remember at least that in spite of such disconcertments, such dismays, as certain of the most thoroughly

Victorian *choses vues* originally treated me to, something yet deeper and finer than observation admonished me to like them just as they were, or at least not too fatuously to dislike – since it somehow glimmered upon me that if they had lacked their oddity, their monstrosity, as it even might be, their unabashed insular conformity, other things that belong to them, as they belong to these, might have loomed less large and massed less thick, which effect was wholly to be deprecated. To catch that secret, I make out the more I think of it, was to have perhaps the smokiest, but none the less the steadiest, light to walk by; the 'clue', as I have called it, was to be one's appreciation of an England that should turn its back directly enough, and without fear of doing it too much, on examples and ideas not strictly homebred – since she did her own sort of thing with such authority and was even then to be noted as sometimes trying other people's with a *kind* of disaster not recorded, at the worst, among themselves.

I must of course disavow pretending to have read this vivid philosophy into my most immediate impressions, and I may in fact perhaps not claim to have been really aware of its seed till a considerable time had passed, till apprehensions and reflections had taken place in quantity, immeasurable quantity, so to speak, and a great stir-up of the imagination been incurred. Undoubtedly is it in part the new – that is, more strictly, the elder – acuteness that I touch all the prime profit with; I didn't know at the time either how much appearances were all the while in the melting-pot or what wealth of reaction on them I was laying up. I cherish, for love of the unbroken interest, all the same, the theory of certain then positive and effective prefigurements, because it leaves me thus free for remarking that I knew where I was, as I may put it, from the moment I saw the state of the London to come brought down with the weight of her abdication of her genius. It not unnaturally may be said that it hasn't been till to-day that we *see* her genius in its fulness – throwing up in a hundred lights, matters we practically acknowledge, such a plastic side as we had never dreamed she possessed. The genius of accommodation is what we had last expected of her – accommodation to anything but her portentous self, for in *that* connection she was ever remarkable;

and certainly the air of the generalised, the emulous smart modern capital has come to be written upon her larger and larger even while we look.

The unaccommodating and unaccommodated city remains none the less closely consecrated to one's fondest notion of her – the city too indifferent, too proud, too unaware, too stupid even if one will, to enter any lists that involved her moving from her base and that thereby, when one approached her from the alien *positive* places (I don't speak of the American, in those days too negative to be related at all) enjoyed the enormous 'pull', for making her impression, of ignoring everything but her own perversities and then of driving these home with an emphasis not to be gainsaid. Since she didn't emulate, as I have termed it, so she practised her own arts altogether, and both these ways and these consequences were in the flattest opposition (*that* was the happy point!) to foreign felicities or foreign standards, so that the effect in every case was of the straightest reversal of them – with black for the foreign white and white for the foreign black, wet for the foreign dry and dry for the foreign wet, big for the foreign small and small for the foreign big: I needn't extend the catalogue. *Her* idiosyncrasy was never in the least to have been inferred or presumed; it could only, in general, make the outsider provisionally gape. She sat thus imperturbable in her felicities, and if that is how, remounting the stream of time, I like most to think of her, this is because if her interest is still undeniable – as that of overgrown things goes – it has yet lost its fineness of quality. Phenomena may be interesting, thank goodness, without being phenomena of elegant expression or of any other form of restless smartness, and when once type is strong, when once it plays up from deep sources, every show of its sincerity delivers us a message and we hang, to real suspense, on its continuance of energy, on its again and yet again consistently acquitting itself. So it keeps in tune, and, as the French adage says, *c'est le ton qui fait la chanson.* The mid-Victorian London was sincere – that was a vast virtue and a vast appeal; the contemporary is sceptical, and most so when most plausible; the turn of the tide could verily be fixed to an hour – the hour at which the new plausibility began to exceed the old sincerities by so much as a single sign. They could truly have been arrayed face to face, I think, for an attentive eye – and I risk even saying that my own, bent upon them, as was to come to pass, with a habit of anxiety that I should scarce be able to overstate, had its unrecorded penetrations, its alarms and recoveries, even perhaps its very lapses of faith, though always redeemed afresh by still fonder fanaticisms, to a pitch that shall perhaps present itself, when they expose it all the way, as that of tiresome extravagance. Exposing it all the way is none the less, I see, exactly what I plot against it – or, otherwise expressed, in favour of the fine truth of history, so far as a throb of that awful pulse has been matter of one's own life; in favour too of the mere returns derivable from more inordinate curiosity. These Notes would enjoy small self-respect, I think, if that principle, not to call it that passion, didn't almost furiously ride them.[7]

1. Gunter's Tea Shop, renowned for its ices and sorbets, was to remain at 7–8 Berkeley Square for a further quarter of a century.
2. *A Small Boy and Others* (1913), pp 309–11.
3. Ibid, p 316.
4. Ibid, pp 321–3.
5. *The Middle Years* (1917), pp 43–6.
6. Ibid, pp 56–8.
7. Ibid, pp 19–25.

Other titles in **THE ENCORE SERIES** published by **Tabb House**

All titles 205 x 135mm.

This series brings neglected traditional writing and classics to the attention of the modern reader, and for the first three titles, paintings by Caeria Strong (Israel) were specially commissioned.
'High quality productions; elegant yet economical editions ideal for both students and the general reader' Publishing News

THE HAUNTING *by* **C. A. Dawson Scott**. *Foreword by* **Francis King**
Mrs Dawson Scott's novel of paranormal suspense, set in a small Cornish port (Padstow) in the 19th century, makes compelling reading.
'The narrative has imaginative power; I recommend this as a late night solitary read' *Literary Review*
248 pp. Hbk. £8.50. Sewn pbk. £3.95.

MALACHI'S COVE and Other Stories and Essays *by* **Anthony Trollope**
Edited with an Introduction by **Richard Mullen**
Travelling and the writing of fiction form the theme of this volume and the reader is taken from Cornwall to Ireland, France and America.
'Doctor Mullen has done a considerable service in selecting some of Trollope's best short stories' *Contemporary Review*
'A handsomely produced book – worthy in every way to stand beside the Barchester novels' *Church Times*
168 pp. Hbk. £7.95. Sewn pbk. £3.50.

ONE POOR SCRUPLE *by* **Mrs Wilfrid Ward**. *Introduction by* **Bernard Bergonzi**
London society life at the turn of the century and the moral conflicts of the protagonists provide the setting and the cause of dramatic interest in this leisurely novel.
'Powerful, haunting and beautiful' *Journal of Pre-Raphaelite Studies.*
400 pp. Hbk. £8.95. Sewn pbk. £3.95

Published in 1989

LONDON STORIES and Other Writings *by* **Henry James**
Edited and with an Introduction by **David Kynaston**
Henry James lived in London for over twenty years and was fascinated by its vastness and its many types and classes. For the first time, his best work on the subject is here gathered together.

In his writing, the contrast between civility of manner and violence of emotion and the cruelties of social existence are minutely observed. This is especially so where, 'In the Cage', a young girl handling the telegrams in a Mayfair post office wonders about the relationships they cryptically express.

In the words of Robert Louis Stevenson about another of the stories in this collection: 'Every touch surprises with its intangible precision; and the effect, when done, is as light as syllabub, as distinct as a picture.'
Cover illustration depicts the National Gallery and St Martin-in-the-Fields by Joseph de Nittis. Pbk £4.95. Hbk £12.95.